Climate Change and Tourism

Responding to Global Challenges

Climate Change and Tourism – Responding to Global Challenges
ISBN: 978-92-844-1234-1 (UNWTO)
ISBN: 978-92-807-2886-6 (UNEP)

Published by the World Tourism Organization and the United Nations Environment Programme
Printed by the World Tourism Organization, Madrid, Spain
First printing 2008
All rights reserved

World Tourism Organization
Calle Capitán Haya, 42
28020 Madrid, Spain
Tel.: (+34) 915 678 100
Fax: (+34) 915 713 733
Website: www.unwto.org
Email: omt@unwto.org

United Nations Environment Programme
15 Rue de Milan
75441 Paris Cedex 09, France
Tel.: (+33) 1 44 37 14 50
Fax: (+33) 1 44 37 14 74
Website: www.unep.fr
Email: unep.tie@unep.fr

Table of Contents

Foreword

The Second International Conference on Climate Change and Tourism (Davos, Switzerland, October 2007) was a milestone event that brought together a wide variety of stakeholders and delivered a clear commitment for action to respond to the climate change challenge. It underscored the need for the tourism sector to rapidly respond to climate change if it is to develop in a sustainable manner, which will require actions to: mitigate greenhouse gas emissions from the tourism sector, derived especially from transport and accommodation activities; adapt tourism businesses and destinations to changing climate conditions; apply existing and new technologies to improve energy efficiency; and secure financial resources to assist regions and countries in need.

The Davos Declaration highlighting these actions is a huge step forward and presents concrete recommendations to the key interest groups involved in tourism. This is indeed necessary, considering that tourism is today one of the world's largest economic sectors, and represents an activity that forms an integral part of modern societies in both developed and developing countries. It is, above all, a vital element in poverty reduction efforts and for the achievement of the UN Millennium Development Goals.

In the context of the Davos meeting, the report "Climate Change and Tourism: Responding to Global Challenges", which was commissioned to a group of prominent researchers, encompasses the status of knowledge on the complex relationship between climate change and tourism. The publication notes the vulnerability of the sector to climate change and the impacts of tourism on climate itself. The report provides an excellent basis to address the global phenomenon of climate change, as well as to develop practical tools that can be used by tourism policy-makers and managers to foster the sustainable growth of the industry. The impacts and opportunities pertinent to the tourism sector are also underlined in the 2007 reports of the Intergovernmental Panel on Climate Change and the Global Environment Outlook.

The Davos Conference and the London Ministerial meeting held in November 2007, together with the release of this report, are an integral part of the common UN system effort to develop a climate change response framework, and constituted the tourism input at the UN Climate Summit held in Bali in December 2007. This process is possible thanks to the close collaboration between the World Tourism Organization, the United Nations Environment Programme and the World Meteorological Organization, and we are confident that it will contribute to the establishment of an effective and comprehensive climate change framework for the post-2012 period. The three agencies have joined forces with the aim of ensuring an effective response to the challenges ahead, in the true spirit of the 'Delivering as one' message of the UN family.

Francesco Frangialli
Secretary-General
World Tourism Organization

Achim Steiner
UN Under Secretary-General
Executive Director
United Nations Environment
Programme

Michel Jarraud
Secretary-General
World Meteorological Organization

Acknowledgements

This publication has been coordinated by Luigi Cabrini and Gabor Vereczi at the Sustainable Development of Tourism Department of UNWTO, in cooperation with Stefanos Fotiou at UNEP and Leslie Malone at WMO.

UNWTO, UNEP and WMO are grateful to the following for their contribution:

Authorship team of the technical study:

Dr. Daniel Scott (Lead Author, University of Waterloo, Canada, Lead of the WMO Expert Team on Climate and Tourism); Dr. Bas Amelung (University of Maastricht, Netherlands); Dr. Susanne Becken (Lincoln University, New Zealand, Oceania/Southeast Asia Representative of WMO Expert Team on Climate and Tourism); Dr. Jean-Paul Ceron (Limoges University, France); Ghislain Dubois (TEC Conseil, France); Dr. Stefan Gössling (Lund University, Sweden and Western Norway Research Institute, Norway); Paul Peeters (Breda University of Applied Sciences, Netherlands); Dr. Murray C. Simpson (University of Oxford, England).

Advisors and reviewers:

UNWTO: Geoffrey Lipman, Eugenio Yunis, Chris Lyle, John Kester, Sandra Carvao, Julian Fischer

UNEP: Charles Arden-Clarke, Martina Otto, Mark Radka, Helena Rey de Assis

WMO: Rupa Kumar Kolli

External reviewers: Martin Brackenbury (International Federation of Tour Operators), Christian Hochfeld (Öko-Institut), Suzana Kahn Ribeiro (Universidade Federal do Rio de Janeiro)

This publication has been financed by UNWTO, UNEP (with a contribution of the French Ministry of Ecology, Sustainable Development and Physical Planning, under the Marrakech Task Force on Sustainable Tourism Development) and WMO.

Introduction

This publication reflects the importance attached by the tourism sector to the impacts of climate change and contains valuable scientific and technical information. It also constitutes an important input in the ongoing commitment of the United Nations to respond to the challenge of climate change. The publication contains two distinct parts.

The first, entitled "The International Debate" collects the main results of a series of events focused on climate change and tourism, which took place in the second half of 2007. The participants at the Davos International Conference (1-3 October 2007) adopted a Declaration, which represents the position of a wide spectrum of tourism stakeholders from the public and the private sector. The Davos Declaration acknowledges the urgency to further assess the impacts deriving from the relation between tourism and climate change and sets out directions for common actions from the tourism sector. At the Ministerial Summit held in London on 13 November 2007 and at the UNWTO General Assembly (Cartagena de Indias, Colombia, 23-29 November 2007) the Davos Declaration was extensively reviewed, and a number of important considerations, which complement and further elaborate on its content, were discussed and adopted.

The London Conclusions and the Resolution adopted by UNWTO Member States in Colombia reflect the consensus reached in these forums and reiterate some key messages: climate change should be addressed without losing sight of other priorities, especially poverty alleviation and tourism contribution to the Millennium Development Goals; there should be no discrimination against developing countries by creating obstacles to their economic development; financial resources should be secured for those especially vulnerable to climate change; a disproportionate burden should not be imposed on the tourism sector; and initiatives to address climate change in the tourism sector should be integrated within the existing UN framework.

The second part is a technical report, which analyzes in detail the relations between tourism and climate change, the impact of climate change at destinations, the adaptation options and strategies and the implications for tourism demand patterns. The report contains as well the first detailed assessment ever made of greenhouse gas emissions from tourism related activities, together with an analysis of mitigation policies and measures.

This study was committed by UNWTO, in cooperation with the United Nations Environment Programme (UNEP) and the World Meteorological Organization (WMO), to a team of prominent experts, with reviews by relevant staff of the three international organizations as well as by other external reviewers. UNWTO elaborated a set of tourism statistical data to be used for the calculation of greenhouse gas emissions while the expert's team took responsibility for the scientific aspects of the technical study relating to climate change, which are based on the broader research carried out by the Intergovernmental Panel on Climate Change (IPCC). The Annexes contain a detailed description on methodology and terminology used for these calculations. A summary of the preliminary findings of this report was presented at the Davos Conference, and it is included as the executive summary of this report.

We wish to thank all those who have contributed to this important work.

Luigi Cabrini
Director, Sustainable Development of Tourism
World Tourism Organization

Part I
The International Debate

Chapter 1

Second International Conference on Climate Change and Tourism
(Davos, 1–3 October 2007)

1.1 Programme of the Second International Conference on Climate Change and Tourism

Opening Session

- Ambassador Dr. Eric **Scheidegger,** Deputy Director of the Secretariat of State for Economic Affairs SECO, Switzerland

- Mr. Francesco **Frangialli,** Secretary-General, UNWTO

- Mr. Shafqat **Kakakhel,** Deputy Executive Director, UNEP

- Mr. R. D. J. **Lengoasa,** Assistant Secretary-General, WMO

- Mr. André **Schneider,** MD and COO, World Economic Forum

Conference Overview and Key Trends

- Prof. Geoffrey **Lipman,** Assistant Secretary-General, UNWTO

- Dr. Youssef **Nassef,** Manager, Adaptation, UNFCCC

- Dr. Daniel **Scott,** UNWTO Expert, Canada Research Chair in Global Change and Tourism, Faculty of Environmental Studies, University of Waterloo

Roundtable Discussion: How the tourism sector responds

Moderated by Ms. Fionnuala **Sweeney,** CNN Anchor

- Dr. Philippe **Rochat,** Executive Director, Air Transport Action Group

- Dr. Sapta **Nirwandar,** Secretary-General, Ministry of Culture and Tourism, Indonesia

- Mr. Renton **de Alwis,** Chairman, Sri Lanka Tourist Board

- Mr. Lelei **Lelaulu,** President, Counterpart International

- Ms. Cathleen **Johnson,** Executive Vice President, General Manager, Global Tourism Director, Edelman Inc.

- Mr. Christopher **Brown,** Chair, UNWTO Business Council, MD/CEO, TTF Australia

- Mr. Ghassan **Aïdi,** President, IH&RA

Plenary Panel Sessions on Adaptation at Tourism Destinations

Panel 1: Coastal Destinations and Small Islands

Moderated by Mr. Gabor **Vereczi,** Chief of Environment and Quality Section, Sustainable Development of Tourism Department, UNWTO

- Mr. Christopher **Rodrigues,** Chairman, VisitBritain

- Dr. Abdulla **Mausoom,** Director-General, Maldives Tourism Board

- Ms. Banuve **Kaumaitotoya,** Permanent Secretary for Tourism and Environment, Fiji

- Mr. Mahmoud **El Kaissouni,** Advisor to the Minister on Environment Affairs, Egypt

- Mr. Michael **Nalletamby,** Director-General, Policy and International Cooperation, Seychelles

- Mr. Andrew **Skeat,** Executive Director, Great Barrier Reef Marine Park Authority, Australia

Panel 2: Mountain Regions and Winter Tourism

Moderated by Mr. Luigi **Cabrini,** Director, Sustainable Development of Tourism Department, UNWTO

- Dr. Shardul **Agrawala,** Principal Economist Climate Change, Environment Directorate, OECD

- Dr. Walter **Ammann,** Conference Chairman IDRC Davos, Swiss Federal Institute for Snow and Avalanche Research SLF

- Mr. Arthur **de Jong,** Mountain Planning and Environmental Resource Manager, Whistler and Blackcomb Mountain, Canada

- H.E. Mr. Predrag **Nenezic,** Minister of Tourism and Environment, Montenegro

- Mr. André **Vallerand,** President, World Centre of Excellence for Destinations of Montreal

Panel 3: Nature-based Destinations

Moderated by Mr. Stefanos **Fotiou,** Programme Officer, Tourism and Environment, UNEP

- Mr. Wayne **Calder,** General Manager, Business Development Group, Tourism Division, Department of Industry, Tourism and Resources, Australia

- Dr. Andreas **Fischlin,** Group Director, Institute of Integrative Biology, Swiss Federal Institute of Technology, Zurich

- Dr. John **Hull,** Senior Lecturer, AUT University, New Zealand

- Ms. Desislava **Mihalkova,** Chief Expert, State Agency for Tourism, Bulgaria

- Ms. Ljubica **Milojevic,** Senior Advisor for International Tourism Affairs, Ministry of Economy and Regional Development, Republic of Serbia

- Mr Engelbert **Ruoss,** Director, Venice Office, UNESCO

- Mr. Bruce **Poon Tip,** CEO, G.A.P. Adventures, Canada

Plenary Panel Session on Mitigation in the Tourism Industry

Panel 1: Transport, Tour Operation and Accommodation

Moderated by Prof. Geoffrey **Lipman,** Assistant Secretary-General, UNWTO

- Mr. Robert J. **Aaronson,** Director-General, Airport Council International
- Mr. Jeff **Gazzard,** Aviation Environment Federation, United Kingdom
- Mr. Jens **Hügel,** Head, Sustainable Development, International Road Transport Union
- Mr. Michel **Lavernhe,** Director of Environmental Affairs, AirFrance
- Mr. Christopher **Lyle,** UNWTO Representative to ICAO and Expert on Aviation Issues
- Dr. Philippe **Rochat,** President, Air Transport Action Group

Panel 2: Transport, Tour Operation and Accommodation

Moderated by Mr. Eugenio **Yunis,** Director of Programme and Coordination, UNWTO

- Mr. Martin **Brackenbury,** President, IFTO
- Ms. Thea **Chiesa,** Associate Director, Head Aviation, Travel & Tourism Industries, World Economic Forum
- Dr. Wolf Michael **Iwand,** Executive Director, Group Corporate Environmental Management/ Sustainable Development, TUI AG
- Dr. Tom **Selänniemi,** Chairman, Tour operators Initiative

Panel 3: Transport, Tour Operation and Accommodation

Moderated by Mrs. Leslie **Malone,** Scientific Officer, WMO

- Mr. Ghassan **Aïdi,** President, IH&RA
- Mr. Antoni **Costa i Costa,** President, Paradores, Spain
- Mr. Peter **de Jong,** President and CEO, PATA
- Ms. Hélène **Roques,** Director, Sustainable Development Department, Accor Group, France

Conclusions and Davos Declaration

Co-chaired by

- Mr. Luigi **Cabrini,** Director, Sustainable Development of Tourism Department, UNWTO
- Mr. Stefanos **Fotiou,** Programme Officer, Tourism and Environment, UNEP
- Prof. Dr. Peter **Keller,** Head Tourism, State Secretariat Economic Affairs, Switzerland
- Prof. Geoffrey **Lipman,** Assistant Secretary-General, UNWTO
- Mrs. Leslie **Malone,** Scientific Officer, WMO

1.2 Conclusions from the Panel Sessions

The following conclusions have been derived from presentations delivered by panellists representing public, private, NGO and research institutions, and the subsequent interventions and debates involving the audience at the Second International Conference on Climate Change and Tourismus, held in Davos, Swizerland, 1–3 October 2007.

1.2.1 Adaptation Responses in Specific Types of Destinations

1.2.1.1 Coastal and island destinations

Conclusions:

Beach tourism remains the dominating market segment, constituting a key part of the economy of most SIDS and developing countries.

Coastal and island destinations are highly vulnerable to direct and indirect impacts of climate change (such as storms and extreme climatic events, coastal erosion, physical damage to infrastructure, sea level rise, flooding, water shortages and water contamination), given that most infrastructure is located within short distance of the shoreline. This high vulnerability often couples with a low adaptive capacity, especially in SIDS and coastal destinations of developing countries.

The strong seasonality of beach tourism has to be taken into consideration, as it can be exacerbated by climate change. In many beach destinations the high tourist season coincides with low water regimes in dry seasons, aggravating water management and environmental issues.

The impacts of climate change and global warming will vary greatly in the different coastal regions, and might bring opportunities as well. For example, in traditional summer beach destinations (like the Mediterranean) shoulder seasons might lengthen, and winter season might be more appealing to tourists, providing opportunities to reduce seasonality and expand the tourism product. Northern coastal areas might benefit from warmer summers, attracting more tourists and lengthening summer season.

Recommended measures:

- 'Soft' coastal protection to prevent erosion (e.g., reforestation of mangroves, reef protection);

- enhanced design, siting standards and planning guidelines for tourism establishments;

- integrate climate change factors into regulatory frameworks for tourism development, such as Environmental Impact Assessment for tourism infrastructure and establishments;

- implementation of tourism development plans within the framework of Integrated Coastal Zone Management (ICZM) processes and spatial planning such as zoning;

- shade provision and crop diversification;

- reduce tourism pressures on coral reefs;

- water conservation techniques, such as rainwater storage, the use of water-saving devices, or waste-water recycling;

- diversification of the tourism product to less-climate dependent and seasonal activities, such as ecotourism;

- education/awareness raising among tourism businesses and their staff, as well as tourists;

- awareness and preparedness to face extreme climatic events and disasters at the national and local levels through improved coordination between disaster management offices, tourism administrations, businesses and host communities;

- improved provision of climatic information to the tourism sector through cooperation with national meteorological services;

- insurance cover (or alternative schemes) for the recovery of infrastructural and other damage;

- drainage and watershed management to reduce flood and erosion risks;

- support protected area management, and other means of the conservation of coastal ecosystems in order to enhance their resilience.

Climate change adaptation can only been implemented effectively in an integrated policy framework. Coordination between agencies to allow mainstreaming of climate change and sustainable development are essential in coastal zones and islands.

Many coastal destinations and most SIDS depend on long-haul flights for their tourism-driven economies. Mitigation policies should be developed in a way that do not jeopardise the tourism sector of these destinations.

1.2.1.2 Mountain and winter tourism destinations

Conclusions:

Mountain regions are important destinations for global tourism. Snow cover and pristine mountain landscapes, the principal attractions for tourism in these regions, are the features that are most vulnerable to climate change. Besides the negative impacts, climate change can also bring opportunities in mountain areas. While winter season might shorten, summer season might lengthen, providing opportunities for other types of outdoor activities and tourism business that supply them (e.g., trekking, hiking, mountain biking, etc.).

Recommended measures:

- Stimulate product and seasonal diversification: e.g., creating spas, all-year tourism;

- implement snow-making, and make it more efficient;

- groom ski slopes to reduce snow depth requirements;

- preserve glacier areas;

- move ski areas to higher altitudes or to colder north slopes;

- improve insurance cover in the face of extreme events and natural disasters (e.g., avalanches);

- promote industry partnerships (integration within resorts, cooperation between resorts) to reduce economic vulnerability and share the cost of snow-making;

- educate and raise awareness among tourists about the impacts of global environmental change on the Alpine landscape;

- combine mitigation and adaptation measures into integrated and coherent strategies;

- improve water use and protect Alpine watersheds;

- improve emergency preparedness, implement and improve warning and evacuation systems, and put avalanche prevention infrastructure into place.

1.2.1.3 Nature-based destinations

Conclusions:

Nature-based tourism relies on a high diversity of tourism resources (landscapes, flagship species, ecosystems, outdoor activities relying on specific resources like water level in rivers for canoeing, etc.). These resources are highly variable in space, and will be affected by climate change in various ways. It is rather difficult to assess the magnitude of climate change impacts in nature-based destinations, given this diversity of resources, compared for example to ski resorts, (relying principally on snow conditions), or coastal resorts (relying mainly on beach and bathing water conditions). Although ecosystems can be highly vulnerable to climate change impacts, probably there are good adaptation options in ecotourism, given the wide range of activities that can be developed and conducted in natural areas. Therefore, there are good possibilities to design effective adaptation strategies for ecotourism and nature-based destinations.

Recommended measures:

- Develop response plans; i.e., water supply planning (in drought susceptible destinations), risk assessment and preparedness strategies, and implement early warning systems (e.g., for flooding);

- improve adaptive capacity of authorities and managers of protected areas through capacity building initiatives, especially in biodiversity hotspots of LDCs and developing countries;

- establish scientific monitoring survey programmes to assess ecosystem changes and take necessary protection measures (monitoring activities could especially focus on species and habitats most vulnerable to climate change impacts and most important for tourism activities);

- promote product diversification, for example: opening up new 'micro destinations' and attractions within and adjacent to an already popular national park or heritage site; diversification is especially important where key elements of the nature-based product are threatened (e.g., polar bear watching in Northern Canada);

- carry out re-design or redefinition of protected areas, for example revision of zoning of certain areas, extending protected area to a larger surface, creation of migratory corridors to allow threatened species to more easily find new geographic ranges;

- reduce or remove external stresses such as pollution and in the case of marine resources, agricultural run-off;

- promote the application of integrated tourism carrying capacity assessment techniques (considering physical, economic, environmental, socio-cultural and managerial aspects) in protected areas as a tool for tourism planning;

- improve visitors and congestion management to prevent overuse of sites and physical impacts of visitation;

- promote mitigation options amongst environmentally conscious eco-tourists, e.g., through offsetting their trips to nature-based tourism destinations;

- ensure active participation of local communities living within or near protected areas, in policy making and management processes;

- take into consideration local and traditional knowledge to develop coping and adaptation strategies;

- develop replicable methodologies and share knowledge across nature-based destinations.

1.2.2 Mitigation Responses in Tourism Sub-Sectors

1.2.2.1 Transportation

Conclusions:

Transportation causes around 75% of the CO_2 emissions generated by tourism, with aviation representing the bulk part of it (40%). Although tourism transport has a relatively small share in current global emissions, there is a need to develop effective mitigation measures, considering its projected dynamic growth. In the mitigation efforts technological development is still a key tool, but it is unable to solve the problem of climate change on its own. Therefore, for effective mitigation in the transport sector there is a need to implement a mix of measures, including technological improvements, regulatory and market based measures, as well as behavior changes. In any market-based measures the position of developing countries should be considered carefully to ensure that poverty reduction objectives are not jeopardized – which might imply increasing flights to deliver tourism exports.

Recommended measures:

- Create a fleet renewal fund;

- provide incentives for increased rate of technological development;

- increase efficiency in routing and air traffic management systems;

- develop and install global guidance for off-setting schemes specifically for use amongst businesses;

- engage an in-depth assessment of the potential impacts of market-based instruments and levies on the different components of the tourism industry (accommodation, tour operators, travel agencies, airlines, railway companies, coach business, ferries, etc.) and on different market segments (short-haul, mid and long-haul, developed and developing countries, domestic and international, etc). Especially for open and closed trading systems, emission reduction incentives, emission taxation and trading can be considered;

- encourage partnerships between different transport and tourism stakeholders with the objective to reduce emissions through optimizing the value chain;

- promote the use of public transport by integrated actions to boost the use of train and coach in developed countries (investment in infrastructure such as large scale high speed train, improvement of international train booking systems, regional train and transport 'on demand', improve inter-modal connections) and actions to safeguard and improve the still highly used rail and coach systems in most developing countries;

- improve consumer awareness and transparency by indicating emissions on transport tickets and product brochures;

- create a standard for carbon footprint labeling on all tourism products, like transport tickets, accommodations, activities and packages;

- involve destinations through actions to create and improve low-carbon transport access (like the Alpine Pearls Project and the Sri Lanka 'Earth Lung' initiative).

1.2.2.2 Tour operators

Conclusions:

Tour operators could play a central role in mitigation, through their capacity in influencing the whole tourism supply chain, and shape demand patterns. They thus could play a role in customers' awareness raising and soft mobility product development. Compared to the transport sector, tour operators and travel agents are probably less sensitive to the possible impacts of mitigation policies: they sell complete products where travel forms part of a complex holiday experience, well-being and pleasure. Innovation is a key factor for effective and timely adaptation.

Recommended measures:

- Develop and implement soft mobility products (low emissions modes of transport, especially train and coach, as well as low emissions in accommodation and activities);

- improve and develop partnerships between tour operators and railways, especially within reservation systems;

- integrate climate change mitigation criteria within existing initiatives of the tour operator industry, such as the Tour Operators' Initiative;

- improve computer reservation systems and global distribution systems (CRS and GDS) in order to calculate GHG emissions, so as to allow travel agents to propose soft mobility products;

- adapt national, regional and local promotion and marketing plans, so as to direct the marketing efforts towards the less carbon intensive markets;

- promote tourism at short-haul distances, domestic or between neighboring countries, specifically within the often less developed regions near the borders;

- develop products with increased length of stay, especially for long-haul and mid haul destinations;

- support destinations to introduce adaptations and mitigation measures;

- use the tourism industry as a 'lobby' for more ambitious national and regional mitigation strategies.

1.2.2.3 Accommodation establishments

Conclusions:

The accommodation sector represents approximately 20% of emissions generated from tourism activities, and is an intensive energy user, but there is huge potential for improving its carbon efficiency. Even using existing technologies and best practices, emissions from the accommodation sector could be reduced by 30–40%. For tourist establishments good energy management should mean good business, due to the savings in the energy bill. An increasing number of hotel chains, motivated by external and internal drivers are documenting their energy use and taking action in order to improve energy-efficiency, reduce energy use and apply renewable energy sources. Some hotel chains have even established climate funds where a small percentage of the profits generated in their hotels is transferred. Energy management issues form integral part of the numerous certification systems and eco-labels working with accommodation establishments on a voluntary basis, and are also actively promoted through international schemes, such as the International Hotels Environment Initiative.

There is no explicit evidence that, at present, tourists deliberately select their accommodation because of such 'green' initiatives; other factors, including comfort, price, and facilities dominate, but there is reason to believe that tourists are supportive of energy-efficient environments.

Tourists on holiday expect and pay for certain luxuries. However, clients may be willing to participate in energy reduction efforts, if it does not greatly diminish their holiday experience, if it is easy (or mandatory), or if it saves them money.

The sector must take steps to become more environmentally sustainable, even if initially there are costs for implementation of the changes (most energy efficient choices prove cost-effective in the longer term), and even if the customers do not demand it as part of their expectations. In order to meet the sustainable development goals for energy-efficient operations, the sector must find a way to avoid the fragmentation driven by competitiveness, and work together in order to shape policies, not just react to them.

Recommended measures:

- Energy conservation and efficiency in buildings and tourist attractions:

    - setting targets and benchmarking, apply certification;

    - integrating sustainability and customer comfort;

    - motivating employees and customers through awareness-raising and through incentives for energy reduction;

    - enhanced building siting, and design (orientation, natural ventilation, insulation, etc.);

    - reducing the need for air conditioning where possible;

    - installation of devices that permit heating, cooling and lighting only when the room is occupied;

    - use of energy-efficient appliances (light bulbs, heat exchangers, etc.);

    - frequent maintenance and cleaning of heating, cooling and refrigeration equipment;

- use of alternative fuels (e.g., biodiesel) and renewable energy sources (e.g., wind, photovoltaic, solar, thermal, geothermal, biomass and waste);

- integrated emission management (including supply chain management) and wider environmental management (e.g., waste), designating manager specified on environmental management systems (EMS) and emission issues;

- awareness-raising among customers on recycling;

- development of an environmental 'Code of Ethics', (checklist or criteria that a hotel chain can provide to its suppliers/providers, to help them perform their services to the sector in an environmentally respectful manner;

- capacity building, and climate change and environment related education for managers of the accommodation establishments and in related sectors; such as architecture, construction and engineering;

- development of a network of climate change focal points in the accommodation sector to promote activities proposed in the Davos Report and Declaration;

- inclusion of energy-efficiency and renewable energy use support programmes in national tourism policies and development plans (Agenda 21, guidelines, regulations, incentives, planning, capacity building, stakeholder cooperation);

- development of links with international policies (e.g., Clean Development Mechanism), cooperation and standards.

Chapter 2

Davos Declaration: Climate Change and Tourism – Responding to Global Challenges

The international community is taking concerted action against climate change around a commonly agreed framework led by the United Nations. This UN framework will seek to establish a long term post-Kyoto roadmap with rapid deployment and targeted milestones. The tourism sector has an important place in that framework, given its global economic and social value, its role in sustainable development and its strong relationships with climate.

To support this action the World Tourism Organization (UNWTO), jointly with the United Nations Environment Programme (UNEP) and the World Meteorological Organization (WMO), with the support of the World Economic Forum (WEF) and the Swiss Government, convened the Second International Conference on Climate Change and Tourism, in Davos, Switzerland, from 1 to 3 October 2007. This event, building on the results of the First International Conference organised on this topic in Djerba, Tunisia in 2003, gathered 450 participants from over 80 countries and 22 international organizations, private sector organizations and companies, research institutions, NGOs and the media, with the aim of responding in a timely and balanced way to climate change imperatives in the tourism sector. In preparation of this Conference the organizers commissioned a report to provide an extensive review of current impacts and analyse options for possible actions.

The Conference agreed that:

- climate is a key resource for tourism and the sector is highly sensitive to the impacts of climate change and global warming, many elements of which are already being felt. It is estimated to contribute some 5% of global CO_2 emissions;

- tourism – business and leisure – will continue to be a vital component of the global economy, an important contributor to the Millennium Development Goals and an integral, positive element in our society;

- given tourism's importance in the global challenges of climate change and poverty reduction, there is a need to urgently adopt a range of policies which encourages truly sustainable tourism that reflects a 'quadruple bottom line' of environmental, social, economic and **climate** responsiveness;

- the tourism sector must rapidly respond to climate change, within the evolving UN framework and progressively reduce its Greenhouse Gas (GHG) contribution if it is to grow in a sustainable manner; this will require action to:

  - **mitigate** its GHG emissions, derived especially from transport and accommodation activities;

  - **adapt** tourism businesses and destinations to changing climate conditions;

  - apply existing and new **technology** to improve energy efficiency; and

  - secure **financial** resources to help poor regions and countries.

The Conference calls for the following actions.

1) **Governments and International Organizations:**

   - Incorporate tourism in the implementation of existing commitments under the United Nations Framework Convention on Climate Change (UNFCCC) and its Kyoto Protocol, and respond to the call by the United Nations Secretary-General for launching, at the 13th session of the

UNFCCC Conference of the Parties in Bali, December 2007, an effective and comprehensive climate change framework for the post-2012 period.

– Implement concrete, simultaneous actions for mitigation, adaptation, technology and financing, consistent with the Millennium Development Goals.

– Provide financial, technical and training support to tourism destinations and operators in developing countries (especially in the least developed countries and Small Island Developing States) to ensure that they can participate in the global climate response framework, through established initiatives, such as the Clean Development Mechanism.

– Promote, at all levels, interdisciplinary partnerships, networks and information exchange systems essential to sustainable development of the sector.

– Collaborate in international strategies, policies and action plans to reduce GHG emissions in the transport (in cooperation with ICAO and other aviation organizations), accommodation and related tourism activities.

– Introduce education and awareness programs for all tourism stakeholders – public and private sector – as well as consumers.

– Develop regional and local climate information services tailored to the tourism sector and promote their use among tourism stakeholders. Build capacities for interpretation and application of this information, strengthening collaboration with WMO's National Meteorological Services.

– Implement policy, regulatory, financial, managerial, educational, behavioural, diversification, research and monitoring measures, for effective adaptation and mitigation.

2)   Tourism Industry and Destinations

– Take leadership in implementing concrete measures (such as incentives) in order to mitigate climate change throughout the tourism value chain and to reduce risk to travellers, operators and infrastructure due to dynamic climate variability and shift. Establish targets and indicators to monitor progress.

– Promote and undertake investments in energy-efficiency tourism programmes and use of renewable energy resources, with the aim of reducing the carbon footprint of the entire tourism sector.

– Integrate tourism in the formulation and implementation of regional, national and local level adaptation and mitigation strategies and implementation plans. The Nairobi Work Programme on Impacts, Vulnerability and Adaptation to Climate Change, coordinated by UNFCCC, represents an important opportunity for the tourism sector to enhance knowledge, increase capacities and stimulate action.

– Strive to conserve biodiversity, natural ecosystems and landscapes in ways which strengthen resilience to climate change and ensure a long-term sustainable use of the environmental resource base of tourism – in particular those that serve as 'earth lungs' (carbon sinks), sequestering GHGs through forest management and other biological programmes, or that protect coastlines (e.g., mangroves and coral reefs).

– Seek to achieve increasingly carbon free environments by diminishing pollution through design, operations and market responsive mechanisms.

– Implement climate-focused product diversification, to reposition destinations and support systems, as well as to foster all-season supply and demand.

– Raise awareness among customers and staff on climate change impacts and engage them in response processes.

3)   Consumers:

– In their choices for travel and destination, tourists should be encouraged to consider the climate, economic, societal and environmental impacts of their options before making a decision and, where possible to reduce their carbon footprint, or offset emissions that cannot be reduced directly.

– In their choices of activities at the destination, tourists should also be encouraged to opt for environmentally-friendly activities that reduce their carbon footprint as well as contribute to the preservation of the natural environment and cultural heritage.

4)   Research and Communications Networks:

– Encourage targeted, multi-disciplinary research on impacts of climate change in order to address regional gaps in current knowledge, develop tools for risk assessment and cost-benefit analyses with which to gauge the feasibility of various responses.

– Include environmental and climate specific subjects in the study curricula of tourism training programmes and extend these to broader educational systems.

– Promote responsible travel that supports 'quadruple bottom line' sustainable tourism, incorporating climate, environmental, social and economic considerations.

– Raise awareness on tourism's economic role as a tool for development, and present information on causes and effects of climate change based on sound science, in a fair, balanced and user-friendly manner.

The Conference

• Sets out a range of specific actions to be taken by all stakeholders in the sector to immediately begin to establish and implement a long range carbon-neutral roadmap.

• Invites governments and international organizations, the tourism industry, consumers, research and communications networks to implement these recommendations, with concrete commitments and action plans, and to use the UNWTO on-line Climate Change and Tourism Information Exchange Service as a platform, for committed stakeholders to register their pledges and activities toward adaptation and mitigation on an on-going basis.

• Stresses the need that UNWTO, in collaboration with UNEP and WMO, continue to lead this process, and to consider convening a Third Conference on Climate Change and Tourism, at an appropriate time in the future, to review progress, to maintain response levels and to identify further needs and actions.

• Urges action by the entire tourism sector to face climate change as one of the greatest challenges to sustainable development, and to the Millennium Development Goals in the 21st Century.

Chapter 3

Conclusions of the Ministers' Summit on Tourism and Climate Change
(London, United Kingdom, 13 November 2007)

The participants to the Ministers' Summit on Tourism and Climate Change gathered in London, UK on 13 November 2007 welcome the initiatives taken by the tourism sector, under the leadership of UNWTO in cooperation with UNEP and WMO, to address the causes and consequences of climate change for the tourism sector.

The participants strongly endorse the Davos Declaration and urge all tourism stakeholders to follow its recommendations. Some delegations made however specific comments, and request the Secretary-General of UNWTO to report on them to the UNWTO General Assembly and at the Bali summit on climate change.

The Delegation of Australia wishes to record the following statement:

"Tourism Ministers support effective global action to address climate change. Policy responses should be balanced and comprehensive and focus on measures which are economically efficient. The tourism sector must play a strong role as part of a broader response to climate change; however it should not be disadvantaged through the imposition of a disproportionate burden either on tourism as a whole or on vital components such as aviation".

The Delegation of Bangladesh wishes to stress that special consideration should be given to Least Developed Countries and Small Island Developing States in the provision of financial, technical and training support to tourism destinations and operators. A specific mention should be made to support their National Adaptation Programmes of Action on climate change through contributions to the UNFCCC LDC Trust Fund. It also suggests to add a specific reference to the UNESCO World Heritage Sites, when describing actions addressed at conserving biodiversity, natural ecosystems and landscape.

The delegation of India wishes to put on record the following statements:

"India is acutely aware of the considerable challenge we face today from climate change. We, like other developing countries, bear an inordinate share of the burden of climate change even though this is due to high-level emissions of developed countries. In such circumstances, we must significantly shore up our abilities to cope with and adapt to climate change. To be able to do so, we need development, which is also the best form of adaptation."

"The UN Framework Convention on Climate Change (UNFCCC) has one of the largest numbers of State Parties of any multilateral instrument. It is, therefore, appropriate that matters relating to climate change are addressed in the UNFCCC. At the UNWTO we need to try and take stock of the situation as it affects our sector and see what can be done to adapt to the inevitability of further global warming, especially as far as developing countries are concerned."

The delegation of Brazil wishes to reinforce the principle of common and differentiated responsibilities (as included in the UNFCCC), especially in the section of the Davos Declaration calling for actions of the different stakeholders. It also suggests to add the following paragraph under the section relating to actions from Governments and international Organizations: "Assist developing countries where the tourism sector is particularly vulnerable to the adverse effect of climate change, in order to allow them to meet the related costs of adaptation".

The delegation of Uruguay suggests adding the following paragraph related to the actions of tourism industry and destinations: "The private sector should proportionally contribute to the costs that imply preventing, mitigating and adapting to climate change".

The delegation of Maldives suggests undertaking awareness activities on the importance of climate change.

Chapter 4

Resolution on Tourism and Climate Change adopted by UNWTO General Assembly, Seventeenth Session
(Cartagena de Indias, Colombia, 23–29 November 2007)

The General Assembly,

Having taken cognizance of the document relative to climate change and tourism and of the report of the Secretary-General.

Taking into account that the effects of climate change have already a serious impact on several tourism destinations; that certain activities relating to the tourism sector generate only a small proportion of the total greenhouse gas emissions; that there is scientific evidence that global warming will continue to increase at an alarming rate if substantial remedial actions are not taken.

1. **Expresses** its appreciation for the active engagement of the UNWTO Secretariat to analyse the complex issues deriving from the inter-relations between climate change and tourism with a view to taking effective measures of adaptation and mitigation, through transfer of advanced clean technologies, to combat the effects of warming on the tourism sector;

2. **Expresses** its appreciation to the Secretary-General for having organized the Djerba Conference on 9-11 April 2003, the Davos Conference on 1-3 October 2007 and the London Ministerial Summit on 13 November 2007, which generated meaningful discussions on climate change and tourism;

3. **Takes note** with satisfaction of the participation in these two events of the tourism authorities of a broad number of countries, and of a wide spectrum of tourism stakeholders from the public and private sector and welcomes the exchange of views on the problems and the actions to be undertaken;

4. **Takes note** of the main elements of the Davos Declaration issued on 3 October 2007 and of the conclusions reached at the London Ministerial Summit on 13 November and emphasizes that the recommendations emanating from these fora should not discriminate against developing countries by creating obstacles to their economic development and in particular of those developing countries located at long distance from tourists generating markets;

5. **Recognizes** the urgent need for the tourism sector to adapt to climate change conditions; to mitigate greenhouse gas emissions in line with the principle of common but differentiated responsibilities included in the United Nations Framework Convention on Climate Change (UNFCCC); to help the transfer of new technologies especially through the clean development mechanism and to make efforts to secure financial resources to assist developing countries which are especially vulnerable to climate change; and **calls** on governments, international organizations, professionals of the tourism sector, media, and other actors to engage in the response to one of the greatest challenges of our times;

6. **Reiterates** the importance for the tourism sector to identify consensus measures to address climate change but without losing sight of all other priorities, especially poverty alleviation and tourism contribution to Millennium Development Goals;

7. **Takes note** with interest of the preliminary findings of the technical study on climate change and tourism undertaken by a group of experts under the supervision of UNWTO in cooperation with the United Nation Environment Programme (UNEP) and the World Meteorological Organization (WMO) and **welcomes** comments from the State members after the final report has been circulated by the Secretary-General; and

8. **Welcomes** the close cooperation established by UNWTO with other relevant agencies of the UN System, and in particular with UNEP and WMO, in view of the forthcoming climate change summit to be held in Bali in December 2007 and of the future actions to be taken within the UN framework, and **urges** UNWTO to work in close consultation with the UNFCCC, which is the appropriate mechanism within the UN system to address issues relating to climate change.

Chapter 5

Statement by Francesco Frangialli, Secretary-General of UNWTO, on the Occasion of the UN Conference on Climate Change
(Nusa Dua, Bali, Indonesia, 12 December 2007)

Mr. President,

Excellencies, ladies and gentlemen,

Tourism contributes to global warming, and, at the same time, is a victim of climate change.

Tourism is a central phenomenon of today's word. It has become globalised. It is growing spectacularly, from 165 millions international arrivals in 1970, to 846 millions last year, and, undoubtedly, 1.6 billion by 2020. And this, without including domestic travel.

A phenomenon of such magnitude could not remain without consequences for the climate on account of the greenhouse gas emissions generated by trips and stays. In turn, the warming caused by major human activities profoundly alters the conditions of tourism development. Small tropical islands and medium-altitude ski resorts are the first destinations to be affected. Others will follow, those for which the product is based on forests, glaciers, biodiversity and wildlife.

*　　*　　*

I have **two messages** for you today.

The **first message** is that the tourism community will not shrink back. It will participate in the common effort led by the United Nations. Two weeks ago, the General Assembly of the World Tourism Organization responsibly engaged itself. A consensus has been forged among our 153 members. I hope this Conference will reach the same level of consensus.

UNWTO members agreed that we should not sidestep the issue, by arguing that the contribution of travel and tourism to greenhouse gas emissions is limited to 5% of the total – half of which for passenger air transport. It is true, but it is not a valid excuse.

You can count on us. We are ready to take up our share of the burden. But, by the same token, we are also within our rights to tell the public opinion and the media: do not unfairly target tourism! It is an activity just as respectable as others, which satisfies needs that are just as essential.

*　　*　　*

I have a **second message:** never forget that tourism generates wealth, creates jobs, and contributes to the alleviation of poverty.

Those who say: "do not travel far from home and avoid taking planes to save several tons of carbon emissions", should think twice. Because these long-haul trips are often to countries that are home to the planet's poorest populations, which – we know – will already be the first victims of warming. These communities, like Bali, would be doubly affected if we also deprive them of the economic contribution of tourism.

*　　*　　*

To the negotiators gathered here, we would like to say: you hold an important part of our industry's destiny in your hands. Having come to Bali, you are tourists yourselves! You are part of the tourism economic pattern, even if you work in this conference room and do not stay on the beach!

As tourists, as travellers, in the decisions you are going to take, do not forget the message of tourism.

I thank you.

Part II
Technical Report

Chapter 6

Executive Summary

6.1 The New Realities of Tourism in an Era of Global Climate Change

Compelling evidence indicates that global climate has changed compared to the pre-industrial era and is anticipated to continue to change over the 21st century and beyond. The Intergovernmental Panel on Climate Change (IPCC) [1] declared that "[…] warming of the climate system is unequivocal." The global mean temperature has increased approximately 0.76° C between 1850–1899 and 2001–2005 and the IPCC [2] concluded that most of the observed increase in global average temperatures since the mid-20th century is very likely (> 90% probability) the result of human activities that are increasing greenhouse gas concentrations in the atmosphere. Discernible human influences now also extend to other aspects of climate, including ocean warming, continental-average temperatures, temperature extremes and wind patterns. [3] Widespread decreases in glaciers and ice caps and warming ocean surface temperature have contributed to sea level rise of 1.8 mm per year from 1961 to 2003, and approximately 3.1 mm per year from 1993 to 2003. The biological response of ecosystems and individual species has been recorded on every continent. [4]

The IPCC has projected that the pace of climate change is very likely (> 90% probability) to accelerate with continued greenhouse gas (GHG) emissions at or above current rates, with the best estimate that globally averaged surface temperatures will rise by 1.8° C to 4.0° C by the end of the 21st century. [5] Even if atmospheric concentrations of GHGs were stabilized at current levels, the Earth would continue to warm as a result of past GHG emissions and the thermal inertia of the oceans. The biological response to this continued warming and sea level rise would continue for several centuries. [6, 7]

Future changes in temperatures and other important features of climate will manifest themselves differently across the regions of the world (Figure 6.1). According to the IPCC, it is very likely that hot extremes, heat waves and heavy precipitation events will continue to become more frequent. It is likely that future tropical cyclones (typhoons and hurricanes) will become more intense, with larger peak wind speeds and more heavy precipitation associated with ongoing increases of tropical sea surface temperatures. There is less confidence in projections of a global decrease in numbers of tropical cyclones. The extension of the regions that will be primary affected by these extreme events with major tourism destinations highlights the need for awareness and preparedness for natural hazards at the local level through systematic capacity building and strategies for disaster risk management. Extra-tropical storm tracks are projected to shift poleward, with consequent changes in wind, precipitation and temperature patterns, continuing the broad pattern of observed trends over the last half-century. Observed decreases in snow cover are also projected to continue.

The environmental and economic risks of the magnitude of climate change projected for the 21st century are considerable and have featured prominently in recent international policy debates. [8, 9, 10] The IPCC concluded with very high confidence [11] that climate change would impede the ability of many nations to achieve sustainable development by mid-century. The Stern Review [12] on the Economics of Climate Change found that the costs of taking action to reduce GHG emissions now, are much smaller than the costs of economic and social disruption from unmitigated climate change.

Figure 6.1 IPCC representation of anticipated regional climate change

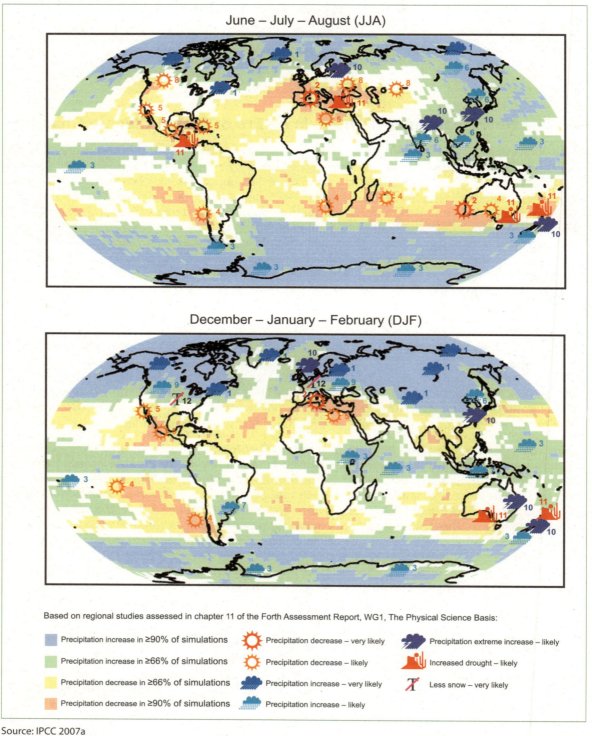

Source: IPCC 2007a

Our lifestyles, economies, health and social well-being are all affected by climate change, and although the consequences of climate change will vary on a regional basis, all nations and economic sectors will have to contend with the challenges of climate change through adaptation and mitigation. Tourism is no exception and in the decades ahead, climate change will become an increasingly pivotal issue affecting tourism development and management. [13], [14], [15], [16], [17], [18]

With its close connections to the environment and climate itself, tourism is considered to be a highly climate-sensitive economic sector similar to agriculture, insurance, energy, and transportation. [19] The regional manifestations of climate change will be highly relevant for tourism destinations and tourists alike, requiring adaptation by all major tourism stakeholders. Indeed, climate change is not a remote future event for tourism, as the varied impacts of a changing climate are becoming evident at destinations around the world and climate change is already influencing decision-making in the tourism sector.

At the same time, the tourism sector is a non-negligible contributor to climate change through GHG emissions derived especially from the transport and accommodation of tourists. [20, 21] Tourism must seek to significantly reduce its GHG emissions in accordance with the international community, which at the "Vienna Climate Change Talks 2007" recognized that global emissions of GHG need to peak in the next 10–15 years and then be reduced to very low levels, well below half of levels in 2000 by mid-century. * The tourism sector can not address the challenge of climate change in isolation, but must do so within the context of the broader international sustainable development agenda. [22, 23] The critical challenge before the global tourism sector is to develop a coherent policy strategy that decouples the projected massive growth in tourism in the decades ahead from increased energy use and GHG emissions, so as to allow tourism growth to simultaneously contribute to poverty alleviation and play a major role in achieving the United Nations Millennium Development Goals (MDG).

> "Climate change as well as poverty alleviation will remain central issues for the world community. Tourism is an important element in both. Governments and the private sector must place increased importance on these factors in tourism development strategies and in climate and poverty strategies. They are interdependent and must be dealt with in a holistic fashion."
>
> Francesco Frangialli, *UNWTO Secretary-General* (2007)

Tourism can play a significant role in addressing climate change if the innovativeness and resources of this vital global economic sector are fully mobilized and oriented towards this goal. The concern of the tourism community regarding the challenge of climate change has visibly increased over the last five years. The World Tourism Organization (UNWTO) and several partner organizations, including UNEP, convened the First International Conference on Climate Change and Tourism in Djerba, Tunisia in 2003. This event was a watershed in terms of raising awareness about the implications of climate change within the international tourism community. The Djerba Declaration recognized the complex inter-linkages between the tourism sector and climate change and established a framework for future research and policy making on adaptation and mitigation. [24] A number of individual tourism industry associations and businesses have also shown leadership on climate change, voluntarily adopting GHG emission reduction targets, engaging in public education campaigns on climate change and supporting government climate change legislation.

> "Far sighted action by the US$ 880 billion international tourism industry will send important signals to governments, industries and the public that mitigation and adaptation to the climate change challenge make economic and environmental sense. It is the kind of leadership that can encourage others to look not only to their exposure and to the risks posed by climate change, but also to the abundant opportunities and benefits of cost effective action."
>
> Achim Steiner, *UN Under-Secretary-General and UNEP Executive Director* (2007)

The scientific community has also responded, doubling the number of scientific publications that examine the interactions of tourism and climate change between 1996–2000 and 2001–2005 [25] and significantly advancing the place of tourism in the IPCC 4th Assessment Report (AR4) relative to previous assessments. [26] In 2006, the World Meteorological Organization (WMO) established an Expert Team on Climate and Tourism in collaboration with the UNWTO, with the broad mandate to advance

---

* The "Vienna Climate Change Talks 2007" represent the latest international negotiations on GHG emission reductions under the auspices of the United Nations Framework Convention on Climate Change. www.unis.unvienna.org/unis/pressrels/2007/unisinf230.html.

the application of weather and climate information in the tourism sector and understanding of the implications of climate change.

6.2 Impacts and Adaptation at Tourism Destinations

The tourism industry and destinations are clearly sensitive to climate variability and change. [27, 28, 29, 30, 31] Climate defines the length and quality of tourism seasons and plays a major role in destination choice and tourist spending. In many destinations tourism is closely linked with the natural environment. Climate affects a wide range of the environmental resources that are critical attractions for tourism, such as snow conditions, wildlife productivity and biodiversity, water levels and quality. Climate also has an important influence on environmental conditions that can deter tourists, including infectious disease, wildfires, insect or water-borne pests (e.g., jellyfish, algae blooms), and extreme events such as tropical cyclones.

There are four broad categories of climate change impacts that will affect tourism destinations, their competitiveness and sustainability.

Direct climatic impacts: Climate is a principal resource for tourism, as it co-determines the suitability of locations for a wide range of tourist activities, is a principal driver of global seasonality in tourism demand, and has an important influence on operating costs, such as heating-cooling, snow-making, irrigation, food and water supply, and insurance costs. Thus, changes in the length and quality of climate-dependent tourism seasons (i.e., sun-and-sea or winter sports holidays) could have considerable implications for competitive relationships between destinations and therefore the profitability of tourism enterprises. Studies indicate that a shift of attractive climatic conditions for tourism towards higher latitudes and altitudes is very likely. [32, 33, 34] As a result, the competitive position of some popular holiday areas are anticipated to decline (e.g., the Mediterranean in summer), whereas other areas (e.g., southern England or southern Canada) are expected to improve. Uncertainties related to tourist climate preference and destination loyalty require attention if the implications for the geographic and seasonal redistribution of visitor flows are to be projected. There are well established vulnerabilities among winter sports destinations to projected declines in natural snowfall. Even with increased snow-making, contractions in the ski industry are very likely in the European Alps, Eastern and Western North America, Australia, and Japan, although projected impacts on destinations in these nations vary in magnitude and over different time horizons. [35, 36, 37]

The IPCC [38] has concluded that changes in a number of weather extremes are probable as a result of projected climate change, including: higher maximum temperature and more hot days over nearly all land areas (very likely), greater tropical storm intensity and peak winds (likely), more intense precipitation events over many land areas (very likely), and longer and more severe droughts in many mid-latitude continental interiors (likely). Such changes will affect the tourism industry through increased infrastructure damage, additional emergency preparedness requirements, higher operating expenses (e.g., insurance, backup water and power systems, and evacuations), and business interruptions.

Indirect environmental change impacts: Because environmental conditions are such a critical resource for tourism, a wide-range of climate-induced environmental changes will have profound effects on tourism at the destination and regional level. Changes in water availability, biodiversity loss, reduced landscape aesthetic, altered agricultural production (e.g., wine tourism), increased natural hazards, coastal erosion and inundation, damage to infrastructure and the increasing incidence of vector-borne diseases will all impact tourism to varying degrees. In contrast to the varied impacts of a changed climate on tourism, the indirect effects of climate induced environmental change are likely to be largely negative. Mountain, island, and coastal destinations are considered particularly sensitive to climate-induced environmental change, as are nature-based tourism market segments. [39, 40, 41, 42, 43] UNESCO has also identified several World Heritage Sites that are critical tourist destinations, to be vulnerable to climate-induced environmental change (e.g., Venice, Italy – sea level rise; Great Barrier Reef, Australia – coral bleaching and mortality; Glacier-Waterton International Peace Park, USA and Canada – glacier retreat; and Chan Chan Archaeological Zone, Peru – El Niño-Southern Oscillation (ENSO) caused flooding and eroding). [44] While our understanding of the impacts of climate change for various destination types has improved since the Djerba Conference, it is important to emphasize that there remain major regional gaps in our knowledge of how climate change will affect the natural and cultural resources critical for tourism in Africa, the Caribbean, South America, the Middle East and large parts of East Asia. [45]

Impacts of mitigation policies on tourist mobility: National or international mitigation policies – that are policies that seek to reduce GHG emissions – are likely to have an impact on tourist flows. They will lead to an increase in transport costs and may foster environmental attitudes that lead tourists to change their travel patterns (e.g., shift transport mode or destination choices). There has been substantial recent media coverage on this topic, specifically as it relates to air travel. Long-haul destinations can be particularly affected and officials in Southeast Asia, Australia-New Zealand, and the Caribbean have expressed concern that mitigation policies could adversely impact their national tourism economy. [46, 47, 48] On the other hand, emission scenario projections developed for this report indicate that opportunities may arise for low carbon emission transport modes like coach and rail. This may also help to re-vitalize destinations that are nearer to the main markets.

Indirect societal change impacts: Climate change is thought to pose a risk to future economic growth and to the political stability of some nations. [49, 50, 51, 52] The Stern Report on the Economics of Climate Change concluded that although a global warming of only 1° C might benefit global GDP, greater climate change would eventually damage economic growth at the global scale, including the stark conclusion that unmitigated climate change could cause a reduction in consumption per capita of 20% later in the 21st century or early 22nd century. [53] Any such reduction of global GDP due to climate change would reduce the discretionary wealth available to consumers for tourism and have negative implications for anticipated future growth in tourism; however there has been no in-depth interpretation of the Stern Report [54] for the tourism sector.

> "Our actions over the coming few decades could create risks of major disruption to economic and social activity, later in this century and in the next, on a scale similar to those associated with the great wars and the economic depression of the first half of the 20th century."
>
> The Stern Report (2006)

Climate change is considered a national and international security risk that will steadily intensify, particularly under greater warming scenarios. [55, 56, 57] Climate change associated security risks have been identified in a number of regions where tourism is highly important to local/national economies. [58, 59, 60] Tourists, particularly international tourists, are averse to political instability and social unrest, [61, 62] and the negative tourism demand repercussions for the climate change security hotspots [63] are very evident. A security-related decline in tourism would exacerbate deteriorating economic performance in these destinations, potentially undermining development objectives in some LDCs. [64, 65, 66, 67]

Destination vulnerability hotspots: The integrated effects of climate change will have far-reaching consequences for tourism businesses and destinations. Importantly, climate change will generate both negative and positive impacts in the tourism sector and these impacts will vary substantially by market segment and geographic region. The implications of climate change for any tourism business or destination will also partially depend on the impacts on its competitors. A negative impact in one part of the tourism system may constitute an opportunity elsewhere. Consequently, there will be 'winners and losers' at the business, destination and nation level. Figure 6.2 provides a summary assessment of the most at-risk tourism destinations for the mid- to late-21st century. Due to the very limited information available on the potential impacts of climate change in some tourism regions, this qualitative assessment must also be considered with caution. Until systematic regional level assessments are conducted a definitive statement on the net economic or social impacts in the tourism sector will not be possible. Furthermore, the outcome most likely will depend on the extent of climate change. The impact on the tourism sector may strongly parallel that of the global economy, where a 1° C temperature rise may result in a net benefit for the world economy, but greater increases increasingly show net declines. [68]

Destination level adaptation: It is now recognised that regardless of the emissions reduction efforts, there is an inevitable need for societies around the world to adapt to unavoidable changes in climate.

[69] It is essential to emphasize that regardless of the nature and magnitude of climate change impacts, all tourism businesses and destinations will need to adapt to climate change in order to minimize associated risks and capitalize upon new opportunities, in an economically, socially and environmentally sustainable manner.

Tourists have the greatest adaptive capacity (depending on three key resources: money, knowledge and time) with relative freedom to avoid destinations impacted by climate change or shifting the timing of travel to avoid unfavourable climate conditions. Suppliers of tourism services and tourism operators at specific destinations have less adaptive capacity. Large tour operators, who do not own the infrastructure, are in a better position to adapt to changes at destinations because they can respond to clients demands and provide information to influence clients' travel choices. Destination communities and tourism operators with large investment in immobile capital assets (e.g., hotel, resort complex, marina or casino) have the least adaptive capacity.

The dynamic nature of the tourism industry and its ability to cope with a range of recent major shocks, including SARS, terrorism attacks in a number of nations, or the Asian tsunami, suggests a relatively high adaptive capacity within the tourism industry overall. The capacity to adapt to climate change is thought to vary substantially between sub-sectors, destinations, and individual businesses within the tourism industry. [70, 71, 72, 73, 74]

> "It is vital for tourism destinations [...] to anticipate the coming changes and to draw their consequences, starting now. [Adaptation] is a long-term project that must be anticipated and carefully prepared beforehand; it is not easy to see this through successfully, because it entails, all at the same time, modifying economic circuits, introducing new technologies, carrying out intensive training, investing in the creation of new products, [...] changing the minds of public authorities, entrepreneurs, host communities and tourists."
>
> Francesco Frangialli, *UNWTO Secretary-General* (2007)

The tourism sector has been adapting its operations to climate zones world-wide, using a diverse range of technological, managerial, educational, policy and behavioural adaptations to deal with climate variability. However, adaptation has figured less prominently in climate change research on tourism than in some other economic sectors (e.g., agriculture). There has been a range of research activities focusing on climate change impacts for destinations or specific tourism sectors (e.g., ski operations), but they generally have not identified properly the range of adaptation options available to tourism stakeholders. Due to a lack of integration of adaptation measures in impact analysis studies, the perspectives on projected impacts may be misleading.

Much more needs to be done to incorporate adaptation into future impact assessments in the tourism sector given its high adaptive capacity. Second, knowledge of the capability of current climate adaptations to cope successfully with future climate change remains rudimentary. [75] An important lesson learned from Hurricane Katrina and the extremely warm winter of 2006–2007 in the European Alps is that adaptations can be overwhelmed by events unexpected and beyond the range of experience of the tourism sector. Such events should be anticipated under climate change, and consequently there is a critical need for the tourism sector to evaluate the effectiveness of current adaptations under projected climate conditions. In an era of global climate change, it will no longer be sufficient to rely on past experience. The information requirements for effective, anticipatory climate change adaptation will be substantial and therefore adaptation is a critical area for future research.

Climate change is slowly entering into decision-making of a range of tourism stakeholders (e.g., investors, insurance companies, tourism enterprises, governments, and tourists); studies that have examined the climate change risk appraisal of local tourism officials and operators have consistently found relatively low levels of concern and little evidence of long-term strategic planning in anticipation of future changes in climate. * [76, 77, 78, 79, 80, 81, 82, 83] There is also some evidence that local tourism

---

*   Key destination vulnerabilities are identified at the sub-regional scale in the full technical report.

operators may be overestimating their adaptive capacity (e.g., capacity to make snow under the warmest scenarios). The incorporation of adaptation to climate change into the collective minds of private and public sector tourism decision-makers ('mainstreaming') remains several steps away. Consequently, there is a real need for effective communication between the climate change science community and tourism operators at the regional and local scale, particularly with respect to the development of climate change scenarios and indicators catered toward local tourism decision-making.

Figure 6.2 Geographic distribution of major climate change impacts affecting tourism destinations*

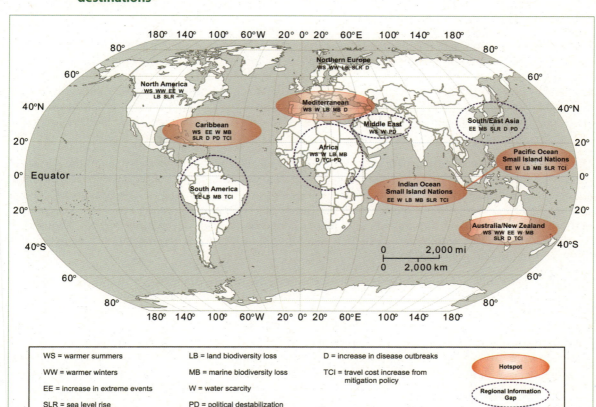

* Key destination vulnerabilities are identified at the sub-regional scale in the full technical report

6.3 Implications of Climate Change for Tourism Demand Patterns

Climate, the natural environment, and personal safety are three primary factors in destination choice, and global climate change is anticipated to have significant impacts on all three of these factors at the regional level. Tourists also have the greatest capacity to adapt to the impacts of climate change, with relative freedom to avoid destinations impacted by climate change or shifting the timing of travel to avoid unfavourable climate conditions. As such, the response of tourists to the complexity of destination impacts will reshape demand patterns and play a pivotal role in the eventual impacts of climate change on the tourism industry. Understanding and anticipating the potential geographic and seasonal shifts in tourist demand will remain critical areas of research in the future.

The evidence available from studies that have explored the potential impact of altered climate conditions for tourist demand suggests that the geographic and seasonal redistribution of tourist demand may be very large for individual destinations and countries by mid- to late-century. [84, 85] Anticipated impacts include a gradual shift in preferred destinations to higher latitudes and to higher elevations in mountainous areas. Tourists from temperate nations that currently dominate international travel (e.g., Northern Europe) are expected to spend more holidays in their home country or nearby, adapting their travel patterns to take advantage of new climatic opportunities closer to home. Tourism seasons will be altered with possibly more tourists travelling in shoulder seasons, or in winter seasons, as climate will be more appealing. This shift in travel patterns may have important implications, including proportionally more tourism spending in temperate nations and proportionally less spending in warmer nations now frequented by tourists from temperate regions. The direct effect of climate change might be significant enough to alter major intra-regional tourism flows where climate is of paramount importance, including Northern Europe to the Mediterranean and the Caribbean, North America to the Caribbean, and to a lesser extent North East Asia to Southeast Asia. However, the net effect of a change in climate on tourist demand at the global scale is expected to be limited, as there is no evidence to suggest that a change in climate will directly lead to a significant reduction of the global volume of tourism.

It is important to emphasize that it is the holistic impact of climate change on tourism environments that tourists will respond to, not just changes in climatic conditions. [86, 87] Tourism demand at the regional scale will also be affected by the range of indirect environmental and social impacts brought about by global climate change. The indirect impacts of global climate change are anticipated to influence tourist demand for specific destinations and perhaps at the regional level where political destabilization may occur, but not affect tourism demand at the global level, unless, as some economic analyses indicate, [88] global economic growth were to be adversely affected by climatic change.

The perceptions of future impacts of climate change are likely to play the central role in the decision-making of tourists and tourism investors alike, as perceptions of climate conditions or environmental changes are just as important to consumer choices as the actual conditions. Perceptions of climate change impacts in a region are often heavily influenced by the nature of media coverage. Speculation and misinformation about the impacts of climate change on tourism destinations already abounds in the media, particularly with regard to the demise of the ski industry and extreme summer temperatures in the Mediterranean region.

The combination of increased awareness of the potential environmental impacts of air travel, as reflected in a number of recent public opinion polls, [89, 90, 91] and national or international mitigation policies that increase the costs of travel, will also have important implications for shaping tourist demand. Current understanding of how price increases for travel may alter tourist mobility remains low. Past studies that have analysed the price sensitivity of air passengers, for example, show moderate [92] inelasticity (–0.7). [93] Recent market surveys have also identified highly varied willingness to pay to offset the environmental consequences of air travel. [94, 95] The perception of transport, and in particular air travel, in relation to its carbon footprint is also likely to be an important influence on tourists' responses to price changes.

Information on tourist climate preferences and key thresholds (i.e., temperature limits for a beach holiday), tourist perceptions of the environmental impacts of global climate change at destinations (i.e., perceptions of coral bleaching, diminished or lost glaciers, degraded coastlines, reduced biodiversity or wildlife prevalence), and tourist perceptions of the environmental impacts of tourism related travel and their willingness to pay to reduce this impact, remain important knowledge gaps that need to be addressed if potential long-range shifts in tourist demand are to be more accurately projected. There is also limited understanding of how climate change impacts will interact with other longer term social and market trends influencing tourism demand (e.g., globalization and economic fluctuations, fuel prices, aging populations in industrialized countries, increasing travel safety and health concerns, increased environmental and cultural awareness, advances in information and transportation technology). [96]

6.4 Emissions from Global Climate Tourism: Status and Trends

The contribution of tourism to human-induced climate change has never been comprehensively assessed. This report represents the first attempt to calculate emissions of CO_2 from three main tourism sub-sectors – transportation, accommodations, and activities – as well as the contribution to radiative forcing (i.e. including all greenhouse gases) for the year 2005. Tourism in this report refers to "[…] the activities of persons traveling to and staying in places outside their usual environment for not more than one consecutive year for leisure, business and other purposes not related to the exercise of an activity remunerated from within the place visited." * Existing databases on tourism are not directly suitable for emission inventories, so UNWTO prepared a specific database for this project with data provided for the baseline year of 2005. ** In order to refine calculations of GHG emissions from the tourism sector and effectively monitor progress on GHG emission reductions in the future, a strategic reassessment of the current system of tourism statistics will be required so that appropriate data are collected at the necessary spatial and temporal resolutions.

While CO_2 is the most important greenhouse gas from human activities, other greenhouse gases also make significant contributions to global warming. In the tourism sector, this is particularly relevant for emissions from aviation, which, at flight altitude, has an enhanced impact on global warming. Radiative forcing is thus used to calculate the entire contribution of tourist (air) travel to global warming. Radiative forcing measures the extent to which emissions of greenhouse gases raise global average temperatures now or at a specified year in the future (estimates of tourism contribution to radiative forcing will be analyzed in the full report).

International and domestic tourism emissions from three main sub-sectors are estimated to represent between 3.9% and 6.0% of global emissions in 2005, with a best estimate of 4.9%.

Table 6.1 Estimated emissions from global tourism (including same-day visitors), 2005 [a], [b]

	CO_2 (Mt)
Air transport	515
Car	420
Other transport	45
Accommodation	274
Activities	48
TOTAL	1,302
Total world [c]	26,400
Share (%)	4.9

(a) Estimates include international and domestic tourist trips, as well as same-day visitors (base year 2005).

(b) Colours represent the degree of certainty with respect to the data and underlying assumptions. Green represents a degree of uncertainty of +/-10%, blue +/-25% and red +100%/-50%.

(c) Annual fossil carbon dioxide emissions (including those from cement production), according to IPCC (2007a), *The Physical Science Basis.*[97]

Table 6.1 shows the results of the emissions for global tourism in 2005. Figure 6.3 shows that in 2005 transport generated the largest proportion of CO_2 emissions (75%) from global tourism, with approximately 40% of the total being caused by air transport alone. Emissions from accommodation and activities were estimated to be substantially lower than transport emissions, but emissions from the accommodation sub-sector are also not negligible.

---

*   As defined by the UNWTO/United Nations Recommendations on Tourism Statistics.

**   Note that this database contains estimates, as not all data needed for calculations are available. For instance, there are only estimates for domestic tourism, whose volume is several times larger than international tourism, particularly in large nations like the United States, Russia, China and Canada.

Figure 6.3 Contribution of various tourism sub-sectors to CO$_2$ emissions (%)

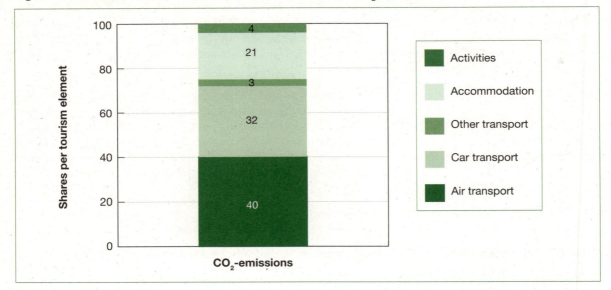

The analysis also showed that emissions can vary greatly per tourist trip, between a few kilograms of CO$_2$ up to 9 t CO$_2$ for long-distance, cruise-based journeys. A globally averaged tourist journey is estimated to generate 0.25 t of CO$_2$ emissions. A small share of tourist trips, however, emits much more than this: while the aviation based trips account for 17% of all tourism trips, they cause about 40% of CO$_2$ emissions from tourism. Long-haul travel by air between the five UNWTO world tourism regions represents only 2.2% of all tourist trips, but contributes 16% to global tourism-related CO$_2$ emissions. In contrast, international tourist trips (i.e., overnight tourist trips) by coach and rail, which account for an estimated 16% of international tourist trips, stand only for 1% of CO$_2$ emissions generated by all international tourist trips (transport emissions only).

These results show that mitigation initiatives in the tourism sector will need to strategically focus on the impact of some particular forms of tourism (i.e., particularly those connected with air travel) if substantial reductions in CO$_2$ emissions are to be achieved. This also implies that climate change mitigation should primarily focus on a minor proportion of tourist trips.

6.5 Mitigation Policies and Measures

Climate change mitigation relates to technological, economic and socio-cultural changes that can lead to reductions in greenhouse gas emissions. Tourism-related emissions are projected to continue to grow rapidly under 'business-as-usual' conditions in contrast to the substantial emission reduction targets the international community agreed was required in the latest round of UNFCCC negotiations ("Vienna Climate Change Talks 2007"), where it was recognized that global emissions of GHG need to be reduced to well below half of the levels in 2000 by mid-century. * Mitigation is thus of particular importance in tourism; however, mitigation policies need to consider a number of dimensions, such as the need to stabilize the global climate, the right of people to rest and recover and leisure **, and attaining the United Nations Millennium Development Goals. As the emission reductions required for tourism to contribute

---

*   The 'Vienna Climate Change Talks 2007' represent the latest international negotiations on GHG emission reductions under the auspices of the United Nations Framework Convention on Climate Change. www.unis.unvienna.org/unis/pressrels/2007/unisinf230.html.

**   The universal right to tourism must be regarded as the corollary of the right to rest and leisure, including reasonable limitation of working hours and periodic holidays with pay, guaranteed by Article 24 of the Universal Declaration of Human Rights and Article 7.d of the International Covenant on Economic, Social and Cultural Rights; (http://www.gdrc.org/uem/eco-tour/principles.html).

meaningfully to the broader emission reduction targets of the international community are substantial, mitigation should ideally combine various strategies, such as voluntary, economic, and regulatory instruments. These can be targeted at different stakeholder groups, including tourists, tour operators, accommodation managers, airlines, manufacturers of cars and aircraft, as well as destination managers. Instruments could also be applied with different emphasis in different countries, so as not to jeopardize the development and poverty reduction opportunity offered by tourism in developing countries. It is clear that for those actors being pro-active in addressing climate change, mitigation offers a range of business opportunities. Given current societal trends, it seems that there will be new, permanent and growing markets for environmentally oriented tourists and many opportunities to develop new low-carbon tourism products.

Four major mitigation strategies for addressing greenhouse gas emissions from tourism can be distinguished:

- reducing energy use;

- improving energy efficiency;

- increasing the use of renewable energy, and;

- sequestering carbon through sinks.

This report has systematically investigated the various options with regard to technological improvements, environmental management, economic and policy measures, and behavioural change, arriving at a number of conclusions:

1) Reducing energy use is the most essential aspect of mitigation, which can be achieved by altering destination development and marketing (tour operators), destination choices (tourists) as well as shifts in transport use from car and aircraft to rail and coach. Changing management practices can be of importance for business tourism (videoconferencing). Tour operators play a key role in this process, as they bundle products into packages that are advertised to and purchased by tourists. Tour operators can also increase length of stay, which would very effectively reduce the carbon footprint per tourist day and increase economic opportunities for destinations. It has to be considered, however, that current tourism trends show an increase of short stays. Overall, tour operators have a considerable influence on creating demand for less carbon intensive journeys by creating attractive products that meet tourists' needs and desires.

    Regarding the most important sector, aviation, the industry favours emission trading over the taxation of fuel or emissions. [98] Aviation is likely to soon enter the European Union Emission Trading Scheme, which will increase the speed at which new technologies are introduced. An even better alternative might be to create an emissions trading scheme entirely for aviation. More efficient technology would be introduced faster, while the profitability of the aviation sector could grow rapidly, as prices for tickets can be increased despite stable costs for operating aircraft.

2) Improving energy efficiency can be another mechanism to decrease energy demand. New technology will significantly reduce the emissions of aviation in a 'business-as-usual' scenario, simply because it saves fuel-costs and improves aircraft performance. Reductions in emissions per passenger km (pkm) are likely to be in the order of 32% between 2005 and 2035. [99] Additional efforts to bring aviation technology to the theoretical limit (50% reduction of emission factors between 2005 and 2035), would contribute to an overall reduction of total emissions from tourist travel (excluding same-day, including all transport modes) by 14% with respect to the 'business-as-usual' scenario. The same overall emissions reduction (14%) may be achieved with strong reductions in the accommodations sub-sector. New technology within car transport has a potential of reducing 7% of all tourist emissions. Note however, that the introduction of new air transport technology takes decades as the market introduction of new technologies is slow, because fleet renewal stretches over several decades due to the long operational life of aircraft. The more rapid introduction of new technologies is thus dependent on environmentally pro-active management decisions that need to be aided by government policy, such as emission trading.

3)   This study found that virtually all sources of renewable energy are relevant for tourism, including wind, photovoltaic, solar thermal, geothermal, biomass and energy regeneration from waste. Several studies have explored the extent to which renewable energy sources can be used for tourism, in particular in island destinations where energy supply based on fossil fuels is expensive and at risk of supply interruptions. These studies come to the conclusion that the use of renewable energy sources is generally economical and technically feasible. [100, 101] For example, in a vast number of destinations in the tropics, investments in solar energy can pay off in as little as two years. Biofuels are another option to contribute to more sustainable transport systems, even though it should be noted that several problems remain unsolved, particularly relating to the sustainability and efficiency of biofuel production and increasing competition over land, especially arable land area. Also the maximum share of biofuels for use in (all) transport is estimated at less than 10%. [102]

4) CO_2 can also be stored in biomass (e.g., through afforestation and avoided deforestation), in aquifers or oceans, and in geological sinks (e.g., depleted gas fields). Within the tourism industry, this is currently practiced through carbon compensation or carbon offsetting, which means that an amount of greenhouse gas emissions equal to that caused by a certain activity (i.e., a flight), will be reduced elsewhere (i.e., through the planting of additional trees). There is still a lot of confusion among tourists about what carbon offsetting is [103] and there is also evidence that particularly hyper-mobile travellers, who account for the major share of the distances travelled and emissions caused, are not ready to support voluntary carbon offsets. [104, 105] There is also a risk that carbon offsetting, which has been initiated as a voluntary form of carbon reductions, is now becoming the means used by the industry to 'reduce' emissions. This effectively means that producer responsibility is turned into customer responsibility, which may be problematic if no action to reduce fuel use is taken. As such, carbon offsetting can be seen as a controversial solution to climate protection, because it potentially diverts from the real causes of the problems and therefore bypasses the structural and technological changes that need to be made to achieve long-term greenhouse gas reductions in the tourism sector. Nevertheless, carbon offsetting does have a role to play in future mitigation efforts in tourism.

In the framework of this report, the expert team developed several scenarios considering different mitigation options, in order to estimate how emission pathways in the global tourism sector might develop in the future. In case of the 'business-as-usual' scenario (which takes into account the UNWTO's *Tourism 2020 Vision* forecast of an average 4% annual growth of international tourist arrivals up to 2020) it was estimated that CO_2 emissions in the global tourism sector may experience a growth of 161% by 2035 (see Figure 6.4).

Figure 6.4 Comparison of current emissions caused by tourist trips (overnight) and projections of emissions for the year 2035 under the assumptions of a 'business-as-usual' scenario

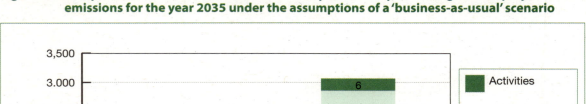

For example, the analysis estimated that emissions may be reduced through the following combination of changed assumptions with respect to a 'business-as-usual' scenario for 2035 (see Figure 6.5):

- If maximum assumed technological efficiencies were achieved for all transport modes, accommodations and activities, this may result in 38% lower emissions.

- Reducing energy use by a combination of transport modal shifts, shifts to shorter haul destinations and increasing average length of stay may result in emission reductions by 44%.

Figure 6.5 Scenarios of CO_2 mitigation potential from global tourism in 2035

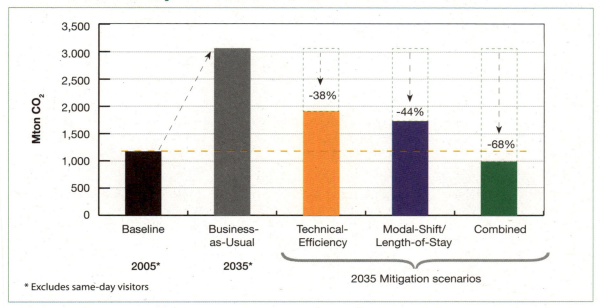

Considering the projected dynamic growth of tourism activities, there is a large task ahead if tourism is to reduce its emissions to the same extent as other economic sectors. For an effective reduction of emissions, the tourism sector needs to apply a combination of mitigation measures. Under the most effective mitigation projection, using a combination of both above measures, the 'business-as-usual' scenario emissions in 2035 could be reduced by 68% *, thus achieving a 16% reduction of emissions with respect to the emissions in 2005.

6.6 The Way Forward to Adaptation and Mitigation in Tourism

Concern about climate change is increasing world-wide and the IPCC has made it clear that global climate change is only just beginning. The impacts of climate change on the tourism sector will steadily intensify, particularly under higher emission scenarios. Climate change would redistribute climate resources for tourism geographically and seasonally and poses a risk to ecosystems worldwide. The nature and intensity of climate change impacts will differ for tourism destinations around the world. The most vulnerable regions are in developing countries, which generally also have less adaptive capacity [106], and this will be a particular challenge for their tourist destinations and their host communities. Climate change impacts on the tourism sector could influence other economic sectors, such as agriculture and local business networks supplying tourism. Conversely, the tourism sector must also be cognizant of the implications of climate change adaptation in other economic sectors, which could have significant impacts on tourism. As the financial sector incorporates a company's climate change strategy, or lack of one, into its investment criteria, it will influence credit rating and insurance rates.

---

*   This figure is less than the sum of the impact of both projections given in the two bullet points, because the different assumed changes interact with each other and sometimes reducing the mutual impact.

Climate change mitigation requires the transformation of energy and transportation systems worldwide, with implications for the cost of travel and tourist mobility. Climate change also has the potential to have an adverse effect on the global economy and poses a security risk in some regions. Consequently, climate change is anticipated to have profound implications that could fundamentally transform aspects of the global tourism sector.

> "Given that climate change is expected to pose an increasing threat to tourism operations in many destinations […], WMO urges governments and the private sector to increasingly use climate information generated through National Meteorological and Hydrological Services […], and to take additional steps towards incorporating climate considerations in tourism policies, development and management plans."
>
> Michel Jarraud, *WMO Secretary-General* (2007)

The unmistakable conclusion of this report is that the significance of climate change to tourism is not in some distant and remote future. Climate change is already influencing decision-making within the tourism sector, including tourists, forward looking tourism businesses and investors, and international tourism organizations. The next generation of tourism professionals will need to contend with virtually all of the broad range of impacts outlined in this report.

Tourism can and must play a significant role in addressing climate change as part of its broader commitment to sustainable development and the United Nations Millennium Development Goals. Tourism as a non-negligible contributor to climate change has the responsibility to reverse the growth trajectory of its GHG emissions over the next three decades to a more sustainable emissions pathway consistent with the actions of the international community. The climate change mitigation potential is thought to be relatively high in the tourism sector because efforts to lower energy consumption and GHG emissions in the sector are still largely in their infancy, and thus far have been generally taken without any vision of a coordinated sector-wide strategic response. [107] Also in this study it is shown that several combinations of strong efforts, including decoupling of the growth of tourism from the growth of tourism transport volumes and technological innovation, may significantly reduce emissions in 2035, without jeopardizing the growth of world tourism in number of trips or guest-nights.

Regardless of the success to reduce GHG emissions by the international community, there will undoubtedly also be costs associated with climate change adaptation. [108] These costs cannot be borne solely by those affected, especially as those most affected are likely to be those less able to take action to cope with the changes (e.g., LDCs, SIDS and local tourism SMMEs). The capacity of the tourism sector to adapt to climate change is thought to be relatively high due to its dynamic nature and therefore there will be important opportunities for tourism to reduce the vulnerability of communities to climate change.

The United Nations Secretary-General Ban Ki-moon has called for action by the international community on climate change to be taken in close coordination with action on poverty alleviation and the Millennium Development Goals. The IPCC further contends that there are significant synergies that can be exploited in bringing climate change to the development community and critical development issues to the climate change community. There is an important opportunity for the tourism sector to show leadership in the development of a coherent policy agenda that integrates both development and climate change perspectives.

This is the time now for the tourism community to collectively formulate a strategy to address what must be considered the greatest challenge to the sustainability of tourism in the 21st century.

Chapter 7

Introduction to the Technical Report

The Earth's climate has demonstrably changed compared to the pre-industrial era and is anticipated to continue to change over the 21st century and beyond. On the basis of accumulating scientific evidence, including observed increases in global average air and ocean temperatures, widespread melting of snow and ice, rising global average sea levels, and a range of biological responses, the Intergovernment Panel on Climate Change (IPCC) [109] declared that "[…] warming of the climate system is unequivocal." The global mean temperature has increased approximately 0.76° C between 1850–1899 and 2001–2005 and the IPCC concluded that most of the observed increase in global average temperatures since the mid-20th century is very likely (> 90% probability) the result of human activities that are increasing greenhouse gas concentrations in the atmosphere.

In addition, the IPCC [110] projected that the pace of climate change is very likely (> 90% probability) to accelerate with continued greenhouse gas emissions at or above current rates, with the best estimate that globally averaged surface temperatures will rise by 1.8° C (low emission scenario) to 4.0° C (high emission scenario) by the end of the 21st century. Even if atmospheric concentrations of greenhouse gases (GHG) were stabilized at current levels, the Earth would continue to warm as a result of past GHG emissions and the thermal inertia of the oceans. The biological response to this continued warming and sea level rise would proceed for many centuries. [111, 112]

The environmental and economic risks of the magnitude of climate change in the 21st century are considerable and featured prominently in international policy debates. [113, 114, 115] The international business community involved in the United Nations Global Compact [116] contend climate change will affect business and society in fundamental and transformative ways. The Stern Review [117] on the Economics of Climate Change concluded that unmitigated climate change could risk major economic and social disruption later in this century and that tackling climate change was a pro-economic growth strategy, with the benefits of strong, early action considerably outweighing the costs of inaction. The IPCC also recently concluded with very high confidence [118] that climate change will impede the ability of many nations to achieve sustainable development pathways, as articulated in the United Nations Millennium Development Goals (MDGs) [119], over the next half-century.

Our lifestyles, economies, health and social well-being are all affected by climate change, and although the consequences of climate change will vary on a regional basis, all nations and economic sectors will have to contend with climate change in one way or another, addressing the challenges of both adaptation and mitigation. Tourism is no exception, as climate change is already affecting decision-making in the tourism sector and will be a pivotal issue affecting the medium and long-term future of tourism development and management. [120, 121, 122, 123, 124, 125]

7.1 The New Realities of Tourism in an Era of Global Climate Change

Because of its close connections to the environment and climate itself, tourism is considered to be a highly climate-sensitive economic sector like agriculture, insurance, energy, and transportation. [126] Indeed, climate change is not a remote future event for tourism, as the varied impacts of a changing climate are becoming evident at destinations around the world. Tourism is affected by a very wide range of environmental and socio-economic factors, and has been continuously adapting to challenges and crisis situations, such as natural disasters, epidemics, terrorism, civil strife or economic downturns, showing great resilience. Therefore, the capacity of the tourism sector to adapt to climate change is thought to be relatively high due to its dynamic nature. Tourism can provide important opportunities for tourism to reduce the overall vulnerability of communities to climate change through sustainable development, particularly in the Least Developed Countries (LDCs) and Small Island Developing States (SIDS). For the effective adaptation in their tourism sector, LDCs and SIDSs will require nonetheless assistance to tackle the adverse effects of climate change, anticipated to be exacerbated due to poverty and environmental needs.

At the same time, the tourism sector is a non-negligible contributor to climate change through greenhouse gas emissions derived especially from the transport of tourists. [127, 128] The tourism sector must therefore respond accordingly to significantly reduce its GHG emissions consistent with the actions of the international community. The climate change mitigation potential is thought to be relatively high in the tourism sector because efforts to lower energy consumption and GHG emissions in the sector are still largely in their infancy and thus far have been generally taken without any vision of a coordinated sector-wide strategic response. [129]

Tourism can play a significant role in addressing climate change if the enormous innovativeness and resources of this vital global economic sector are fully mobilized. Consistent with the position of the United Nations [130] and the IPCC [131], the tourism sector should not address the challenge climate change in isolation, but do so in the context of the broader international sustainable development agenda. The critical challenge before the global tourism sector is to develop a coherent policy strategy that decouples the projected massive growth in tourism in the decades ahead from increased energy use and GHG emissions, so as to allow tourism growth to simultaneously contribute to poverty alleviation and play a major role in achieving the United Nations MGDs.

> "Climate change as well as Poverty alleviation will remain central issues for the world community. Tourism is an important element in both. Governments and the private sector must place increased importance on these factors in tourism development strategies and in climate and poverty strategies. They are interdependent and must be dealt with in a holistic fashion."
>
> Francesco Frangialli, *UNWTO Secretary-General* (2007)

7.2 Moving Forward on Understanding the New Realities

The response of the tourism community to the challenge of climate change has visibly increased over the last five years. The World Tourism Organization (UNWTO), together with the World Meteorological Organization (WMO), the United Nations Environment Programme (UNEP), the United Nations Convention to Combat Desertification (UNCCD), the United Nations Educational, Scientific and Cultural Organization (UNESCO) and the Government of Tunisia hosted the First International Conference on Climate Change and Tourism in Djerba, Tunisia in 2003. The conference aimed at developing awareness among government administrations, the tourism industry and other tourism stakeholders about the salience of climate change impacts occurring or anticipated to affect tourism destinations and the need to carefully consider the consequences of climate change mitigation policies on tourism as well as the obligation of the tourism sector to be a part of the solution by reducing its greenhouse gas emissions. The recognition within the Djerba Declaration of the complex inter-linkages between the tourism sector and climate change and the need to take adaptation and mitigation measures, established a comprehensive framework for future research and policy making. [132] The Davos Conference and Declaration built on the consensus reached in Djerba and took further the policy debate focusing on concrete responses that the different stakeholder groups can take.

Subsequent workshops sponsored by the European Science Foundation (Milan 2003), the North Atlantic Treaty Organization (Warsaw 2003), the European Forum on Integrated Environmental Assessment (Genoa 2004), and the Experts on Climate Change and Tourism group (eCLAT) (Netherlands 2006, Paris 2007) and the Marrakech Task Force on Sustainable Tourism further contributed to the development of collaborative research and practical case studies by a network of international tourism stakeholders and scientists. For example, UNWTO initiated pilot adaptation projects in Fiji and Maldives through the Global Environmental Facility (GEF) in collaboration with UNEP and the United Nations Development

Programme (UNDP). Climate change and tourism have been also prominent at the UN Conference on Small Islands, held in Mauritius in 2005, where UNWTO held a special event on tourism. In 2005, at the Fourteenth Session of the Commission for Climatology, [133] the World Meteorological Organization (WMO) established an Expert Team on Climate and Tourism with the broad mandate, to be carried out in collaboration with the UNWTO, to advance the application of weather and climate information in the tourism sector and understanding of the implications of climate change.

Individual tourism industry associations and businesses have also shown leadership on climate change. Recognizing the risk climate change poses to the future of the ski industry, the National Ski Areas Association in the USA initiated the 'Keep Winter Cool' Campaign in 2003, in order to raise public awareness of the potential effects of global climate change, reduce GHG emissions of the ski industry, and encourage others to take action to reduce their GHG emissions (including lobbying government officials to pass climate change legislation). This campaign has now been adapted for use in Canada and Australia. Aspen Ski Company (USA) was one of the first in the tourism sector to develop a corporate policy on climate change and adopt legally binding greenhouse gas emission targets in 2001. For a number of years now, the New Zealand Tourism Industry Association has promoted awareness of the issue of climate change by offsetting the emissions from the trips made by participants to its annual conference.

The scientific community has also responded, with multi-disciplinary contributions from tourism studies, economics, geography and environmental management, development studies, sociology and psychology doubling the number of scientific publications that examine the interactions of tourism and climate change between 1996–2000 and 2001–2005. [134] This rapidly developing area of tourism research contributed to a significant advancement of the place of tourism in the IPCC 4th Assessment Report (AR4) relative to previous assessments. [135, 136] Tourism was discussed in two volumes of the AR4, that of Working Group 2 (WG2), which focuses on the impacts, adaptation and vulnerability of natural and human systems to climatic change, and, much more briefly, in the volume of Working Group 3 (WG3), which focuses on the GHG emissions from different economic sectors and groups of countries and possible mitigation strategies.

Box 1 Role and structure of the IPCC

The scientific community involved in understanding past-present-future climate change and its implications for natural and human systems is increasingly large. The Intergovernmental Panel on Climate Change (IPCC) plays a decisive networking and synthesis role and, though in an informal manner, in orienting future research. The IPCC was established in 1988 by the United Nations Environment Programme and the World Meteorological Organization "[…] to assess on a comprehensive, objective, open and transparent basis the scientific, technical and socio-economic information relevant to the understanding of the risk of human-induced climate change, its observed and projected impacts and options for adaptation and mitigation". As part of its mandate, the IPCC periodically produces assessment reports which are based in the latest peer-reviewed scientific literature, undergo extensive multiple rounds of scientific and government review, and involve thousands of scientists and government officials world-wide. Because the conclusions are validated both by the scientific community and by governments they are a highly authoritative, key reference for decision-makers in the international community. The IPCC is comprised of three Working Groups that focus on different aspects of the climate change issue, each of them with its special relevance to tourism:

- **Working Group 1** – assesses the mechanisms of the climate system and the magnitude of climate change;

- **Working Group 2** – assesses the vulnerability of socio-economic and natural systems to climate change, negative and positive consequences of climate change, and options for adapting to it; and,

- **Working Group 3** – assesses options for limiting greenhouse gas emissions and otherwise mitigating climate change.

Within the WG2 report, there is considerable diversity in how prominently tourism is in the regional chapters and key geographic gaps on impacts exist. Whereas there are substantial sections dedicated to tourism in the chapters on Africa, Australia, Europe, and North America, there is hardly any consideration of tourism in the chapters on Asia and Latin America. Even among the regions with dedicated sections on tourism, information availability varies substantially. For example, while the impacts of climate change on tourism are anticipated to be very important in Africa, there are almost no tourism specific studies available on this continent. Given the regional distribution of global tourism receipts and relative importance of tourism to the economies to some nations in the Caribbean and Southeast Asia, these regional gaps need to be redressed in the future. The "Industry, Settlement and Society" chapter of the report and the "Small Islands" chapter also devoted substantial discussion to tourism. Tourism is however all but absent in some of the other chapters by WG2, where some discussion could be expected, for example the chapters on "Human Health", "Freshwater Resources", and the critical inter-linkages between "Climate Change and Sustainability".

Tourism received minimal attention by WG3, with tourism only being mentioned where the potential impacts of adaptation measures in the tourism sector on emissions (e.g., higher energy consumption resulting from increased use of air-conditioning) and the potential impacts of mitigation policies are discussed. The prominence of tourism in overall transport emissions might have been expected to be acknowledged more explicitly.

Tourism is an activity whose effects are distributed in many economic sectors, such as transport, accommodation and agriculture. Tourism is also characterised by both the significance of its contribution to GHG emissions and its substantial overall economic importance. An assessment of emissions from tourism would thus help to develop mitigation strategies in particular within the critical field of air transport (see Chapter 11). With minimal discussion of GHG emissions and mitigation within the tourism sector and very limited discussion of the impacts of climate change on tourism or possible adaptation strategies within the AR4, there is currently no peer-reviewed, synthetic and worldwide review of the relationships between climate change and tourism. This report is intended to help close this information gap.

7.3 Purpose and Scope

This report presents a synthesis of the demonstrable progress made since the Djerba Conference in 2003 on the complex interactions between tourism and global climate change. It summarizes the state of knowledge about current and future likely impacts of climate change on tourism in diverse destinations around the world and possible impacts on tourist demand, current levels and trends in GHG emissions from the tourism sector, and an overview of policy and management responses adopted by the key stakeholder groups (international organizations, public administrations, the tourism industry) with respect to adaptation to and mitigation of climate change. The report focused primarily on new science and policy developments that have occurred since the Djerba conference in 2003. Extensive references are imbedded throughout the report to assist those seeking to acquire further information about particular case studies or specific research topics. The text is also illustrated with boxes that describe case studies of impacts or examples of adaptation and mitigation practice from around the world.

The technical report is based on an extensive review of scientific literature and policy and management responses to climate change and is intended to provide extensive background information for high-level technical debate and the search of possible courses of action at the Second International Conference on Climate Change and Tourism (Davos, Switzerland, 1–3 October 2007). The outcomes of the Second International Conference on Climate Change and Tourism and the Ministerial Summit in London (13 November 2007), were transmitted by UNWTO to the UN Climate Change Summit in Bali, Indonesia (3-14 December 2007).

7.4 Who this Report is for

The report is principally aimed at the tourism industry and governments (local through national levels), who will have the primary responsibility of developing mitigation and adaptation strategies to respond to the challenges that global climate change will bring to the tourism sector. International agencies including UNEP, UNWTO, UNDP, the World Health Organization and the World Meteorological Organization and their regional and national entities, development agencies, non-governmental organizations (NGOs), and the investment community will also find the report relevant for decision-making that involve interactions with the tourism sector.

Chapter 8

Advances in Climate Change Science and Implications for the Tourism Sector

Over the past decade quite significant progress has been made in the science of global climate change and its potential implications for natural and human systems. As indicated in Chapter 7, substantial progress on the complex interactions between climate change and tourism has occurred in the past five years. This Chapter first situates the recent concern about the consequences of climate change for tourism within the context of existing knowledge about the relationship between tourism and climate and weather, which has developed over the last 30 years. The importance of local-regional scale climate analysis for tourism is emphasized. The Chapter also provides a brief overview of recent advances in our understanding of global climate change and an overview of the state of climate change science, as outlined in the IPCC AR4, is then provided both at a global scale and at a regional level in order to inform discussion of possible impacts on tourism in subsequent chapters.

8.1 Distinguishing Weather, Climate, and Climate Change

8.1.1 Definitions

Weather is the state of the atmosphere at a moment in time, as determined by the simultaneous occurrence of several meteorological variables (temperature, wind, cloud cover, precipitation) at a specific geographical location. Weather is an element of the environment that nobody can escape. That weather is good or bad is subjective, and depends on personal preferences, activities, and personal health. Weather is what tourists actually experience when at a destination, affecting their activities and holiday satisfaction. Weather also affects key aspects of tourism operations, including infrastructure, activity programming, and operating costs.

Climate is usually defined as 'average weather' for a specific location. More rigorously, climate is the state of the climate system, including a statistical description in terms of the mean and variability of meteorological variables over a specified period of time. Averages of climate elements calculated over a uniform and relatively long period covering at least three consecutive ten-year periods are usually referred to as Climate Normals * under the Technical Regulations. [137] 'Climatological Standard Normals' are averages of climate data computed for the specific 30-year periods of 1931–1960, 1961–1990, and (next) 1991–2020. Climate normals are used as a 'benchmark' against which recent or current observations can be compared, including providing a basis for many anomaly-based climate data sets such as the time series of global mean temperature anomalies. Climate normals are also used, implicitly or explicitly, to serve as a prediction of the conditions most likely to be experienced in a given location. Climate is what a tourist would anticipate experiencing at a specific destination and time, whereas they might be confronted with weather that may not match these climatic expectations. Climate is a key factor considered consciously or implicitly during travel planning and it is an important attribute taken into account in locational planning, infrastructure development and destination marketing.

Climate change refers to a statistically significant variation in either the mean state of the climate or in its spatial (micro-local) or temporal (seasonal) variability, persisting for an extended period (typically decades or longer). [138] Tourism depends not only on average, but also on detailed characteristics of

---

* Note that it is widely recognized that the mean is an incomplete descriptor of climate and that standard deviations, extreme values, etc, are also essential.

climate: the duration of showers or the number of hours with clouds is probably more important for this activity than the absolute amount of rain. Climate change may be due to natural internal processes or external forcings (e.g., fluctuation in solar energy), or to persistent anthropogenic changes in the composition of the atmosphere or in land use.

8.1.2 Relationships between Climate, Weather and Tourism

The relationship between tourism and climate has been studied for a long time. [139] In the 1970s, applied climatologists examined the climatic thresholds that defined the season length for a wide range of tourism activities. [140, 141, 142, 143] In the 1980s, biometeorologists and others studied how climatic variables affected the physical comfort of tourists and developed rating systems to evaluate and compare the climates of tourism destinations. [144, 145, 146] More recent work has focused on validating climate rating systems for tourism in the marketplace. [147, 148, 149] The suitability of a given climate (and weather) varies for different types of tourism, as does the satisfaction of an individual tourist depending on country of origin, age or other factors. [150, 151] Some types of tourism require very specific climate conditions, for example beach tourism, winter sports, or health-wellness tourism. Climatic conditions and their suitability to tourism can differ at a micro scale from one side of the mountain to the other, within a range of a few kilometres according to altitude or even at a smaller scale under the influence of human developments (e.g., urban heat island) or tourism infrastructure (e.g., tourist resorts – both new [La grande Motte in Languedoc, France] and old [on the French Riviera] – have been designed to reduce wind speeds to enhance tourist comfort). More recent work has focused on the role of weather and climate in travel motivation, destination choice, and holiday satisfaction for tourists as well as the range of uses of weather and climate information by tourism operators and other tourism stakeholders (investors, insurers, regulators). [152, 153, 154, 155, 156, 157, 158, 159]

8.1.3 The Importance of Weather Forecasts and Climate Prediction for the Tourism Sector

"A major limiting factor to the predictability of weather beyond several days is a fundamental dynamical property of the atmosphere. In the 1960s, meteorologist Edward Lorenz discovered that very slight differences in initial conditions can produce very different forecast results."

Le Treut et al. (2007)

Weather, in many regions of the world, can be forecast now for up to a week with good reliability and it is expected that similarly reliable forecasts will be extended to upwards of ten days over the next 10–15 years. Weather forecasts are improving at a local scale, though some extreme phenomena such as tornadoes cannot (yet) be predicted with sufficient lead time for effective response to the risk. Improvements to weather forecasts and the development of early warning systems are of particular interest to the tourism sector. Improvements in weather forecasting benefit tourists in their short term decision-making related to travel planning (i.e., departure time-date and destination choice) and activities. Early warning systems also reduce the safety risks associated with extreme events, such as storms, cyclones, or avalanches. [160, 161] The improved accuracy of weather forecasts is also important for tourism operators. Improved forecasts benefit operational decisions, such as irrigation, snow-making, activities programming, maintenance and staff scheduling, and route planning (cruise ships and airlines). Improved forecasting is also desirable because inaccurate forecasts can be detrimental to the tourist experience and tourism demand, for example when people go on ski, beach or camping trip and do not find the expected good weather, or do not go because of the forecast of poor weather that does not actually materialize.

Seasonal climate prediction covers periods from one month, to several years, but typically is for three month periods. The availability of seasonal predictions is expanding, following upon recent advances in the understanding and modelling of climatic processes. Through the analysis of the global or regional phenomena affecting regional and local climate and weather (e.g., El Niño, North Atlantic and Arctic oscillations), meteorologists combine global forecasting methods and statistics, to determine probabilities for a given season (e.g., probability the next summer will be warmer or dryer than average – (see Figure 8.1) – or the number of intense tropical storms expected in a region). Some Meteorological services, such as US National Oceanic and Atmospheric Administration (NOAA), issue seasonal forecasts more than one year in advance, for parameters such as temperature and precipitation. The use of seasonal prediction has been limited in the tourism sector thus far, [162] although there are a number of potential uses that are anticipated to increase as seasonal prediction improve further: fuel supply procurement, marketing, setting insurance premiums, inventory management, or cruise line destination planning.

One of the reasons for the slow integration of weather and climate information into decision making is the uncertainty associated with the forecasts or predictions. Uncertainty is an unavoidable fact in any climate projection, prediction, or assessment, but uncertainty is very different from no information. Weather and climate experts strive to help users understand inherent uncertainty, and to learn how to handle it, and thereby to be fully aware of the risks and benefits when making decisions regarding a climate-sensitive activity. In a "Climate Risk Management" approach, decisions are never based on a single scenario. Rather, risks and benefits are assessed over the range of possible scenarios, in such a way that catastrophic loss is minimized, and over time, the best outcomes are realized. The challenge is for the meteorological and tourism communities to work together to find the decisions and policies that are amenable to such an approach, and to seize upon them.

In recent years, new partnerships between meteorological institutions and tourism stakeholders have developed. [163] This cooperation has taken multiple forms, from new forecasts for tourism destinations, improved media training and cooperation to deliver forecasts related to tourism, to specific contracts between meteorological services and destinations, tour operators and other stakeholders. UNWTO and WMO have begun new collaborations to improve the availability and use of weather and climate information in the tourism sector. WMO has established a new Expert Team on Climate and Tourism [164] with part of its mandate to work with National Meteorological and Hydrological Services and tourism professionals to develop tailored climate products for application to tourism and develop new information on risk assessment to build on the WMO-UNWTO *Handbook on Natural Disaster Reduction in Tourism Areas.*

Figure 8.1 A global seasonal weather forecast for summer 2007 temperatures, issued in March 2007

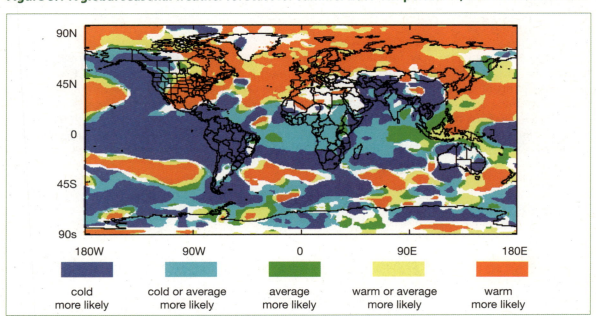

Source : UK Met Office (2007)

8.2 Advances in the Understanding of Global Climate Change

The methods used to explore future climate shows that the uncertainties are linked to research tools currently available and some others to the evolution of human activities over the span of several decades (e.g., population and economic growth, evolution and implementation of new technology). Climate being a statistic of daily weather over a long period implies that it is necessary to work with statistics, trends, indicators of variability, and confidence levels, all of which make it difficult to deliver clear messages to diverse audiences.

Two types of approaches can be used to describe the nature of potential future climate change.

Scenarios

Scenarios are the main method used to explore the future of climate. In order to develop future climate scenarios, the future of GHG emissions from human activities need to be considered. Two categories of GHG emission scenarios must be distinguished; those that do not consider policies to mitigate emissions (e.g., IPCC Special Report on Emission Scenarios (SRES)) and those that do (i.e., stabilisation scenarios). The IPCC SRES scenarios are classified into four families according to their global-regional and the development-environmental orientations:

- The A1 storyline and scenario family describes a future world with very rapid economic growth, low population growth, and the rapid introduction of new and more efficient technologies.

- The A2 storyline and scenario family describes a very heterogeneous world. The underlying theme is self-reliance and preservation of local identities.

- The B1 storyline and scenario family describes a convergent world with the same low population growth as in the A1 storyline, but with rapid changes in economic structures toward a service and information economy, with reductions in material intensity, and the introduction of clean and resource-efficient technologies.

- The B2 storyline and scenario family describes a world in which the emphasis is on local solutions to economic, social, and environmental sustainability.

The different GHG emission trajectories over the 21st century from these SRES scenarios are outlined in Figure 8.2.

When the SRES emission scenarios are run through several extensively validated Global Climate Models (GCMs), the estimated range of global warming is 1.8° C to 4.0° C by the end of the 21st century. [165] This range is due to the uncertainty about future GHG emissions linked to unpredictable socio-economic conditions and to the different responses of GCMs to the same amount of emissions. Thus, these scenarios deliver results that policy makers sometimes find difficult to use. Often, policy makers want to know what they need to do in order to keep climate change within boundaries that they perceive as 'acceptable'. This is a question to which stabilisation scenarios are more suited to provide an answer.

Figure 8.2 Scenarios for global temperature in the 21st century

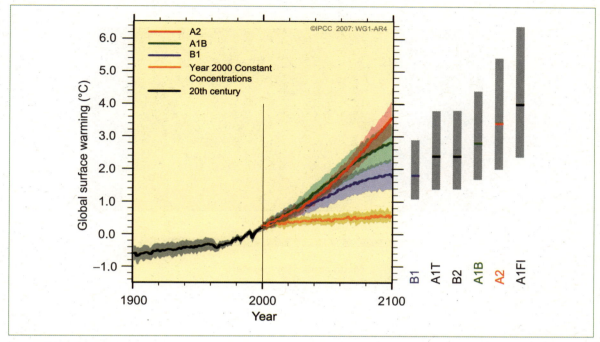

Source: IPCC 2007a

Stabilization scenarios also explore a wide range of future GHG conditions, typically ranging from atmospheric CO_2 concentrations of 450 ppm to 1000 ppm (current levels are estimated at 380 ppm). Some stabilization scenarios can be considered proxies for 'policy scenarios' because they are very near to the objectives of some governments in developed countries: they imply that emissions per unit of GDP would need to be just one quarter of current level by 2050. [166] Such stabilisation scenarios require very ambitious GHG reductions policies to control energy demand, produce carbon neutral energy, capture and store CO_2 from energy production.

Analogues

Another approach to describe what future climate conditions might be like is to refer to similar conditions when they occurred in the past. This approach facilitates more effective communication with some audiences. For example, one can point out that if global average temperatures were approximately 5° C cooler, then climate conditions would resemble those during the last ice age and that the changes we may witness by the end of the 21st century are of a similar magnitude but in the opposite direction. Another example is the European heat wave of 2003, which is an analogue for average summer temperature conditions the region might face in the later decades of this century. Under certain climate change scenarios the annual mean temperature of Paris would be near to that of Toledo now (Figure 8.3). [167] The use of climate analogues assumes that major climate processes remain stable, whereas unprecedented CO_2 concentrations associated with high GHG emission scenarios may trigger new and uncertain climate processes. [168]

Figure 8.3 Spatial climate analogue for European cities for 2100 (a)

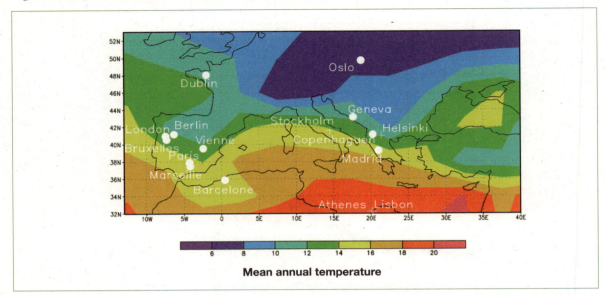

(a) Map of Europe and Mediterranean basin, with a few cities at the location of their future climate analogue, i.e. a location that presently enjoys a climate close to their future climate. The model used is Hadley Centre HafRM3H model.

Source: Hallegatte, S. et al (2005)

The use of climate analogues is a promising avenue for exploring the potential impacts of climate change on tourism. Anomalous weather events can be studied to learn the behavioural response of tourists, how successful climate adaptations by tourism operators were, the extent of economic impacts, the recovery period for visitation, and identify additional adaptation measures that might be required by the tourism industry and government. This approach offers some advantages over other research approaches because it focuses on the observed responses of the entire tourism marketplace to real climatic conditions, and captures the integrated effects of simultaneous supply and demand-side adaptations. Climate analogues have been successfully applied in other fields of research, but remain under utilized in the tourism sector.

8.2.1 Regional and Local Climate Change: Why Downscaling is Critical for Tourism

Tourism, as an economic sector, is greatly influenced by the local environment, its climate and its climate-influenced natural resources. Moreover, the effect of climate on tourism is strongly influenced by the perceptions of tourists. Instead of the average temperature, what is important is the 'thermal comfort' of clients, and rather than average precipitation, the frequency and length of rain showers count for the quality of a tourism experience. Therefore, research into the impacts of climate change on tourism depends on the performance of regional and local climate scenarios, as well as on the sort of parameters that can be modelled at these scales.

Box 2 Using a climate change analogue approach to examine climate change vulnerability of the New England (USA) ski industry [169]

The record warm winter of 2001–2002 (+8° C warmer than climatically normal temperatures for the 1961–1990 baseline period) is representative of projected future average winter climate conditions in the New England region under a high greenhouse gas emission scenario for the 2040–2069 period. This winter was used as a climate change analogue to examine how a wide range of ski area performance indicators (ski season length, hours of snow-making operation, total skier visits, visitation by time of year, average season passes sold, and operating profit as a percentage of total gross revenue) were affected by anomalously warm conditions. Comparison of ski area performance indicators for the 2001–2002 analogue year with the climatically normal (for 1961–1990 period) years of 2000–2001 and 2004–2005, revealed substantial differences. The ski season length was 11% shorter in the analogue year. Snow-making hours increased by 12% in the analogue season and the amount of power utilized for the purpose of creating snow was almost 35% higher than during average ski seasons. Visitation during the climate change analogue season was 12% lower versus the climatically normal winters. The combination of increased snow-making costs, decreased season length, and lower visitation rates, caused financial strain that reduced operating profits for the 2001–2002 season by 19% versus climatically average seasons. Analysis of impact on different sized ski resorts (categorized by lift capacity) further revealed that smaller ski areas experienced larger impacts.

Tourism decision makers need clear and reliable conclusions of impact assessments. To answer this need, tourism research must adequately portray the differences between climate change scenarios produced by different climate models and downscale GCM scenarios to regional and local levels in order to describe the variability of climate, to present the probability of extreme events, and, above all, to 'translate' model outputs into indicators that are important for the tourism sector (e.g., number of rainy days, length of showers, thermal comfort, duration of the snow season, forest fire frequency and intensity). One of the key recommendations of the "Climate and Tourism on the Colorado Plateau Workshop" [170], that involved representatives from research, industry, and environmental organizations, was for better communication and characterization of certainties and uncertainties in climate variability and change projections to the tourism industry and for the development of indicators catered toward local tourism decision-making. Additional workshops like this one would be highly valuable in identifying regionally specific weather and climate information needs of the tourism industry.

Projecting future climate change at local scales is difficult because the resolution of GCMs is too coarse to take into account local features of climate. Climate modellers and meteorologists utilize several techniques to produce regional-local scale climate scenarios, including Regional Climate Models (RCMs), statistical weather generators and weather forecast simulations. RCMs are higher resolution climate models that are usually better able to reproduce regional climate processes than GCMs. The application of RCM scenarios in climate change impact assessments has been restricted because of the limited range of GHG emission scenarios available. Weather generators are inexpensive computational tools that replicate the statistical attributes of a local climate and can be used to produce site-specific, multiple-year climate change scenarios at the daily timescale. [171] Tourism researchers have used these techniques in climate change impact assessments. In order to obtain even more precise local results, an additional technique can be to introduce some human experience in the downscaling process. Local weather analysts, who are experts on local specificities, can be involved to take into account localized micro-climate effects (e.g., coastal effects of marine winds on a tourist location). The IPCC has provided guidelines for best practice in downscaling [172], nonetheless, downscaling generally increases the uncertainties and margins of error associated with climate change scenarios.

Box 3 Recommendations for impact assessment studies in tourism

Climate change impact assessments in many socio-economic sectors, including tourism, have often employed a very limited range of climate change scenarios to explore the potential impacts of climate change; sometimes using only one GCM or a single GHG emission scenario (e.g., IPCC A2 scenario or another SRES scenario). Such an approach does not adequately represent the uncertainty in future climate conditions and produces an unrealistically narrow assessment of the potential impacts and possible adaptation requirements. Climate change assessments, in tourism, as in other sectors*, should better take into account of the uncertainty in climate change scenarios. In any study, the minimum requirement is to be transparent about climate change scenarios utilized, including the GHG emission scenarios and the climate models used. As recommended by the IPCC, impact assessments should incorporate multi-GCM/RCM and multi-emission scenario combinations to represent the full range of possible future climates for a study area. Since developing several scenarios is costly and time-consuming, alternate strategies are possible, such as presenting the whole range of scenarios for a limited number of critical parameters and selecting a representative set of climatic scenarios for use in the impact analysis (e.g., the warmest and driest scenario as well as the least warm and wettest scenario). This requires a general improvement in the availability of user friendly climate change scenario data, which has been an important barrier in some regions. To overcome this barrier, some countries, such as Canada, have made all currently available GCM data available in a user friendly format for any location. For example, see the Climate Change Scenario Network (http://www.ccsn.ca/).

8.3 Latest Results on Past and Future Climate Change

8.3.1 The Changing Climate

The IPCC AR4 [173, 174] summarized the growing evidence from multiple natural systems that indicate that the global climate is changing. Eleven of the last twelve years rank among the 12 warmest years in the record of global surface temperature since 1850 (Figure 8.4). The warming trend over the last 50 years (0.13° C per decade) is nearly twice that for the last 100 years (Figure 8.4). The total temperature increase from 1850–1899 and 2001–2005 is 0.76° C. Widespread decreases in glaciers and ice caps and warming ocean surface temperature have contributed to sea level rise. Global average sea level rose at an average rate of 1.8 mm per year over 1961 to 2003, and at approximately 3.1 mm per year from 1993 to 2003. The biological response of ecosystems and individual species has been recorded on every continent. [175]

---

*   It is important to note that impact assessment studies in the tourism sector are not especially weaker than those conducted in other sectors.

Figure 8.4 Recorded changes in global average temperature since 1850

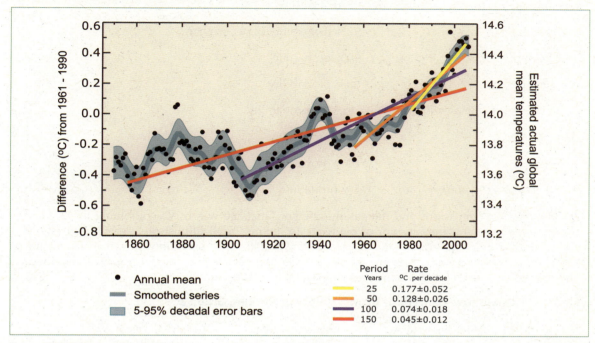

Source: IPCC 2007a

8.3.2 Human Influence on Climate Change

"Most of the observed increase in global average temperatures since the mid-20th century is very likely (>90% probability) due to the observed increase in anthropogenic greenhouse gas concentrations."[176] Discernible human influences now extend to other aspects of climate, including ocean warming, continental-average temperatures, temperature extremes and wind patterns.[177]

Box 4 The language of uncertainty in the IPCC AR4 [178]

Assessments of climate change science by the IPCC have always recognized the importance of communicating uncertainties to policy makers. In the AR4 Working Group II on impacts and adaptation, the following terms were used to indicate 'degree of confidence in being correct' and 'likelihood of occurrence', as based on the collective judgment of the authors using the observational evidence, modeling results, and theory that they have examined.

Terminology for degree of confidence in being correct

- *Very high confidence*   At least 9 out of 10 chance

- *High confidence*   About 8 out of 10 chance

- *Medium confidence*   About 5 out of 10 chance

- *Low confidence*   About 2 out of 10 chance

- *Very low confidence*   Less than 1 out of 10 chance

Terminology for likelihood of the occurrence/outcome

- *Virtually certain*   > 99% probability of occurrence

- *Very likely*   > 90% probability

- *Likely*   > 66% probability

- *About as likely as not*   33 to 66% probability

- *Unlikely*   < 33% probability

- *Very unlikely*   < 10% probability

- *Exceptionally unlikely*   < 1% probability

In AR4 WG 3 on emissions and mitigation, another language was used, combining the level of expert agreement and the amount of evidence (scientific publications) on a specific question. These two factors were combined into a qualitative matrix of uncertainty shown in Figure 8.5 Since human choices were more involved in a mitigation perspective, the concepts of 'likelihood' and 'confidence' used in WG 2 appeared less suitable to Working Group 3.

Figure 8.5 Qualitative definitions of uncertainty in Working Group 3

Level of agreement (on a particular finding) ↑	High agreement, limited evidence	High agreement, medium evidence	High agreement, much evidence
	Medium agreement, limited evidence	Medium agreement, medium evidence	Medium agreement, much evidence
	Low agreement, limited evidence	Low agreement, medium evidence	Low agreement, much evidence

Amount of evidence (number and quality of independent sources) ⟶

Source: IPCC 2007c

8.3.3 Global Climate Change in the 21st Century

The recently completed AR4 [179] highlighted the following key global scale climate changes that are projected to take place over the 21st century):

- "For the next two decades, a warming of about 0.2° C per decade is projected for a range of SRES emission scenarios." [180]

- Figure 8.2 shows that based on the SRES emission scenarios the best estimate is that global average temperatures would increase 1.8° C to 4° C by 2100. There are two notable caveats to this estimate. First, the recent growth of emissions [181] is on a trajectory that exceeds the most pessimistic of SRES scenarios. Second, there is a risk of feedbacks in the climate system that may increase warming. [182] Models used to date do not include uncertainties in climate-carbon cycle feedback nor do they include the full effects of changes in ice sheet flow. [183]

- There is no historical analogue to indicate what might happen with such a rapid warming over current temperatures.

- The temperature increase in the 21st century represents only 50 to 90% of the eventual warming that could result from SRES emission scenarios. The level at which temperatures eventually stabilize depends on how fast GHG emissions will be reduced.

- "Warming is expected to be greatest over land and at most high northern latitudes, and least over the Southern Ocean and parts of the North Atlantic Ocean" [184]

- Observed decreases in snow cover are projected to continue.

- "It is very likely that hot extremes, heat waves and heavy precipitation events will continue to become more frequent." [185]

- "It is likely that future tropical cyclones (typhoons and hurricanes) will become more intense, with larger peak wind speeds and more heavy precipitation associated with ongoing increases of tropical sea surface temperatures. There is less confidence in projections of a global decrease in numbers of tropical cyclones." [186]

- "Extratropical storm tracks are projected to move poleward, with consequent changes in wind, precipitation and temperature patterns, continuing the broad pattern of observed trends over the last half-century." [187]

- "There is now higher confidence in projected patterns of warming and other regional-scale features, including changes in wind patterns, precipitation and some aspects of extremes and of ice." [188]

8.3.4 Regional Climate Change in the 21st Century

Future changes in temperatures and other important features of climate will manifest themselves differently across the regions of the world. Very concise summaries of the current understanding of how regional climates may change have been developed by the IPCC [189] and are provided below.

Africa

Warming is very likely to be more significant than the global annual mean warming throughout the continent and in all seasons, with drier subtropical regions warming more than the moister tropics. Annual rainfall is likely to decrease in much of Mediterranean Africa and the northern Sahara, with a greater likelihood of decreasing rainfall as the Mediterranean coast is approached. Rainfall in southern Africa is likely to decrease in much of the winter rainfall region and western margins (Figure 8.6). There is likely to be an increase in annual mean rainfall in East Africa. It is unclear how rainfall in the Sahel, the Guinean Coast and the southern Sahara will evolve.

Mediterranean and Europe

Annual mean temperatures in Europe are likely to increase more than the global mean. Seasonally, the largest warming is likely to be in northern Europe in winter and in the Mediterranean area in summer. Minimum winter temperatures are likely to increase more than the average in northern Europe. Maximum summer temperatures are likely to increase more than the average in southern and central Europe. Annual precipitation is very likely to increase in most of northern Europe and decrease in most of the Mediterranean area. In central Europe, precipitation is likely to increase in winter but decrease in summer. Extremes of daily precipitation are very likely to increase in northern Europe. The annual number of precipitation days is very likely to decrease in the Mediterranean area. Risk of summer drought is likely to increase in central Europe and in the Mediterranean area. The duration of the snow season is very likely to shorten, and snow depth is likely to decrease in most of Europe (Figure 8.6).

Asia

Warming is likely to be well above the global mean in central Asia, the Tibetan Plateau and northern Asia, above the global mean in eastern Asia and South Asia, and similar to the global mean in Southeast Asia. Precipitation in boreal winter is very likely to increase in northern Asia and the Tibetan Plateau, and likely to increase in eastern Asia and the southern parts of Southeast Asia. Precipitation in summer is likely to increase in northern Asia, East Asia, South Asia and most of Southeast Asia, but is likely to decrease in central Asia. It is very likely that heat waves/hot spells in summer will be of longer duration, more intense and more frequent in East Asia. Fewer very cold days are very likely in East Asia and South Asia. There is very likely to be an increase in the frequency of intense precipitation events in parts of South Asia, and in East Asia (Figure 8.6). Extreme rainfall and winds associated with tropical cyclones are likely to increase in East Asia, Southeast Asia and South Asia.

North America

The annual mean warming is likely to exceed the global mean warming in most areas. Seasonally, warming is likely to be largest in winter in northern regions and in summer in the southwest. Minimum winter temperatures are likely to increase more than the average in northern North America. Maximum summer temperatures are likely to increase more than the average in the southwest. Annual mean precipitation is very likely to increase in Canada and the northeast USA, and likely to decrease in the southwest. In southern Canada, precipitation is likely to increase in winter and spring but decrease in summer (Figure 8.6). Snow season length and snow depth are very likely to decrease in most of North America except in the northernmost part of Canada where maximum snow depth is likely to increase (Figure 8.6).

Central and South America

The annual mean warming is likely to be similar to the global mean warming in southern South America but larger than the global mean warming in the rest of the area. Annual precipitation is likely to decrease in most of Central America and in the southern Andes, although changes in atmospheric circulation may induce large local variability in precipitation response in mountainous areas. Winter precipitation in Tierra del Fuego and summer precipitation in south-eastern South America is likely to increase (Figure 8.6). It is uncertain how annual and seasonal mean rainfall will change over northern South America, including the Amazon forest. However, there is qualitative consistency among the simulations in some areas (rainfall increasing in Ecuador and northern Peru, and decreasing at the northern tip of the continent and in southern northeast Brazil).

Figure 8.6 IPCC representation of anticipated regional climate change

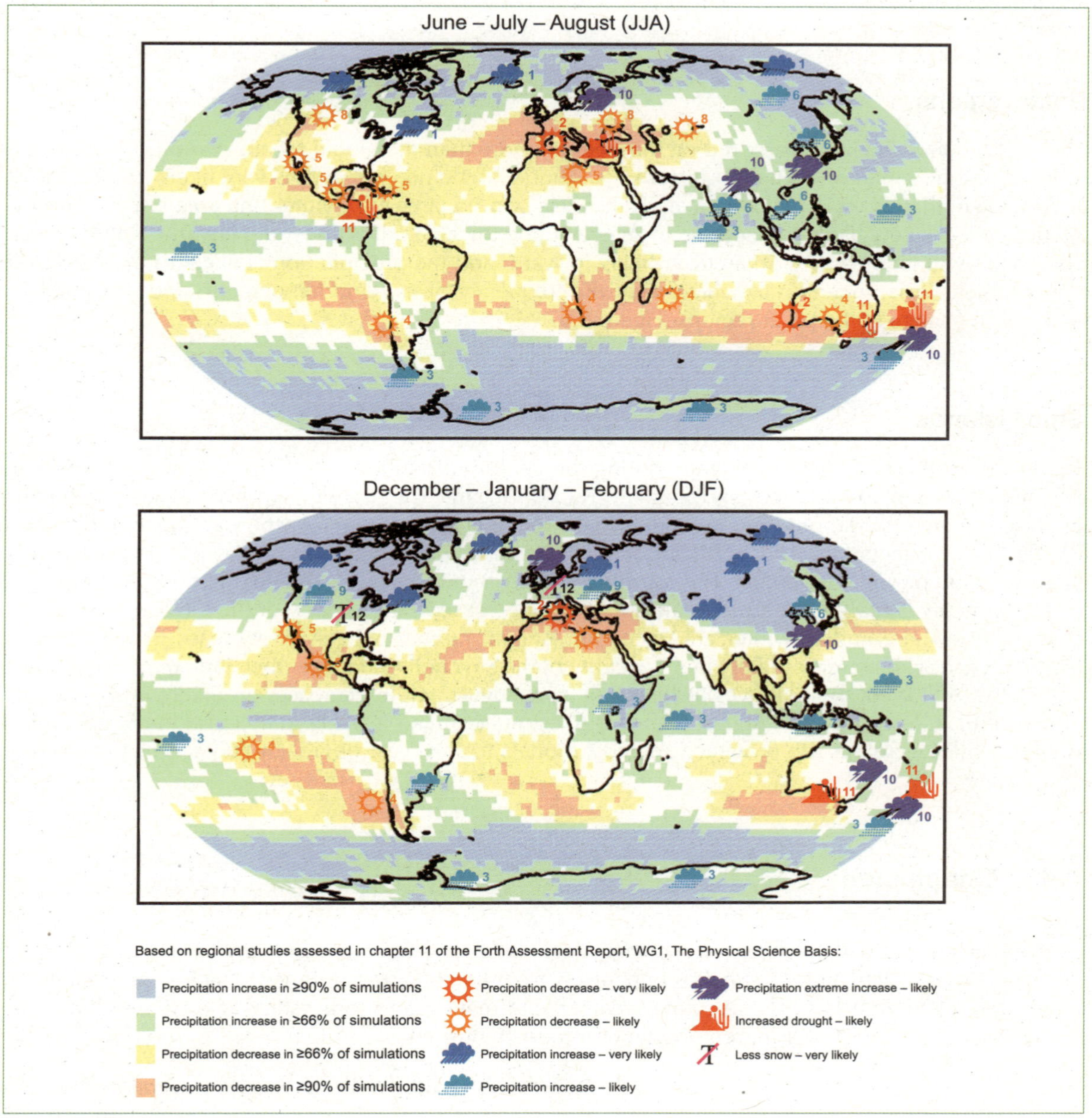

June – July – August (JJA)

December – January – February (DJF)

Based on regional studies assessed in chapter 11 of the Forth Assessment Report, WG1, The Physical Science Basis:

- Precipitation increase in ≥90% of simulations
- Precipitation increase in ≥66% of simulations
- Precipitation decrease in ≥66% of simulations
- Precipitation decrease in ≥90% of simulations
- Precipitation decrease – very likely
- Precipitation decrease – likely
- Precipitation increase – very likely
- Precipitation increase – likely
- Precipitation extreme increase – likely
- Increased drought – likely
- Less snow – very likely

Source: IPCC 2007a

Australia and New Zealand

Warming is likely to be larger than that of the surrounding oceans, but comparable to the global mean. The warming is less in the south, especially in winter, with the warming in the South Island of New Zealand likely to remain less than the global mean. Precipitation is likely to decrease in southern Australia in winter and spring. Precipitation is very likely to decrease in south-western Australia in winter. Precipitation is likely to increase in the west of the South Island of New Zealand. Changes in rainfall in northern and central Australia are uncertain. Increased mean wind speed is likely across the South Island of New Zealand, particularly in winter. Increased frequency of extreme high daily temperatures in Australia and New Zealand, and a decrease in the frequency of cold extremes is very likely. Extremes of daily precipitation are very likely to increase, except possibly in areas of significant decrease in mean rainfall (southern Australia in winter and spring). Increased risk of drought in southern areas of Australia is likely (Figure 8.6).

Polar regions

The Arctic is very likely to warm during this century more than the global mean. Warming is projected to be largest in winter and smallest in summer. Annual arctic precipitation is very likely to increase. It is very likely that the relative precipitation increase will be largest in winter and smallest in summer. Arctic sea ice is very likely to decrease in its extent and thickness. It is uncertain how the Arctic Ocean circulation will change. The Antarctic is likely to warm and the precipitation is likely to increase over the continent. It is uncertain to what extent the frequency of extreme temperature and precipitation events will change in the polar regions (Figure 8.6).

Small islands

Sea levels are likely to rise on average during the century around the small islands of the Caribbean Sea, Indian Ocean and northern and southern Pacific Oceans. The rise will likely not be geographically uniform but large deviations among models make regional estimates across the Caribbean, Indian and Pacific Oceans uncertain. All Caribbean, Indian Ocean and North and South Pacific islands are very likely to warm during this century. The warming is likely to be somewhat smaller than the global annual mean. Summer rainfall in the Caribbean is likely to decrease in the vicinity of the Greater Antilles but changes elsewhere and in winter are uncertain. Annual rainfall is likely to increase in the northern Indian Ocean with increases likely in the vicinity of the Seychelles in December, January and February, and in the vicinity of the Maldives in June, July and August, while decreases are likely in the vicinity of Mauritius in June, July and August (Figure 8.6). Annual rainfall is likely to increase in the equatorial Pacific, while decreases are projected by most models for just east of French Polynesia in December and January.

8.4   Conclusion

> "Climate change will constitute an increasing risk for tourism operators in many destinations. With many tourism activities heavily dependent on the climate and insurance policies increasingly affected by natural hazards, accurate weather information and forecasting of extreme climatic events are becoming ever more important for tourism businesses."
>
> Francesco Frangialli, *UNWTO Secretary-General* (2005)

The use of weather and climate information in the tourism sector is on the rise, but there are still large opportunities to enhance decision-making in the sector with existing meteorological information and by developing new tailored forecast products. [190, 191] The importance of utilizing available weather and climate information will only increase in an era of climate change. Improving the use of weather and climate information in the tourism sector is a challenge that will require closer collaboration between the climate and tourism research communities, national meteorological services, tourism authorities and the tourism industry. The recent collaboration between the WMO and UNWTO to establish an Expert Team on Climate and Tourism is an important initiative to facilitate this collaboration at an international level. In addition, mechanisms such as Regional Climate Outlook Forums (RCOFs) provide an opportunity to extend multidisciplinary training and awareness building at regional and national levels. RCOFs are held regularly in a number of regions around the world and foster direct interaction between climate prediction specialists and user groups, including the tourism sector, in the development of consensus-based regional climate predictions and related product.

The IPCC [192] has projected that climate change will continue throughout the 21st century, even if large-scale reductions in GHG emissions occur over the next several decades. The regional manifestations of climate change that are summarized above are highly relevant for tourism. The impacts of these regional climatic changes and possible adaptation strategies need to be analysed in detail, in order to account for the different geographical and societal contexts of tourism around the world. That is the purpose of the following Chapters.

Chapter 9

Impacts and Adaptation
at Tourism Destinations

The tourism industry and destinations are clearly sensitive to climate variability and change. [193, 194, 195, 196, 197] Climate defines the length and quality of multi-billion dollar tourism seasons and plays a major role in destination choice and tourist spending. In many destinations tourism is closely linked with the natural environment. Climate affects a wide range of the environmental resources that are critical to tourism, such as snow conditions, wildlife productivity and biodiversity, water levels and quality. It also influences various facets of tourism operations (e.g., snow-making, irrigation needs, heating-cooling costs). The major types of climate change impacts projected by the IPCC [198, 199] that have the greatest potential significance for the tourism sector are outlined in Table 9.1

Table 9.1 Major climate change impacts and implications for tourism destinations

Impact	Implications for tourism
Warmer temperatures	Altered seasonality, heat stress for tourists, cooling costs, changes in plant-wildlife-insect populations and distribution, infectious disease ranges
Decreasing snow cover and shrinking glaciers	Lack of snow in winter sport destinations, increased snow-making costs, shorter winter sports seasons, aesthetics of landscape reduced
Increasing frequency and intensity of extreme storms	Risk for tourism facilities, increased insurance costs/loss of insurability, business interruption costs
Reduced precipitation and increased evaporation in some regions	Water shortages, competition over water between tourism and other sectors, desertification, increased wildfires threatening infrastructure and affecting demand
Increased frequency of heavy precipitation in some regions	Flooding damage to historic architectural and cultural assets, damage to tourism infrastructure, altered seasonality
Sea level rise	Coastal erosion, loss of beach area, higher costs to protect and maintain waterfronts
Sea surface temperatures rise	Increased coral bleaching and marine resource and aesthetics degradation in dive and snorkel destinations
Changes in terrestrial and marine biodiversity	Loss of natural attractions and species from destinations, higher risk of diseases in tropical-subtropical countries
More frequent and larger forest fires	Loss of natural attractions; increase of flooding risk; damage to tourism infrastructure
Soil changes (e.g., moisture levels, erosion and acidity)	Loss of archaeological assets and other natural resources, with impacts on destination attractions

Climate change will have both negative and positive impacts on the tourism sector and these impacts will vary substantially by market segment and geographic region. Consequently, there will be 'winners and losers' at the business, destination and nation level. Importantly, all tourism businesses and destinations will need to adapt to climate change in order to minimize associated risks and capitalize upon new opportunities, in an economically, socially and environmentally sustainable manner. The vulnerability of tourism is particularly concerning in those areas where tourism constitutes the major livelihood of local communities, as it is the case in many developing countries and Small Island Developing States.

While it remains beyond its scope to examine the full range of impacts upon the diversity of tourism destinations around the world, the subsequent section will offer a detailed discussion of potential impacts on three major destination types with established vulnerabilities: mountains, islands and coastal zones, and natural-cultural heritage areas. The following section will focus specifically on climate change adaptation, outlining the wide portfolio of adaptations available (both potential strategies and those already being utilized by the tourism industry to cope with natural seasonality and climate variability) and provide illustrative examples of adaptation in mountain, islands and coastal areas, and natural-cultural heritage areas.

9.1 Impacts on Tourism Supply

9.1.1 Overview

There are four broad categories of climate change impacts that could affect tourism destinations, their competitiveness and sustainability, three of which will be covered in this Chapter.

- **Direct climatic impacts** – including geographic and seasonal redistribution of climate resources for tourism, and changes in operating costs (heating-cooling degree days, insurance premiums).

- **Indirect environmental change impacts** – including climate induced-environmental changes such as water shortages, biodiversity loss, decline of landscape aesthetic, increase in vector-borne disease, damage to infrastructure.

- **Impacts of mitigation policies on tourist mobility** – including changes in tourist flow due to increased prices; alterations to aviation routes; changes in the proportions of short-haul and long-haul flights. This aspect will be discussed in detail in Chapters 10 and 12.

- **Indirect societal change impacts** – including the consequences of the broader impacts of climate change on societies, such as changes in economic growth, development patterns, social-political stability and personal safety in some regions. These will have 'knock-on' effects on operations, employment and security issues in tourism and related sectors.

Direct impacts from a changed climate

Direct impacts include changes in climate-related push-pull factors *, changes in operating costs as a result of climate change and change to patterns of extreme weather events. Climate itself is a principal resource for tourism, as it co-determines the suitability of locations for a wide range of tourist activities and is a principal driver of the seasonality of demand. In general, adequate climatic conditions are key for all types of tourism activities, ranging from conventional beach tourism to special interest segments, such as eco-, adventure-, and sport tourism. Furthermore, at some destinations, climate represents the primary attraction on which tourism is predicated. One of the most direct impacts of projected climate change on tourism will be the redistribution of climatic assets among tourism regions. Changes in the length and quality of climate-dependent tourism seasons (i.e., sun-and-sea or ski holidays) could have considerable implications for competitive relationships between destinations and therefore the profitability of tourism enterprises.

An analysis of 143 North American cities identified the potential for a substantive redistribution of climate resources for tourism in the later decades of the 21st century, particularly under high emission scenarios. [200] The number of cities in the USA with 'excellent' or 'ideal' ratings in the winter months is likely to increase, so that southern Florida and Arizona could face increasing competition for winter sun holiday travellers and the seasonal 'snowbird' market (originating from Canada and the northern states

---

*   Push-pull factors: unfavourable climate condition in country/place of origin of tourists and favourable conditions at destinations.

of the USA). In contrast, lower winter ratings in Mexico suggest it could become less competitive as a winter sun-and-sea destination.

Similarly, significant shifts in tourism climate suitability patterns have been projected for Europe towards the end of the 21st century [201], and these will alter the push-pull factors influencing decisions about tourist destinations. The Mediterranean region is projected to become much less attractive for tourism in summer and more attractive in spring and autumn. Simultaneously, the traditional source regions of the majority of tourists to the Mediterranean, particularly Northern Europe, are projected to themselves become more suitable for tourist activities year round, particularly in the summer. As a result it seems likely that more of these travellers might opt to stay within their own region at this time, as well as more people travelling from southerly regions to Northern Europe during the summer months to escape hot summer temperatures in the Mediterranean. [202] The implications of projected changes in the tourism climate resource over the 21st for intra- and inter-regional travel demand are discussed in more detail in Chapter 10.

Another direct business impact of climate change on tourism would be changes in seasonal operating costs, such as heating and cooling, snow-making, irrigation and water supply and annual insurance costs. Although the energy expenses of the accommodation sector vary by location and by type of accommodation, it has been estimated that energy costs expressed in terms of gross hotel revenues typically range from 3–6%, but can be as high as 10% for some historic and luxury hotels. [203] A large portion of overall energy consumption in the accommodation sector is related to space heating-cooling [204] and therefore changes in heating-cooling degree-days have considerable implications for energy costs in some regions.

Table 9.2 illustrates the projected change in heating and cooling degree-days (HDD and CDD) in two important tourism destinations in Canada under a moderate climate change scenario. In temperate destinations like Canada the implications for energy costs will be mixed, with reduced heating costs but increased cooling costs. In warmer climates the cost implications are likely to be unidirectional towards increased cooling costs.

Table 9.2 Projected changes in heating- and cooling degree days[a] relative to 1961–1990 (%)

Destination	2040–2069		2070–2099	
	HDD	CDD	HDD	CDD
Toronto-Niagara Falls	−23	+239	−35	+478
Vancouver-Whistler	−29	+82	−42	+161

(a) Degree-days are the accumulated departures of temperature above or below a particular threshold value. In this analysis 18° C is used as an indication of space heating or cooling requirements.

Source: Scott, D. and Jones, B. (2006a)

A third direct impact of changes in climate is weather extremes. The IPCC [205] has concluded that changes in a number of weather extremes are probable as a result of projected climate change, including: higher maximum temperature and more hot days over nearly all land areas (very likely), greater tropical storm intensity and peak winds (likely), more intense precipitation events over many land areas (very likely), and longer and more severe droughts in many mid-latitude continental interiors (likely). Increased tropical storm intensity would affect the tourism industry through increased infrastructure damage, additional emergency preparedness planning, higher operating expenses (e.g., insurance, backup water and power systems, and evacuations), and business interruptions.

Indirect impacts from environmental change

Because environmental and climatic conditions are such a critical resource for tourism, any subsequent changes will have an inescapable effect on the industry. Changes in water availability, snow cover, the loss in biodiversity at destination level, degradation of the aesthetics of destination·landscapes, agricultural production, increase of natural hazards, coastal impacts, damage to infrastructure and the increasing incidence of vector-borne diseases all impact on tourism in various ways.

In this Section some of the relationships between these changes and tourism impacts are examined in summary. Other climate-induced environmental changes are described in more detail in the following Sections of this Chapter when examining implications for key tourism destinations; mountains, islands and coastal zones, and natural and cultural heritage destinations.

The projected decrease in rainfall levels in some of the world's major tourism regions will very likely affect current destinations, as well as future developments. In some areas this issue relates to potential water scarcity, both shortages in water for basic needs as well as water distribution problems, relating to competition for water between different sectors (e.g., agriculture and tourism), or between different forms of use in tourism establishments (e.g., rooms, kitchen, cleaning, swimming pools, maintenance of gardens, golf courses etc.) as opposed to their uses such as agriculture. UNEP [206] notes that the tourism industry is an intensive water user, and the impacts of wasteful and inefficient use of the water resources can be very detrimental. Examples include evidence from Israel, where water use by hotels along the River Jordan is thought to be contributing to the drying up of the Dead Sea, with the water level having dropped 16.4 metres since 1977. Additionally, golf tourism has an enormous impact on water withdrawals – an eighteen-hole golf course can consume more than 2.3 million litres a day. [207] On average, a golf course requires 10–15,000 m³ of water per hectare/year. A golf course covers between 50–150 hectares, which means that the annual consumption of a golf course is around 1 million cubic metres per year, the equivalent of the water consumption of a city of 12,000 inhabitants. [208] These negative consequences of tourism on water supplies have to be considered in the broader context with the many and varied positive consequences tourism brings to an area, including economic stability and trade.

In addition to water problems relating to rainfall declines in some areas, water supplies stored in glaciers and snow cover are also projected to decline, resulting in reduced water availability in summer seasons in regions supplied by melt water from major mountain ranges. These mountain areas are not only popular tourist destinations but more critically, they are also areas where more than one-sixth of the world population currently lives. [209]

Conversely, water excesses such as flooding, usually related to extreme weather events, will impact on both natural and cultural heritage attractions in many regions. For example, major geological problems identified for Italian cultural heritage sites relate to floods and associated landslides. [210] In Peru, intense precipitation during the 1997–1998 El Niño events have significantly contributed to increased groundwater levels, causing damage to the earthen architectural structures at the Chan Chan Archaeological Zone in the north of the country. [211] In the context of natural heritage attractions of particular importance to tourism, it is estimated that 16% of the world's coral reefs have been destroyed in the 1997–1998 El Niño event. [212] In south and east Africa, this was compounded in 2000 by widespread flooding resulting in increased rates of dying off of coral reefs, from 18.6% in 1999 to 51.3% in 2001. [213] Coral reefs are a major tourist attraction in many coastal and island areas around the world, so any long-term damage arising from such incidents will have major implications for the industry.

The major impacts of climate change on biodiversity, ecosystems and landscapes can be categorized into three broad areas: [214, 215, 216, 217]

- impacts at different spatial scales; ecological communities, along environmental gradients, at the regional level;

- impacts on different environments: soil, rivers and estuaries, sea and coastal zones, terrestrial ecosystems;

- impacts on specific areas such as protected areas.

Between 20 and 30% of plant and animal species assessed so far are likely to be at risk of extinction if increases in global average temperature exceed 1.5 – 2.5° C. [218] The changes in biodiversity will, in turn, impact on tourism by affecting, for example, the levels or the very existence of endemic species, animal populations, birdsong, the flowering of plants, coral reef, and the type and cover of forests. [219, 220, 221, 222] See additional discussion on biodiversity impacts on natural and cultural heritage in Section 9.1.4.

Landscape aesthetics, the presence of natural hazards and the extent of damage to infrastructure will be affected by climate-induced environmental change in a number of ways; e.g., flooding, coastal erosion, desertification, an increase in frequency and intensity of extreme events such as hurricanes and tropical storms, and changes in geomorphology. For example, future climate change has the potential to increase significantly the nature, frequency and magnitude of natural hazards in mountain regions via the processes of glacier retreat and the melting of permafrost. [223, 224, 225] Because glaciers are coupled to their slope and valley-floor, retreat impacts upon these in a number of complex ways including heightened risk of rockfalls, glacial lake outburst floods, large-scale debris flow events and increasingly dynamic valley floors that are susceptible to deep and rapid river entrenchment. These form significant natural hazards which in many glaciated mountain regions of the world increase the vulnerability of destinations and socio-economic infrastructure in such regions. Furthermore, recent research has shown that mountain slopes underlain by permafrost are at high risk of future instability with climate warming. [226, 227]

The health status of millions of people will be impacted by projected climate change-related exposures, particularly those regions with a low adaptive capacity. [228] Countries identified as having the lowest adaptive capacity are predominantly in Sub-Saharan Africa, and developing countries in Asia and Central Asia, with regions experiencing conflict situations and small-island states also included in this category. [229, 230] Direct impacts from extreme weather events and environmental change will have consequences on morbidity and mortality, but the indirect impacts may be more significant. The greatest impacts are likely to be caused by proportionally small increases in diseases that currently have major impacts already, but which will become more widely prevalent, such as diarrhoea, malnutrition and vector-borne diseases. [231, 232] Though some of the regions most severely impacted are not, on a world scale, major tourist destinations when the number of trips is considered (e.g., sub-Saharan Africa), it must be recognized that tourism can be of a significant importance to their economy and their communities' livelihoods.

The ability of some destinations to provide tourist facilities, services and products will be compromised by these indirect impacts from climate change. Alterations in the spatial distribution of vector-borne diseases are anticipated, so that diseases such as malaria (Figure 9.1), dengue fever, viral encephalitis and Lyme disease are projected to occur in regions where they have been previously unknown. Potential disease transmission rates may increase substantially for diseases such as malaria (P. falciparum – Figure 9.1), where the risk of transmission is projected to double in across Western Europe and Eastern United States by the 2020s and large parts of central Asia, Mexico and regions of South America by the 2050s. [233] These developments will compromise infrastructures in some destinations, and their ability to cater adequately for tourism, as well affecting tourists themselves who will be exposed to new risks when travelling.

Figure 9.1 Future transmission potential for the malaria parasite *Plasmodium falciparum* relative to the baseline period (1970s = 1, doubling = 2) [a]

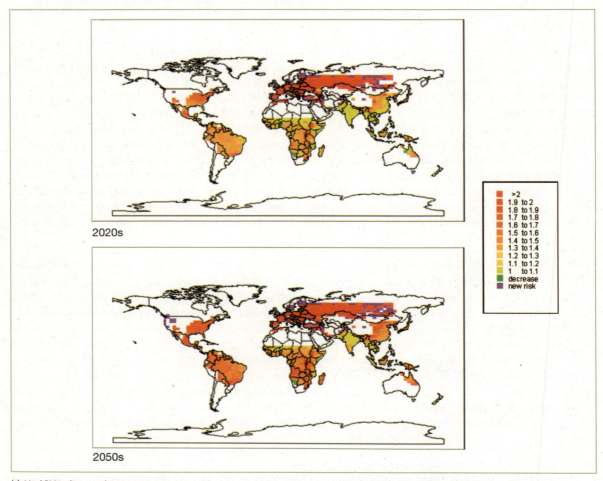

[a] HadCM3 climate change scenario (monthly mean temperature and precipitation) for the 2020s and 2050s

Source: Martens, P. et al (1999)

Climate change is also expected to have some impacts on food production that will have subsequent implications for tourism. Agricultural productivity is projected to decrease at even small temperature increases (1–2° C) in developing nations, particularly those at lower latitudes. [234] Adverse impacts on food supplies would risk increases in nutritional deficits, gastro-intestinal infections and psychological stresses, placing additional burdens on local health services [235], with consequent impacts on all sectors, including tourism.

Other shifts in agricultural production will not affect the health of local populations or the ability to supply the local tourism industry, but rather affect the attractiveness of destinations for specific tourism markets. A primary example is the impact of climate change on wine production, particularly high-quality vintages, and the implications for wine tourism. Wine grapes have acute environmental sensitivity and there are indications that climate change is already affecting the taste of wines from some regions. Regions that are currently producing high-quality grapes at the margins of their optimal climatic zone may be thrust into a climate that is no longer suited to the grapes now grown. Areas of France, Australia and California that are renowned for high-quality wines are projected to see grape growing conditions impaired by mid to late-century. [236, 237] Conversely other more pole ward wine growing regions (Southern England, southern New Zealand, southern British Columbia Canada) are projected to be able to produce higher-quality vintages and may benefit from a shift in wine tourism over time. [238]

Societal Change, including impacts of economic disruption and political instability

> "Our actions over the coming few decades could create risks of major disruption to economic and social activity, later in this century and in the next, on a scale similar to those associated with the great wars and the economic depression of the first half of the 20th century."
>
> The Stern Review (2006)

Climate change is thought to pose a risk to future economic growth and to the political stability of some nations. [239, 240, 241, 242] Although not without debate [243], the Stern Review is generally considered to be the most comprehensive assessment of the economics of global climate change. It concluded that although a rise of only 1° C might benefit global GDP, greater climate change would eventually damage economic growth at the global scale, including the stark conclusion that if we do nothing to stem climate change, there could be an eventual permanent reduction in consumption per capita of 20% later in the 21st century or early 22nd century.[244] These costs would not be shared evenly, with a disproportionate burden falling on the poorest countries. The uneven distribution of climate change burdens raises questions of international and intergeneration fairness and justice. Anthropogenic climate change has been brought about predominantly by the activities of developed countries, while some of the most acute impacts will fall on developing countries. [245, 246, 247, 248] As noted previously, many such developing countries are likely to have a low adaptive capacity and therefore an inability to adapt to or manage these impacts of climate change in an effective way.

The Stern Review notes that tackling climate change is a pro-growth strategy for the longer term, with the benefits of strong, early action considerably outweighing the costs of inaction. Any reductions of global GDP due to climate change would likely have negative implications for anticipated future growth in tourism spending, however there has been no in depth interpretation of the Stern Review [249] for the tourism sector.

> "If climate protection policy fails (mitigation) [...] it is likely that from the mid 21st century local and regional conflicts will proliferate and the international system will be destabilized, threatening global economic development and overstretching global governance structures."
>
> German Advisory Council on Global Change (2007)

Climate change is considered a national and international security risk that will steadily intensify, particularly under greater warming scenarios. [250, 251, 252, 253] Regional climate change impacts such as degradation of fresh water resources, declining food production, increased storm related disasters, and trans-boundary environmental migration could overwhelm local capacities to respond and result in violence and the destabilization of fragile governments. Climate change associated security risks have been identified in a number of regions where tourism is highly important to local-national economies: Caribbean and Central America, Mediterranean North Africa, and China. [254, 255, 256, 257, 258] A security-related decline in tourism would exacerbate deteriorating of economic performance in these destinations.

There is crucial interdependence between tourism, economies, community livelihoods and the environment, and climate change is likely to undermine development objectives in many developing countries. [259, 260, 261, 262, 263, 264] Most developing nations do not have sufficient human, financial and technical capital to effectively address climate change, particularly those countries with a wide range of existing socio-economic and environmental challenges. The more dramatic impacts of climate change (including flood, drought, risk of unstable food security, decrease in public health and disease, and loss of biodiversity) will increase the vulnerability of already vulnerable regions potentially resulting in increased poverty.

Factors such as widespread poverty, recurrent droughts, a dependence on natural resources and biodiversity make sub-Saharan Africa more acutely vulnerable to the impacts of climate change than most other regions in the world. [265, 266, 267] Inequitable land distribution, an over dependence on rain fed agriculture, disease and governance issues also combine to ensure that the consequences of climate change in Africa will have inevitable 'knock-on effects' on the tourism sector and the livelihoods of the communities' that rely on tourism. [268]

This Section has provided an overview of the main impacts of climate change on tourism demand and supply. The subsequent Sections will cover in more detail issues relating to the three major destination types with recognised vulnerabilities: mountains, islands and coastal zones, and natural-cultural heritage areas.

9.1.2 Mountain and Winter Sports Destinations

Mountain regions are important destinations for global tourism. Snow cover and pristine mountain landscapes are the principal attractions for tourism in these regions are the features that are most vulnerable to climate change. [269, 270, 271]

Winter sports tourism

> "Climate change is the most pressing issue facing the ski industry today."
>
> Patrick O'Donnell, *Chief Executive Officer of Aspen Skiing Company* [272]

The impact of climate change on the snow-based sports tourism industry is potentially severe. The multi-billion Euro international winter sports industry* has been repeatedly identified as at risk to global climate change due to the close linkage between economic performance and climate through the availability of natural snow and suitable climatic conditions to make snow. Known vulnerabilities exist in Australia, Austria, Spain, Canada, France, Germany, Italy, Switzerland, and the United States, however the projected impacts on destinations in these nations vary in magnitude and over different time horizons. [273, 274] The key climate change impacts of interest to the winter sports industry relate to 'natural snow reliability' and also 'technical snow reliability' (i.e., cold temperatures to make snow). The latter is important in areas where snow-making is almost universal among ski areas and covers a high proportion of skiable terrain.

European Alps

A considerable number of studies have been completed on the impact of climate change on skiing in the European Alps. [275, 276, 277, 278, 279, 280] The most comprehensive was recently conducted for the Organization for Economic Cooperation and Development. [281] It determined that the number of ski areas that were considered 'naturally snow reliable' ** dropped from 609 (91%) to 404 (61%) under a +2° C warming scenario and further declined to 202 (30%) under a +4° C warming scenario. By comparison, climate change scenarios for the European Alps project an annual warming of 2.3 to 3.3° C by mid-century and 2.9 to 5.3° C by the end of the 21st century, and even more pronounced warming in winter months. [282, 283] The impacts varied among the five nations examined, with the ski industry in Germany found to be the most at risk. Snow-making is already a widespread climate adaptation in the region, with the proportion of skiable terrain currently equipped with snow-making estimated at 50% in Austria, 40% in Italy, 18% in Switzerland, 15% in the French Alps, and 11% in Germany (Bavaria).

---

*   The ski industry, not including apparel and equipment sales = Euro 9 billion (see Scott 2006b); snowmobile industry = Euro 18 billion (International Snowmobile Manufacturers Association 2007); there are limited data on the economic value of other winter sports, such as nordic skiing, ice fishing or snowshoeing

**   Defined as the upper half of a ski area having at least a 30 cm natural snow base for 100-days.

Critically, the heavily cited OECD analysis did not account for snow-making. It therefore does not reflect the operating realities of many ski operators and has likely overestimated the potential damages to these businesses. Major uncertainties on the impacts for businesses also relate to the acceptance of customers to ski on partially snow covered ski runs, such as illustrated in Figure 9.2, or the potential for large reductions in opportunities for Nordic skiing at low mountain elevations.

The winter of 2006-2007 was the warmest on record over most parts of the Alps and estimated to be the warmest winter in the past millennium in some locations. [284, 285] The impact of this record warm winter on the ski industry is still being tabulated, but the delayed opening of the season and inability to make snow in some locations were prominent impacts. Analysis of this climate change analogue will provide important new information on the ability of ski areas to operate and remain profitable under conditions similar to those projected decades from now.

Figure 9.2 Partially operating ski area near Salzburg, Austria (mid-January 2007)

Photo credit: Stadel, B.

Scotland

Trends in ski season length at the Cairngorm ski area in Scotland from 1972 to 1996 reveal a shorter average season, but at the highest elevation ski lift (1,060–1,150 m) there was no change. [286] Based on an analysis of the exceptionally mild winter of 1988–1989, it has been suggested that ski areas above 1,000 m would still have sufficient natural snow cover for skiing in warmer winters. [287] However, the warm winter of 1988–1989 was not compared against future climate change scenarios for this region, so the future operation of ski areas in Scotland remains uncertain.

Eastern North America

Snow-making is integral to the ski industry in Eastern Canada and the US and most ski areas have virtually complete coverage of their skiable terrain. A second generation of climate change assessments, which account for snow-making, have substantially improved our understanding of the risk climate change poses to the ski industry in this region. [288, 289] Advanced snow-making systems substantially lower the vulnerability of ski areas in eastern North America to climate change at least through the middle of the 21st century. Ski season losses are projected to range from 8–46% in Ontario and 4–34% in Quebec depending on the climate change scenario, with high emission scenarios causing much larger impacts. [290, 291] In New England, with advanced snow-making capabilities, only one of 14 locations was projected to lose greater than 25% of its ski season under low emission scenarios by mid century.

However, high emission scenarios had a much greater impact, with eight locations projected to lose 25% or more of their ski season by mid-century and half losing 45% or more of their ski season by the end of the 21st century. [292]

In order to limit ski season losses to the levels described above, mid century snow-making requirements were projected to increase by 62–151% in Ontario, 18–150% in Québec, and 3–86% in New England. At the end of the century, several locations required more than double the machine-made snow of today, while in other locations warm temperatures made snow-making unfeasible during parts of the winter months.

Another major snow-based winter sport in North America is snowmobiling, which in some regions (Midwest, Plains-Prairies, New England, Ontario and Quebec) exceeds skiing in terms of number of participants and economic impact. According to the International Snowmobile Manufacturers Association the annual economic impact of snowmobiling is US$ 25 billion in the US and Canada. [293] The snowmobiling industry in North America is much more vulnerable to climate change than is the ski industry, because it is completely reliant on natural snowfall. Under high emission climate change scenarios a reliable snowmobile season disappears from most regions of eastern North America (New England, southern Ontario and Quebec, and the Midwest states) with developed trail networks by mid-century and earlier in some areas. [294, 295]

Western North America

Although the Rocky and Sierra Nevada Mountains are home to some of North America's most widely known winter tourism destinations, the implications for major ski areas in the region have not yet been comprehensively examined. Considering only changes in natural snow conditions, the ski season in the Sierra Nevada Mountains of California was projected to decrease 3–6 weeks by mid-century and 7–15 weeks by the end of this century. [296] Taking snow-making into account, ski seasons at high elevation ski areas near Aspen Colorado were projected to decrease by 10 days in the next two decades and become 28–70 days shorter by 2100. [297]

A recent media release proclaimed that the 'Ski Industry in Rockies May Be Shut Down by 2050'. [298] However, this analysis did not examine the impact of climate change on any key performance indicator of the ski industry, such as operational ski days (season length), capacity to operate during economically key holiday periods, snow-making requirements and costs, or skier visits. Consequently, such a conclusion is unfounded and highlights the need for sound science on this issue so that misinformation that could be damaging to the ski industry is not propagated to investors and skiers.

Australia

Under a warming scenario of +3° C and precipitation decline of 20%, none of Australia's ski areas were projected to have enough natural snow cover to remain financially viable. [299] However, with sufficient investment in snow-making systems and necessary water supply, it was estimated that all of the ski areas would be able to cope with the impact of projected climate change over the next 25 years but not likely through to mid-century. [300]

The preceding summary of impacts focused on average changes to ski seasons and not extreme seasons. Inter-annual variability is very likely to be more pronounced under climate change, creating increasingly challenging business conditions. It may not matter to ski area operators if every ski season by mid-century is a couple of weeks shorter, as much of the season loss will occur at the beginning and end of the season when skier visits are relatively low. [301] Conversely, two or three consecutive extremely warm winters, could cause substantive economic losses and if frequent enough perhaps adversely affecting skier perceptions and demand in the longer term.

Beginner ski runs are typically found at lower elevations, where the general finding is that the impact of climatic change would be more pronounced. Most people learn to ski on these lower-lying beginner slopes and the implications of fewer such slopes for discouraging beginning skiers or possibly diminishing the industry's client base over time remains uncertain. There are divergent views on how best to manage this risk. Some regard market-based contraction of the sector as healthy, while others contend there is essential to retain these 'nursery ski areas' through subsidies, for regional economic reasons and the future of the ski industry. [302, 303, 304, 305]

With the possible exception of the Australian and Scottish ski industries, which appear to be entirely at risk to moderate or high warming scenarios over the next 50 years, the probable consequence of climate change will be a contraction in the number of ski operators in most regional markets. Although climate change would contribute to the demise of many ski businesses, it could advantage some of the ski operations that remain. If skier demand remained relatively stable, as it has in some climate change analogue years (see Box 2), remaining ski businesses would be in a position to gain market share through diminished competition. The socio-economic implications of a climate change induced contraction of the ski tourism marketplace for communities have yet to be examined, but it is clear that both communities that are at risk of losing ski operators and those where ski operations are likely to persist will need to adapt to climate change, though for very different reasons. The former will need to adjust to reduced winter tourism spending, lost employment, and potentially declining real estate prices, while the latter will need to plan for increased visitation, congestion, and perhaps greater development pressures. [306, 307] What is clear is that adaptation to maintain skiing as a central cultural and economic component of many alpine communities in an era of climate change will require significant economic investment and careful environmental planning. The adaptation options available to ski operators and communities are further discussed below.

Changing Alpine Landscapes

Nature-based tourism is also a vital component of tourism in mountain regions of the world. Climate change is projected to have substantial impacts on sensitive mountain environments, with implications for the attractiveness of mountain environments for tourism and the occurrence of natural hazards. A survey of Mountain Biosphere Reserve (MBR) managers in 2004 about the impacts of climate change found that the impacts on tourism and recreation were the most frequent concern, identified by 80% of MBRs around the world. [308] Although the central question was deceptively clear – how will climate change affect this economically critical sector – answers from MBR managers remain elusive.

Climate-induced environmental change has been documented in several mountain ranges of the world that are key tourism destinations (the European Alps, Rockies, Andes, and Himalayas). Glaciers provide some of the most dramatic scenery that attract tourists to mountain destinations (e.g., visitors per year: Franz Josef Glacier, New Zealand 250,000 [309]; Columbia Ice Fields, Banff National Park, Canada 600,000 [310]; Los Glaciares National Park, Argentina 167,000 [311]). An estimated 7,000 km^2 have been lost from mountain glaciers in the last 40 years. [312] Glacier extent has decreased by 30–40% in the European Alps during the 20th century [313] and a similar decrease of 25% has been recorded in the Canadian Rockies over the same period. [314] Glacier National Park in the USA has lost 115 of its 150 glaciers over the past century and scientists estimate that the remaining 35 glaciers will disappear over the next 30 years. [315] In addition to aesthetic impacts for tourism, shrinking of glaciers modify the water-storage capacities of mountains, thus affecting downstream ecosystems and water supply in some destinations.

Figure 9.3   Retreat of Muir and Riggs glaciers in Glacier Bay National Park and Preserve (Alaska, USA)

Photo credit: Global Warming Art [316]

Climate change also has serious implications for the biodiversity of mountain ecosystems. Many alpine species have limited capacity to move to higher altitudes in response to warming temperatures and displacement by lowland species. This is especially true of isolated populations on 'mountain islands', where, with nowhere to go, the danger of localized extinctions is considerable. The loss of colourful mountain meadows and upslope migration of the tree line have been observed in mountain ranges of North America [317] and in the European Alps, and some plants previously found only on mountaintops have disappeared. [318]

Certain natural processes which pose hazards to people and development in mountain regions have accelerated as a result of recent warming and deglaciation, including glacier avalanches, landslides and slope instability caused by glacier debuttressing and permafrost melting, and outburst floods from moraine- and glacier-dammed lakes. [319] Changes in natural hazards in mountain destinations pose an increased risk to tourists and tourism infrastructure. The unprecedented melting of the Belvedere Glacier during the summer of 2002, for example, created a new glacial lake that Italian government engineers feared threatened to destroy the alpine resort near the town of Macugnaga. [320]

In contrast, the warmer climate conditions that are projected to drastically reshape alpine landscapes will also provide opportunities for mountain destinations to extend the warm-weather tourism season (including activities like hiking and mountain biking) [321, 322] and provide comfortable climatic conditions as a retreat from the heat in urban centres and valleys. [323, 324] The implications of climate change for altered seasonal tourist demand and tourist perceptions of projected changes in the physical landscape in mountain regions are further discussed in Chapter 10.

9.1.3 Impacts on Islands and Coastal Zones

Islands and coastal zones are among the most vulnerable tourist destinations to climate change. The main observed and projected climatic changes in island destinations are an increased intensity and frequency of extreme events, sea level rise, changes in ocean circulation, and changes in natural ecosystems. [325, 326, 327, 328]

Extreme events

There is high confidence that the most immediate and more significant consequences of climate change are likely to be changes in the nature of extreme events (e.g., flooding, tropical cyclones, storm surges, heat waves) and climatic variability (e.g., droughts, and prevailing winds accelerating coastal erosion, see Figure 9.4). [329, 330, 331, 332] Coastal areas are particularly vulnerable to extreme wind events. Wind-storm disasters account for about one-third of all natural disasters throughout the world (by number, fatalities and economic losses), whilst accounting for more than two-thirds of the corresponding insured losses and major wind-storm disasters and the losses generated by them have increased drastically in recent decades. [333] An increase in the frequency of extreme cyclones has occurred in the last decade and is projected to continue, bringing more extreme wind events. [334]

Figure 9.4 Erosion of shoreline and damage to tourism infrastructure due to hurricane Ivan in Tobago

Photo credit: Simpson, M. C.

The causal relationship between climate change and the observed increase in extreme events is still under debate. Some scientists highlight the role of Atlantic Multi-decadal Oscillation patterns, as opposed to global warming activities, in the recorded 20–30 year storm cycles, the latest of which commenced in 1995. The heavy hurricane toll of 2004 and 2005 in the Gulf of Mexico is seen as indicative of the development of this cycle, preceded by the last active cycle during 1940–1960. [335, 336]

However, there is much compelling evidence that the current levels of tropical cyclone activity are largely a response to climate change from anthropogenic causes. [337, 338, 339] In the North Atlantic regions, the observed 20–30 year variations in tropical cyclone and hurricane frequency over the past century have been characterised by a 50% increase in cyclone activity with each subsequent multi-decadal cycle through the last 100 years. These increases are closely correlated with increasing sea surface temperatures (SSTs): "[…] a substantial 100-year trend leading to related increases of over 0.7° C in SST and over 100% in tropical cyclone and hurricane numbers." [340] Anthropogenically-produced greenhouse gases have contributed to a general trend, whereby raised SSTs, and increased tropical cyclone and hurricane numbers are "[…] substantially influenced by greenhouse warming." [341]

Variations in cyclones, hurricanes and typhoons in many small-island tropical and sub-tropical regions are dominated by El Nino events and characterised by decadal variability. In addition, increases in the distribution of tropical storm increases in one area are mirrored by decreases in other areas. [342] Although the number of cyclones and cyclone days has decreased in most areas during the past decade, there has been a large increase in the number and proportion of extreme hurricanes (categories 4 and 5). [343] These increases in hurricane intensity coincide with an increase in sea surface temperatures. Sea temperature warming has ranged from 0 to 0.5° C per decade between 1971 and 2004, for the Caribbean, Indian Ocean and Mediterranean regions. [344] Evidence appears to indicate the correlation between higher sea temperatures and increasing hurricane intensity, and there appears to be a general trend towards more frequent intense hurricanes. [345]

Box 5 Extreme storm events in the Caribbean

Caribbean small islands states (SIS) are extremely vulnerable to hurricanes. Future warming is likely to lead to greater hurricane force intensity and destructive potential, and subsequently increased hurricane-related losses across coastal regions. [346] There has been a marked increase in activity since 1994 with a very high level of hurricane activity in the 2004–2005 seasons. This has been attributed to increased sea surface temperature (SST) coupled with anomalies in wind patterns, particularly in 2005 with the highest SST recorded since 1870 across the western tropical Atlantic and Gulf of Mexico, [347] leading to record tropical storm activity, with 15 named storms making landfall in the Atlantic basin. [348]

Figure 9.5 North Atlantic hurricanes have increased with sea surface temperature

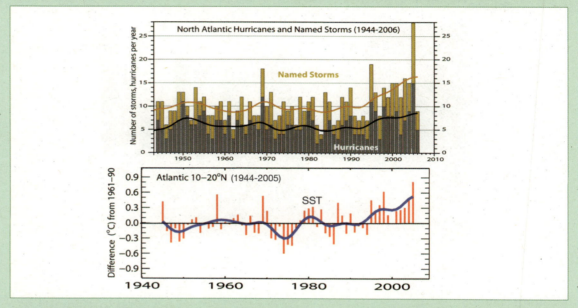

Source: Pachauri and Jallow (2007) [349]

Seasonal records for the number of tropical storms (42) and hurricanes (24) in the Mexican Gulf were established by the combination of the 2004 and 2005 hurricane seasons. During the hurricane season in 2004 and 2005 anomalies in sea surface temperature existed in the main hurricane development region along with anomalies in sea level pressure and in the trade-winds.

Figure 9.6 Selection of major gulf hurricanes in 2004-2005

Source: Saunders and Lea (2006) [350, 351]

The losses experienced in Honduras and Nicaragua from Hurricane Mitch in 1999 totalled more than the combined GDP of both countries and over 7000 people died in Honduras. [352] Similarly, the major cyclone that hit Bangladesh in 1991 resulted in a storm surge of 7 metres and winds of 235 miles/hour; over 138,000 people were killed and 840,000 homes destroyed, with over 12 million people impacted by the cyclone. [353]

The economic impact of strong storm events on tourism is substantial. The ten-day closure and clean-up following Hurricane Georges in 1998 resulted in tourism revenue losses of approximately US$ 32 million in the Florida Keys. [354] The economic impact of the four hurricanes that struck Florida in 2004 was estimated to be several times larger. However, this revenue was not lost to the industry as whole, as other US destinations such as Arizona and California benefited from the transfer of large numbers of visitors not going to Florida. [355] With 26 tropical storms and 14 hurricanes, the 2005 hurricane season was one of the most active and destructive in history, spawning three of the most intense North Atlantic storms on record, including Hurricane Katrina with its associated environmental, social and economic impacts. Hurricane Katrina caused extensive damage to the tourism infrastructure in New Orleans and Coastal Mississippi, with major losses in tourism, convention business and gambling expected for some time after the event. [356]

Sea level rise

Sea level rise is of major importance to tourism given that most tourism activities take place in coastal zones. Further global sea level rises could range from 31 to 65 cm by 2100, aggravating coastal erosion and leading to the loss of beaches. [357] This is primarily a consequence of the expansion of sea water (70–75%), as a result of the increase in oceanic temperatures, and of the continued melting of mountain glaciers and small ice caps. [358] In a few countries the sea level has fallen due to tectonic uplift; however, overall, sea level is projected to rise, at an escalating rate. Even small rises in sea level will result in significant erosion and submersion of land, increased flood hazard, contamination of freshwater aquifers, loss of protective coral reefs, mangrove areas and sand beaches which will increase exposure to hurricanes and storm surges in coastal zones. In small island regions especially, much of the biological diversity and most of the population, agricultural land and capital assets are located in these areas and so at risk. [359] This has major implications for tourism which needs to be assessed. In the Indian Ocean, the Maldives average only 1.5 meters above sea level and projected rates of sea level rise are likely to inundate large areas of the different islands and atolls. Of the archipelago's 1,192 islands and coral atolls, 194 are inhabited, and the beaches on 60% of those are already facing varying degrees of erosion and encroachment. Other low lying islands, such as the Bahamas and Kiribati, face similar problems. [360] One-quarter of the Indian population live along the coastline and are to a great extent dependent on coastal livelihoods. Sea level rises ill have major impacts in these areas especially in the Bay of Bengal area which also experiences seasonal monsoon and cyclonic patterns. [361]

In Europe, the EUROSION study [362] into the management of coastal erosion throughout the EU reported that 20% of the European shoreline is retreating and/or is being artificially stabilised. Its findings indicated that for Europe, the value of economic assets located within 500 metres of EU coastline, and at risk from sea level rises (including those related to infrastructure, industry, agriculture and tourism), is 500 to 1,000 Billion.

Ocean circulations

Sophisticated computer-based global climate models are now used to estimate global winds and ocean currents. Ocean currents have a large influence on local climatic conditions. Changes in rainfall variability and tropical cyclone characteristics in the South Pacific, for example, are strongly dependent on El Niño Southern Oscillation (ENSO). El Niño manifests in a decrease in precipitation for areas in the Western Pacific (e.g., Australia). As the El Niño develops, the extent of its influence on global weather increases, resulting in anomalous weather and climate conditions worldwide. This includes a decrease in tropical storm activity in the Atlantic Ocean, droughts in the Caribbean and Central

America, increased tropical storm activity in the Eastern Pacific, and wet conditions in the Southern USA and Eastern Africa. The drought, floods and fires that inflict Southeast Asia during an El Niño have a major impact on the region's tourism industry, due in part to the haze resulting from man-made fires reducing visibility, impeding air traffic and increasing health risks. [363, 364]

Ecosystems

Coastal and island ecosystems are affected by the above mentioned climate change impacts. Most directly, extreme events can destroy ecosystems, such as mangrove forests, tropical forests or coral reefs. In the South African Cape Floral Region, some lowland areas are threatened due to sea level rises, which will have consequences both for the coastal ecosystem itself and for the buffering of associated ecosystems. [365] Coral reefs especially are a crucial resource for tourism and other sectors. In many destinations, reefs are the key pull factor (as a visitor attraction) for tourists, and therefore a major economic asset; "[…] more than half of the tourists currently visiting the regions along the Great Barrier Reef are 'reef-interested', and, as these tend to be relatively big-spending, they represent 70% of the total tourism expenditure in these regions." [366] The increasing sea surface temperature and increasing acidity of the water will have an important impact on marine life and coral reefs [367] (Figure 9.7).

Figure 9.7 Coral bleaching in Tobago

Photo credit: Simpson, M. C.

Box 6 Impact and adaptation in Mauritius [368]

Tourism destination and situation: Island of Mauritius, Indian Ocean – SCUBA Diving.

Climate change impact: More frequent and intense cyclones and El Niño phenomena killing and/ or damaging the coral reefs.

Adaptation strategy/strategies: Coastal Zone Management (CZM) has reduced local pollution levels thereby attempting to increase resilience of the reef to local and global environmental change (although findings of the study show that the state of coral reefs are only relevant for a minor share of specialized and experience divers).

Organization implementing the adaptation strategy: Mauritius Government.

9.1.4 Impacts on Natural and Cultural Heritage

The natural resource base for tourism includes both human-shaped environments and the relatively unmodified components of the environment, such as natural terrestrial, coastal and marine ecosystems and landscapes, surface and ground water, as well as the atmosphere. Cultural heritage assets are also a foundation of tourism; visitation to places for their historic, archaeological, architectural or indigenous value underpins the industry in many destinations.

The natural environment is often very important in determining the demand for tourism, especially for nature-based tourism. Tourists are attracted to national parks because they represent an aesthetically pleasing and healthy environment, and they contain varied and interesting biodiversity. The impact of climate change on biodiversity and natural landscapes may have a negative influence on their amenity value and hence on visitor numbers. [369] However, tourists have been shown to adapt in the long run to major changes in landscape (e.g., the Italian and French Rivieras through the twentieth century). In some cases there are likely to be both costs and benefits. In the Arctic, a longer summer season is likely to benefit cruise tourism and activities such as whale-watching whilst shorter winters could reduce the range of Arctic fauna and flora which attracts some visitors. [370]

The following are examples of some of the impacts on biodiversity that may occur as a result of climate change, which in turn will impact on tourism. [371, 372, 373, 374, 375, 376]

- The survival of rare and isolated populations in fragmented habitats may directly or indirectly be affected by climate change; the loss of keystone or iconic species has important implications for ecotourism. For example, the unique polar bear tourism industry (Figure 9.8) that has developed in the northern town of Churchill, Canada is threatened by declining sea ice conditions on Hudson Bay. Projections are that over the next 30 years, sea ice conditions may deteriorate to the point that the polar bear population may collapse in this region.

Figure 9.8 Polar bear watching

Photo credit: Dawson, J.

- Endemic species are highly sensitive to change and therefore more vulnerable; e.g., over the past twenty years one-hundred and ten endemic frog species (around 67%) of the population in the popular tourist destination of the Costa Rican cloud forests and rainforests have become extinct. [377] Such extinctions can be due to non-climatic changes to the environment such as urban or agricultural expansion, but similar changes will result from climate-related changes as well. [378]

- Animal populations may be affected by environmental stress or indirectly through changes in vegetation. In some circumstances, migration may occur but however, where populations are unable to migrate due, for example restrictions of mountainous terrain or lack of migration corridors, local extinction is likely to occur. [379]

- Coastal areas are especially vulnerable to natural disturbances where loss of habitats, habitat fragmentation and biological invasions may occur. The unique habitats and wildlife of the low-lying Northwestern Hawaiian Islands are threatened by sea level rise, and these islands are important nurseries for popular species such as sea turtles and migratory birds. [380] Increased temperature will affect the incubation and life cycle of loggerhead turtle eggs on the much visited island of Komodo. [381, 382] Higher temperatures skew the sex ratio towards a predominance of females, which may or may not enhance the fertility of the population but any possible beneficial effects will be nullified as nesting opportunities decrease through a loss of nesting beaches due to sea level rise.

- Rising sea levels will have impacts on coastal ecosystems, for example mangrove forests and wetland areas, including the potential squeezing out of habitats especially where coastal margins are backed by areas of intense human use or steep physical terrain which also reduces fresh water availability. [383]

- Ecosystems that are already under stress, such as coral reefs that are not adequately protected by coastal zone management plans, will be the most likely to be severely affected by climate change. Corals have shown a high sensitivity to minor increases in temperature, rising sea temperatures will further affect the distribution and survival of these marine resources. [384]

- Temporal shifts in seasons may increase the ranges of insects and diseases [385], and affect birdsong [386, 387] and the flowering of plants. [388, 389]

- The number of invasive species and their dissemination is likely to increase and already existing invasive species are expected to expand their areas. For example in the Cape Flora region of South Africa, a popular destination for tourists, trees and shrubs from Australia, California and the Mediterranean introduced in the nineteenth century are predicted to become far more prevalent and further threaten the high endemism in the region [390]; four out of five protected areas in South Africa are predicted to lose 10–40% of their plant species by the year 2050. [391]

- Drought and desertification may occur in tropical and sub-tropical zones, changing patterns of precipitation and evaporation are of critical importance, and extreme flooding will have implications for large areas.

- Increased frequency and magnitude of extreme events such as cyclones and storm surges will result in loss of land area and impacts on nesting colonies and activities for seabirds and turtles, and the migratory patterns of species. [392]

Many of these issues are influenced by human-induced activity other than climate-related changes, such as development, shipping, mining and fishing. However, there is evidence that climate change will impact on natural ecosystems in a marked way. [393] The significance of these impacts for tourism is diverse. Natural heritage sites are major attractions for tourism, and climate-induced changes in these environments will impact on tourist activity. Conservation International noted in a report on tourism and biodiversity that "[…] biodiversity [and related aspects] is essential for the continued development of the tourism industry". [394] However, it also noted the lack of awareness of the often important synergies between tourism development and nature conservation, [395, 396] and the decline of tourism because of climate change could exacerbate conservation challenges in some regions.

Cultural heritage includes considerations of built heritage (historic and architectural), archaeological heritage and socio-cultural heritage. Architectural heritage may be affected by climate change in a number of ways. The most obvious is the direct effect of rising sea level on those structures that are near the coast and that may be flooded or damaged by coastal erosion. Increased rainfall resulting in rising water tables will have a effects on the foundations or the fabric of buildings. [397] The drainage of land areas may be affected, with consequent increases in area flooding, with consequences for buildings and accessibility. Architectural heritage can also be affected by increased wind speeds, either through damage to roofs, or through increased wind loading on walls. The latter may adversely affect ruined buildings such as monasteries or tower houses many of which are in exposed locations. In many cases the impacts of climatic conditions will lead to very high costs in order to save world renowned destinations such as Venice. [398]

Socio-cultural heritage is an ever more popular attraction for tourists, and cultural activities, as well as indigenous and folk traditions are among the most fragile aspects of a society. Many have already disappeared through processes of globalisation, mechanisation, urbanisation, emigration and other factors. The cultural consequences of physical climate change impacts on landscapes and buildings may reinforce current trends towards the abandonment and break-up of communities leading to the loss of rituals and cultural memory. [399] Such attractions as local arts and crafts, dances and traditional agricultural land-uses are important draws for tourists in destinations such as Australia, Africa and Asia. [400] Traditional skills such as boat-building, fishing and navigation, as well as the way in which boats are used are based on local conditions of tide, current, wind and wave. If any of these aspects are altered the suitability of a boat for its purpose may be adversely affected, so that the boat design may no longer be of use, or the navigation skills used may have to change. [401] Similarly, if marine resources such as coral reefs, fish stocks and mangrove forests are altered or diminished by climate change this will affect the attractiveness and food supplies in a destination, and the livelihoods of local people. Coral reefs cover 0.2% of the ocean floor but contain 25% of marine species globally. They provide livelihoods to 100 million people globally and provide the basis for industries (tourism, fishing) worth an annual net benefit of US$ 30 billion. [402] Similarly, one hectare of mangroves is estimated to deliver products and services worth up to US$ 900,000 (timber and wood chippings, fish spawning, and habitat for economically important species). [403]

In 2005, the UNESCO World Heritage Centre (WHC) initiated an assessment of the impacts of climate change on World Heritage; the report, containing twenty-six case studies of natural and cultural heritage, was published in 2007. [404] These case studies illustrate impacts that have already been observed and some of those that can be expected in the future. Changes in World Heritage sites due to climate change will affect a range of tourism segments including nature-based tourism, ecotourism, cultural tourism, dive tourism, safari tourism and study tourism. The study found, for example, that buried archaeological evidences could be rapidly lost if the stratigraphic integrity (organization of levels and types) of soils changed due to changes in precipitation levels, permafrost melting and floods. The report states that: the melting of glaciers worldwide will alter the appearance of some mountainous regions dramatically affecting their aesthetic beauty; it found problems for the conservation of biodiversity hotspots listed as natural World Heritage sites; and that the conservation of properties listed as cultural heritage built in coastal lowlands is threatened by increased sea level rise and coastal erosion. The report also confirmed the threat of widespread bleaching and potential death of coral reefs due to sea temperature changes and increased levels of carbon dioxide dissolved in the oceans. In addition, changes in wetting and drying cycles will induce crystallization and dissolution of salts and affect other popular tourist sites such as wall paintings, frescos and rock art.

The UNESCO report provides indications of the extent of changes and likely timescales. Regarding the impacts to Venice, according to moderate change scenarios, Venice is likely to be flooded daily by 2100, with a net loss in altitude of 54 cms. In Australia, projections indicate that by 2100, warming on the Great Barrier Reef will be between 2–5° C. This will result in large-scale bleaching and widespread coral death. The frequency of bleaching events is increasing at a rate of about 1.6% more each decade and bleaching thresholds will be reached on an annual basis well before 2100. [405]

> **Box 7 Selected World Heritage sites and potential impacts** [406]
>
> **Kilimanjaro National Park, Tanzania**
>
> - At 5,895 m, Mount Kilimanjaro is the highest mountain in Africa, a volcanic massif with a snowy peak standing in isolation over the savannah – World Heritage List in 1987.
>
> - Approximately 30,000 tourists visit Kilimanjaro each year bringing valuable revenue to the parks authority and local communities.
>
> - If current trends are not changed (losing more than half a metre in thickness each year) this will lead to the complete disappearance of the Kilimanjaro ice fields in less than 15 years. [407]
>
> - Consequences for tourism include reduced landscape aesthetics and decreased visitation.

Great Barrier Reef Marine Park, Australia

- Largest coral reef eco-system in the world; 2,100 km in length, 1,500 species of fish and 400 species of coral – World Heritage List in 1981.

- Approximately 1.8 million visitors per year, generating over AU$ 5.1 billion. In 2005 approximately 820 authorized tourist operators and 1,500 vessels and aircrafts were permitted to operate in the Park.

- The Great Barrier Reef has been observed as being susceptible to sea-temperature increase, sea level rise, increased storm frequency and intensity, changing precipitation patterns, drought, land run-off, oceanic circulation and ocean acidity. Severe coral bleaching has been observed in a number of areas in 1998, 2002 and in 2006.

- Consequences for tourism include reduced attractiveness of destination and quality of tourist experience (i.e., snorkeling and SCUBA diving), and decreased visitation reducing economic sustainability of operators.

Chan Chan Archaeological Zone, Peru

- Capital of the ancient Chimu Kingdom and the largest and most important prehispanic earthen architecture cities in the Americas – List of World Heritage in Danger in 1986.

- Approximately 3.5 million tourists visit Peru every year and Chan Chan is one of the most popular destinations. [408]

- Chan Chan has consistently suffered from the El Niño-Southern Oscillation (ENSO) phenomenon, extreme precipitation and flooding, eroding and affecting the base of the earthen architecture structures.

- Consequences for tourism include reduced attractiveness of destination, decreased visitation and increased risk to visitor safety.

City of London Sites, England

- Westminster Palace; Westminster Abbey and The Tower of London; and the buildings at Greenwich date, respectively, from medieval times; Norman (11th/12th Century); and the 17th and 18th centuries – all site World Heritage List in late 1980s, except for Greenwich (1997).

- Over 12 million international tourists visit London every year and the Tower of London, on the banks of the Thames receives approximately 2 million overseas visitors per annum.

- The predominant impacts of climate change on these sites are sea level rise and an increased incidence of flooding arising from high tides and storm surges caused by low pressure systems traveling over the north sea and the funneling of water from the southern North Sea into the Thames Estuary. [409, 410, 411]

- Consequences for tourism include reduced attractiveness of destination and quality of tourist experience, increased risk to visitor's safety and reduced visitation.

9.2 Adaptation to Climate Change

9.2.1 Overview

> "It is meaningless to study the consequences of climate change without considering the ranges of adaptive responses."
>
> Adger and Kelly (1999)

The IPCC [412] indicated that the need for societies around the world and economic sectors like tourism to adapt to climate change in the decades ahead is inescapable. The inevitability of the need to adapt to future climate change and the realization that adaptation is occurring today partially explains why there has been an explosion of research and policy interest in adaptation to climate change over the past five years. [413] Adaptation has figured less prominently in climate change research on tourism than in some other economic sectors (e.g., agriculture) and remains an important knowledge gap, particularly with respect to destinations. [414]

Adaptation to climate change refers to an adjustment in natural or human systems in response to actual or expected climatic stimuli or their effects, which moderates harm or exploits beneficial opportunities. Adaptation can be pursued by societies, institutions, individuals, governments. It is motivated by economic, social or environmental drivers, by many means, for example social activities, market activities, local or global interventions. [415] The implementation of adaptation measures in the tourism sector should consider the time horizon of climate change impacts which is illustrated in Figure 13.1. The information requirements, policy changes and investments that are required for effective adaptation by tourism destinations will require decades in some cases, and therefore the process of adaptation needs to commence in the very near future for destinations anticipated to be among those impacted by mid-century.

Figure 9.9 Relative adaptive capacity of major tourism sub-sectors

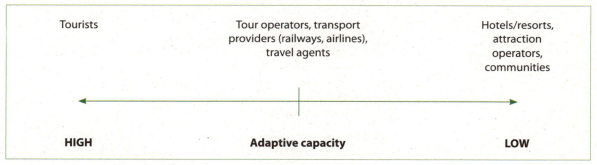

Tourists	Tour operators, transport providers (railways, airlines), travel agents	Hotels/resorts, attraction operators, communities
HIGH	**Adaptive capacity**	**LOW**

Source: Scott, D. and Jones, B. (2006a)

The dynamic nature of the tourism industry and its ability to cope with a range of recent shocks, including SARS, terrorism attacks in a number of nations, or the Asian tsunami, suggests a relatively high climate change adaptive capacity within the tourism industry overall. The capacity to adapt to climate change is thought to vary between the sub-sectors of the tourism industry. [416, 417, 418, 419, 420, 421] Figure 9.9 illustrates the relative adaptive capacity of major sub-sectors. Tourists have the greatest adaptive capacity (depending three key resources; money, knowledge and time) with relative freedom to avoid destinations impacted by climate change or shifting the timing of travel to avoid unfavourable climate conditions. The implications of their potential adaptations to climate change are discussed in Chapter 10. Suppliers of tourism services and tourism operators at specific destinations have less adaptive capacity. Large tour operators, who do not own the infrastructure, are in a better position to adapt to changes at destinations because they can respond to clients demands and provide information to influence clients' travel choices. Destination communities and tourism operators with large investments in immobile capital assets (e.g., hotel, resort complex, marina, or casino) have the least adaptive capacity.

Table 9.3 Portfolio of climate adaptations utilized by tourism stakeholders

Type of adaptation	Tourism operators/ businesses	Tourism industry associations	Governments and communities	Financial sector (investors/insurances)
Technical	• Snow-making • Slope contouring • Rainwater collection and water recycling systems • Cyclone-proof building design and structure	• Enable access to early warning equipment (e.g., radios) to tourism operators • Develop websites with practical information on adaptation measures	• Reservoirs and desalination plants • Fee structures for water consumption • Weather forecasting and early warning systems	• Require advanced building design or material (fire resistant) standards for insurance • Provide information material to customers
Managerial	• Water conservation plans • Low season closures • Product and market diversification • Regional diversification in business operations • Redirect clients away from impacted destinations	• Snow condition reports through the media • Use of short-term seasonal forecasts for the planning of marketing activities • Training programmes on climate change adaptation • Encourage environmental management with firms (e.g., via certification)	• Impact management plans (e.g., 'Coral Bleaching Response Plan') • Convention/ event interruption insurance • Business subsidies (e.g., insurance or energy costs)	• Adjust insurance premiums or not renew insurance policies • Restrict lending to high risk business operations
Policy	• Hurricane interruption guarantees • Comply with regulation (e.g., building code)	• Coordinated political lobbying for GHG emission reductions and adaptation mainstreaming • Seek funding to implement adaptation projects	• Coastal management plans and set back requirements • Building design standards (e.g., for hurricane force winds)	• Consideration of climate change in credit risk and project finance assessments
Research	• Site Location (e.g., north facing slopes, higher elevations for ski areas)	• Assess awareness of businesses and tourists, as well as knowledge gaps	• Monitoring programs (e.g., predict bleaching or avalanche risk, beach water quality)	• Extreme event risk exposure
Education	• Water conservation education for employees and guests	• Public education campaign (e.g., 'Keep Winter Cool')	• Water conservation campaigns • Campaigns on the dangers of UV radiation	• Educate/inform potential and existing customers
Behavioural	• Real-time webcams of snow conditions • GHG emission offset programs	• GHG emission offset programs • Water conservation initiatives	• Extreme event recovery marketing	• Good practice in-house

The tourism sector has adapted its operations to climate zones world-wide. As Table 9.3 illustrates, a diverse range of technological, managerial, policy and behavioural adaptations are currently in use by various tourism stakeholders to deal with climate variability at the destination level. Climate adaptations are rarely undertaken in isolation, but, as the example in Box 8 illustrates, commonly involve multiple adaptations that are very specific to the destination climate and its tourism products. The location specific nature of climate adaptation will eventually create a complex mix of adaptations being practiced in the tourism sector across the globe. This Section of the Chapter will concentrate on the discussion of specific adaptation strategies available for coping with two of the major impacts of climate change (extreme events and changing availability of environmental resources), adaptation strategies in two of the most vulnerable destinations types – mountains and coasts-islands, and the need for adaptation at a national policy level.

Box 8 Climate adaptations used in major tourism event programming by the National Capital Commission of Canada [422]

Winterlude Festival (February) – adapting to warm temperatures and lack of snow

- Moved programming from ice-covered lakes to land locations;

- used refrigerated trucks for the ice sculpture carving contest;

- lengthened the festival from ten days to a three-weekend event to increase the probability of suitable weather;

- implemented snow-making to ensure adequate snow supply for skiing and sledding;

- developed a Nordic ski track setter for low-snow conditions and concentrated Nordic ski race trails shaded terrain that required less snow;

- developed collaborations with local museums to offer package deals that promote non-climate-dependent activities.

Tulip Festival (May) – adapting to mismatch of tulip phenology and event schedule

- Planted tulip bulbs in shady locations;

- planted bulbs with different rates of maturation;

- erected snow fences to increase snow cover on flower beds to delay bulb maturation;

- irrigated flower beds during warm/early springs to delay bulb maturation.

Photo credit: Johnstone, T. (2007)

Canada Day Celebrations (July) – adapting to extreme temperatures

- Educated the public about heat stress;

- provided shade tents and cooling stations;

- position medical staff on stand-by at major events;

- implemented water quality advisory system in swimming areas.

Photo credit: Johnstone, T. (2007)

9.2.2 Adaptation to Extreme Events and Natural Disasters

Climate change provides additional incentives to ensure that new tourism infrastructures are designed and built in such a way that climate change risks will not result in premature deterioration or failure. Similarly, existing infrastructure may have to be modified if current performance standards are inconsistent with the changed climatic conditions. For example, tourist accommodation in tropical areas should be built or retrofitted to be cyclone-proof; i.e., withstand both high average wind speeds and extreme conditions. Windows and doors are generally the weak points susceptible to breakdown by wind pressure and blowing debris. Once failure occurs, wind pressure builds up inside the building, and in seconds may lift the roof off a building hurricane shutters can also provide effective protection (see Figure 9.10).

Figure 9.10 Windows shutters as a protection against hurricanes

Photo credit: Becken, S.

Tourism depends on an intact ecosystem and on institutional structures that can respond to the needs of local people and visitors. Therefore, disaster preparedness and management (against natural or human-made hazards) should be an essential part of any destinations' integrated management plan. Responding to this challenge UNEP has developed a process that assists local communities to increase their level of preparedness and response to disasters. APELL, standing for Awareness and Preparedness for Emergencies at the Local Level, is a process designed to create public awareness of hazards and to ensure that communities and emergency services are adequately trained and prepared to respond. [423] The UNEP Disaster Risk Reduction in Tourism Destinations programme using the APELL process has been established to improve disaster awareness, develop local and national strategies to enhance environmental and coastal planning process, aid risk identification and management, as well as ultimately to improve the trust relationship between visitors and their destination, in three Asian coastal locations (Kanniyakumari in Tamil Nadu State of India, Patong in Phuket and Pi-Pi Island in Krabi of Thailand).

Early warning systems are essential for climate change adaptation. Early warning relates to extreme wind events, storm surges, flooding and heat waves. The early warning of a heat wave will reduce health risks, including mortality. For example, after the 1995 heat wave in the USA, the city of Chicago initiated an 'extreme heat conditions plan'. This involves local agencies, communications tests, stepped responses to early forecasts, a 24-hour 'hotline' and other interventions such as opening air-conditioned shopping malls at night time to those individuals most vulnerable to heat. During a comparable heat wave in 1999, heat-related morbidity and mortality were almost halved, relative to expected levels. [424] Currently, over nine European countries and two dozen cities worldwide have weather-watch warning procedures using various systems to forecast days expected to experience an increase in the average number of deaths due to excessive heat. [425]

As an adaptive strategy, insurance against extreme weather events is critical for tourism, just as "[...] weather and climate are 'core businesses' for the insurance industry". [426, 427] From the perspective of tourist destinations, insurance enables the industry to spread the burdens of those climate-related risks which cannot be avoided by other adaptation measures. In turn, the insurance industry faces the prospect of a growth in the number and size of claims from the tourism industry and tourists, as a consequence of increases in extreme events and climate variability. 19 out of the 20 most costly natural disasters (in terms of property insurance losses) in Australia have been weather related. Hailstorms in Sydney in 1999 proved to be the most costly (AU$ 2.2 billion). Changes to the expected frequency of such weather events are of considerable importance to the insurance industry. [428] Insurance claims relating to climate and tourism, including mortality and sickness while travelling, increased accidents between home and destination or at the tourist destination, structural damage to tourist facilities and hotels, service interruptions, and large-scale bush or forest fires. Events like these drive up insurance premiums potentially making them unaffordable for many (especially smaller) tourism operators. However, it is possible to reduce premiums by proactive adaptation. Premiums for cyclone insurance in Fiji, for example, can be reduced substantially if the insured party introduces measures such as improving building structures, having emergency plans in place, conducting staff training (e.g., for evacuation procedures), and making sufficient provisions for water, food and fuel storage. [429] Information exchange between insurance companies, the tourism sector and those at risk from climate change is essential in order to shape adaptation measures and premiums, and also to reduce uncertainty associated with future risks.

The Association of British Insurers [430] estimates that even small increases in the intensity of hurricanes in the Gulf of Mexico-Caribbean, typhoons in Japan, and windstorms in Europe could increase annual damage costs in these major insurance markets by two-thirds by the end of the 21st century. To reflect the changed risk, regional insurance premiums would need to increase an estimated 20 to 80% in the Gulf of Mexico-Caribbean, 20 to 80% in Japan, and 0 to 15% in Western Europe.

Adaptation by the insurance sector is already occurring in the Caribbean and Gulf of Mexico. The move of some insurers in the USA to reduce coverage in Florida and the Gulf of Mexico is an example of a risk reduction strategy by the insurance industry. [431] One regional insurer in the Caribbean recently dropped coverage of 48 beach front properties across the region and increased premiums an average of 16%. [432] Such changes in insurability will have major implications for future tourism reinvestment and development in high hurricane risk regions like the Caribbean.

The extension of the regions with major tourism destinations that will be primary affected by extreme climatic events highlights the need for awareness and preparedness for natural hazards at the local level through systematic capacity building and strategies for disaster risk management.

Box 9 Adaptation to extreme events in Fiji [433, 434]

Tourism destination and situation: Coastal tourist resorts, Fiji.

Climate change impact: Extreme wind events (cyclones) and storm surges leading to structural damage and shoreline erosion.

Adaptation strategies: To prevent damage from storm surges and sea level rise, resorts are now built at least 2.6 m above mean sea level and 30 m off the high tide mark (these standards might be reviewed in the future). The building code prescribes that structures need to withstand wind speeds of 60 km per hour. Again, the building code is under review. Individual businesses (at least the larger resorts) have evacuation plans, insurance cover and procedures before the start of the cyclone season, such as staff training, water and food storage, first aid kits, trimming of trees and a direct line to the Meteorological Service for early warnings.

Organization implementing the adaptation strategy: A range of Government Departments (e.g., Town and Country Planning, Ministry of Health, Fiji Meteorological Service) and tourism businesses themselves.

Figure 9.11 Small island chains of Yasawa and Mamanuca with small-scale tourism facilities are particularly vulnerable to climate change impacts and extreme events

Photo credit: Vereczi, G.

9.2.3 Adaptation to Changes in Environmental Resources: Conservation of Natural Ecosystems to Enhance their Resilience and the Rational and Efficient Use of Scarce Resources

Conservation of biodiversity and maintenance of ecosystem structure and function are important climate change adaptation strategies in relation to tourism's natural resource base. Establishing and enforcing protected areas is generally considered to be one of the most appropriate strategies for ensuring that terrestrial, freshwater and marine ecosystems are resilient to the additional pressures arising from climate change. The impact of climate change on protected areas is also an important issue, with changes influencing species drift and altering ecosystems. [435]

The resilience of coral reefs is of particular concern, as most of the effects of climate change are stressful rather than beneficial. [436] Reef systems that are jointly affected by global climatic and local human stresses will be the most vulnerable. Coral reefs are a critical component of coastal protection in tropical areas, in addition to shaping wider ecosystems, harbouring high levels of biodiversity and providing significant fisheries and tourism income. [437, 438] Maintaining natural coastal defences provided by the coral reefs or mangroves offers protection for coasts and island from storm and wave damage. [439] In one study assessing the links between sea level rises, biodiversity and economic activity [440] it was demonstrated that approximately one third of the beaches on some Caribbean islands may be lost through coastal squeeze, hurricanes could reduce coral cover by 17%, and that this loss of beaches and coral cover could have a significant impact on tourism within the region. Local conservation measures include education and awareness programmes, tertiary treatment of sewage and disposal via a long off-shore pipeline; monitoring systems that show the relative efficacy of adaptation measures; enforcement of fishing quotas and designation of exclusion zones and seasons. In addition, it is now common to ban destructive fishing practices as well as removal of reef resources for the aquarium trade, construction materials, navigation improvements, and medicinal and pharmaceutical applications. There has been also a range of reef rehabilitation and restoration techniques and projects developed, although the slow growth of corals makes the process lengthy and whether these strategies will be sufficient to secure the future of corals remains to be seen.

Alleviating water shortages requires substantial investments in storage facilities or desalinisation plants. This will be especially the case for resorts some distance from plentiful sources of surface or ground water. Water supply is challenging in arid destinations and on small islands. Adaptation measures at the resort level involve both actions on supply and demand, such as:

- infrastructure improvements (e.g., rainwater collectors);

- water conservation (including the application of water-saving devices and guest education);

- sustainability planning (e.g., considering long-term weather forecasts);

- water source management (e.g., in the case of springs);

- monitoring health and environmental protection (quality of water);

- recycling (use of treated water for irrigation).

Supply-side deficiencies in water treatment and distribution systems need to be addressed, such as leaks in ageing pipes, as do behavioural issues such as reducing consumption patterns. [441] For water management it is also important to take into account increased risk associated with heavy rainfall, drought and other extreme weather conditions. Inadequate water supply is a significant problem in many tourism areas around the world and is often brought about by over development (demand exceeding supply capacity) and climate variability. [442] Some of the most common technical adaptations to increase water supply for tourism operations are: water transfers (pipelines or tankers), reservoirs, and desalination plants, which have both financial and environmental impact implications. [443]

Box 10 Impact and adaptation in Thailand [444]

Tourism destination and situation: Heavily developed tourism island of Phuket, Thailand.

Climate change impact: Water shortages brought about by climate variability.

Adaptation strategy/strategies: Multi-year water supply plan including construction of new dams, development of abandoned mines as water sources, expanded water transmission and recycling systems. Plus a revised fee structure for water consumption and initiation of water conservation campaigns.

Organization implementing the adaptation strategy: Tourism Authority of Thailand, together with other national agencies.

Box 11 Water impact and adaptation in Majorca [445]

Tourism destination and situation: Spanish tourist island of Majorca (heavily developed).

Climate change impact: Water shortages brought about by climate variability and demand exceeding supply capacity. Saline intrusion into local aquifers.

Adaptation strategy/strategies: Construction of two large-capacity desalination plants and additional water pipeline transfers from the mountainous north side of the island.

Organization implementing the adaptation strategy: Spanish Government.

Box 12 Water impact and adaptation in Tobago [446, 447]

Tourism destination and situation: Tobago, the Caribbean.

Climate change impact: Water shortages for accommodation providers and tour operators due to increasing incidence of droughts.

Adaptation strategy/strategies: Small-scale structural adaptations: including retrofitting buildings with rainwater collectors, increasing storage tank capacity, converting toilets to saltwater supply, and adding diesel powered desalination capacity. Plus non-structural adaptations: including water conservation education for employees and guests, revised landscaping practices and limited use of pools.

Organization implementing the adaptation strategy: Conducted by individual accommodation providers and tour operators.

9.2.4 Adaptation in Mountain Destinations

There are a wide range of climate change adaptation options that will allow mountain destinations to cope with reduced natural snowfall, increased natural hazards (e.g., avalanches, rock slides), and position themselves to take advantage of longer warm weather tourism seasons. For some adaptation options, there will also be important barriers that will need to be overcome for successful implementation.

Climate change adaptations available to the ski industry consist of the actions of several stakeholders as outlined in Figure 9.12. The availability of these adaptation options will be context-specific and vary according to geographic characteristics (e.g., microclimate, available high elevation terrain for expansion, and distance to large urban markets), government jurisdiction (e.g., water access rights, snow-making restrictions) and business model (e.g., centralized versus decentralized ownership of ski destination infrastructure, independent ski operator versus ski conglomerate).

Figure 9.12 Climate adaptation options in the ski industry

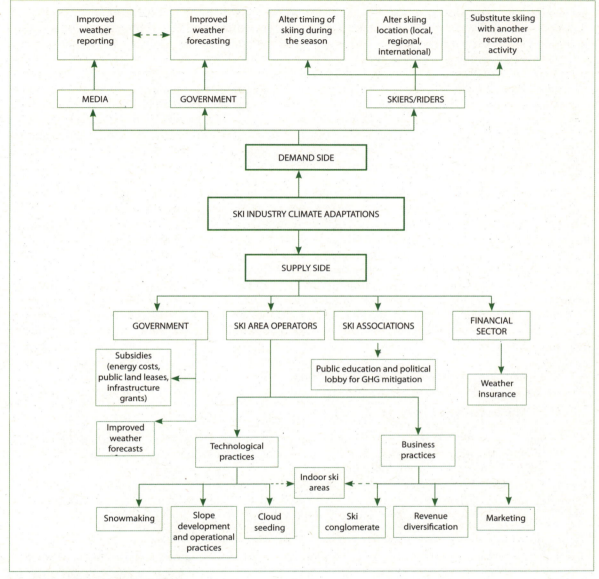

Source: Scott, D. and McBoyle, G. (2006)

The importance of snow-making as an adaptation to climate variability and change cannot be overstated. In eastern North America and Australia, snow-making is almost universal among ski operators. In other ski regions such as Western Europe, western North America, East Asia (Japan-Korea-China), and South America, snow-making is not as extensively used, but continuing to grow [448, 449] and in some areas, such as Austria and Italy, already widespread. [450] With advanced snow-making in place, many ski area managers in North America, Australia and Austria are highly confident in their capacity to negate the impacts of future climate change. [451, 452, 453, 454] For example, almost half of Austrian ski area managers felt that with further adaptation of snow-making their businesses would continue to be viable for at least another 75 years. [455] Assessments that test the capacity of ski areas to physically produce a reliable snow-base with snow-making under climate change are presently limited to North America and Australia, so that this confidence in the adaptive capacity provided by snow-making may be over-estimated in other regions.

Large increases in snow-making requirements under climate change scenarios raise questions about the sustainability of this adaptation strategy in certain locations (Box 13). Communities and environmental organizations have expressed concern about the extensive water use and chemical additives associated with snow-making. Even where snow-making is climatically feasible and water supplies can be secured, the additional infrastructure and energy costs associated with large increases in snow-making volumes at higher average temperatures may be uneconomic for some ski operators. Concerns have also been raised that the increased costs of snow-making, particularly for smaller operators at lower elevations, may again drive skiing to become a 'sport for the rich'. [456] Regulation of the development and operation of snow-making systems differs across and within nations. In regional ski markets, such as the European Alps or New England states, varied government regulations and support for snow-making (through energy or water subsidies) may provide a competitive advantage to certain ski areas. For example, chemical-bacterial additives to facilitate snow-making at temperatures near or even above freezing are allowed in Switzerland [457], but banned in Germany, offering a competitive edge to Swiss ski areas.

Other important technical adaptation strategies that have been questioned from a sustainability perspective include glacier preservation and expansion of ski areas into higher elevations. Glacial retreat is observed to be a global trend [458] and ski areas have utilized two distinct strategies to preserve glaciers deemed important to their operations. [459] With the increased recession of glaciers in the Alps in recent years, notably the record warm summer of 2003, ski areas in Switzerland and Austria, have installed large sheets of white polyethylene on critical areas of glaciers to protect the ice from ultraviolet radiation and restrict melting during summer months. [460] In Canada, the Whistler-Blackcomb ski resort is considering an engineering plan to maintain the Horstman Glacier at the top of Blackcomb Mountain by installing snow fences and using snow-making near the summit to provide additional snow inputs for the glacier. [461, 462] The development of new skiable terrain at environmentally sensitive higher elevations, where snow cover is more reliable and a longer ski season possible, has also a commonly identified adaptation strategy. [463, 464, 465] Thirty-six ski areas in Austria applied for permits to expand their operations into higher elevations in 2002–2003. [466]

Box 13 The sustainability of snow-making

Although concerns have been raised about the environmental impacts of snow-making, little scientific research has been conducted on its differential regional impacts on mountain vegetation, watersheds or energy use and related GHG emissions. Studies have found snow-making to have a localized affect on ski slope vegetation composition and biodiversity of high alpine plants by altering spring soil temperature and moisture, as well as the introduction of phytopathogenic bacteria (used as nuclei to enhance ice crystal formulation). [467, 468]

Concerns about the tremendous water use by snow-making have largely been focused on the impact of water withdrawals from natural water bodies, and there is little knowledge of inter-watershed transfers of water or any regional impact on water cycle from snow-making. When water for snow-making is withdrawal from natural water bodies (streams and lakes), water levels may be reduced at critical times of the year, impacting fish and other marine species. Some jurisdictions have strict regulations governing water withdrawals for snow-making. For example, the State of Vermont (USA) implemented a 'February Mean Flow' standard, where water withdrawals for snow-making are not permitted when natural watercourses are at or below the average mean flow. To reduce impacts on natural watercourses, many ski areas have constructed reservoirs to 'stockpile' water during high flow periods (spring freshet) for winter use. No estimates of total water withdrawals or reservoir storage capacity are available for any ski region.

The sustainability of snow-making has also been questioned on the basis of energy use and related GHG emissions. Snow-making as been referred to as a 'perverse' climate change adaptation because the large projected increase in snow-making under climate change scenarios [469] will further contribute to the very problem of adaptation. In tourism, similar arguments could be made of air conditioning in the Mediterranean, Caribbean or other tropical destinations.

While the large energy use for snow-making is a very valid concern, both technical and regionally specific social factors must be considered in evaluating its sustainability. Technologically, snow-making can be done with renewable energy and thus not contribute further to climate change. In the United States, 58 ski resorts now purchase renewable energy (primarily wind) for part of their operational energy use, and 28 purchase 100% of their energy needs from renewable sources. A number of ski areas are also building on-site renewable capacity. For example, the Whistler Resort in British Columbia, Canada, has built both a micro-hydro plant (run-of-river) and wind turbines that generate enough power for all of its snow-making, lift and resort operations. Increasing the energy efficiency, particularly of older systems which can be improved 25–50%, and the use of renewable power must be a urgent goal for all ski areas that use snow-making.

The broader social context of regional tourism activity must be considered when determining the net impact of additional snow-making activity on GHG emissions. If local ski areas are forced to close because of unreliable natural snow conditions, potentially thousands of skier visits may be displaced to other ski destinations or other forms of tourism. Alternate ski destinations may be nearby (less than 100 km away), but as was found in a study of potential ski area closures in the New England region of the USA [470], in many cases ski tourism may be transferred 500 km or more, with attendant emissions from car, coach, rail or even air travel. If no alternate ski holiday is available regionally, skiers may opt for much more GHG intensive travel options. For example, the poor ski conditions in the European Alps in the winter of 2006–2007 generate a much higher than usual number of European skiers visiting ski resorts in the Rocky Mountains of North America. More comprehensive analysis of the GHG intensity of holiday options and the potential adaptation of winter sports tourists is required to understand the net emissions impact of additional snow-making.

Figure 9.13 The widespread climate adaptation of snow-making

Photo credit: Boyne USA Resorts, Inc.,

Product and market diversification are common adaptation strategies to cope with the business challenges of pronounced tourism seasonality. Over the past three decades, many ski areas in North America and Europe have diversified their operations beyond traditional ski activities to include the provision of skiing and snowboarding lessons, accommodation and retail sales. The *Economist*[471] referred to the transition of major ski resorts in North America from ski areas to winter theme parks, as the 'Disneyfication' of the winter sports industry. A similar pattern was found for visitors to winter resorts in France and Switzerland. [472, 473] Many ski resorts have made substantial investments to provide alternate activities for non-skiing visitors (e.g., snowmobiling, skating, dog sled-rides, indoor pools, health and wellness spas, fitness centres, squash and tennis, games rooms, restaurants, and retail stores). A number of former 'ski resorts' have further diversified their business operations to become 'four season resorts', offering non-winter activities such as golf, boating and white-water rafting, mountain biking, paragliding, horseback riding and other business lines. [474] In some mountain resorts (e.g., Whistler-Blackholm Resort in British Columbia, Canada) summer revenues now exceed winter revenues. At many larger resorts, real estate construction and management have also become a very important source of revenue. Many larger ski areas have profited from the sale of condominiums and other real estate, as well as the management of these properties on behalf of their owners (i.e., helping owners rent out the properties when they are not using them). During the sales phase of new real estate developments, real estate has often replaced resort operations as the prime source of revenue at some ski areas.

Another technical adaptation to marginal snow reliability has been the emergence of indoor ski domes. The first known indoor skiing slope, the 'Casablanca Dome', opened in Belgium in 1986 and since then, many technological advances have been incorporated into the more than 50 indoor ski domes operating globally in 2005. [475] The majority of ski domes are in Europe and Japan, with the largest facility now operating in Dubai. No ski domes are in operation in North America, but one is in the planning phase for New Jersey. The major value of indoor ski domes as a potential climate change adaptation is in encouraging early ski interest in urban areas as the forerunner of future skier demand at traditional resorts. For example, with low elevation ski areas near major urban markets in the eastern US (e.g., Boston, New York) expected to be highly vulnerable to climate change, the development of indoor ski domes in these major markets could be an important strategy by the US ski industry to maintain continued market development.

9.2.5 Adaptation in Small Island Destinations

There is a wide range of climate change adaptation measures for island destinations, addressing the different impacts of increased temperatures, changed precipitation and wind, and sea level rise. [476, 477] A list of possible adaptation measures in small islands and coastal zones is given in Table 9.4. There are also a number of barriers to the successful implementation of measures. Adaptation measures for cyclones and storm surges, for example, include 'soft' coastal protections, improved building design, and insurance cover. Soft coastal protection includes the reforestation and conservation of mangrove forest or other shore-stabilising vegetation that act as natural buffer. In the past, the preferred option was to construct ('hard') seawalls, which are costly, affect the aesthetic of the shore and are often rather ineffective in the medium- to long-term, causing further erosion around structures or transferring erosion problems to other nearby areas. Currently there is a lack of demonstration projects for the soft, alternative options in tourism.

Information is critical in facilitating adaptation to climate by the tourism sectors of small island destinations. For example, many meteorological services issue seasonal climate forecasts towards the beginning of each season. The tourism industry uses such information to devise appropriate marketing strategies well in advance and hotels begin planning for cyclones and other extreme events. In the case of Mauritius, the Comoros and the Seychelles, hotels respond to drought warning by assessing water needs and securing alternative sources of supply, and to cyclone warnings by taking such precautionary measures as:

- removal of surplus branches from trees, especially those near to buildings and electric and telephone installations;

- harvesting of fruits such as coconuts, so as to avoid accidents and to provide emergency food;

- inspection of the internal communication system, entertainment facilities, water pipe and underground cables; and

- servicing of the sewerage system.

Table 9.4 Possible adaptation measures for tourism in small island countries and barriers to implementation

Adaptation measures	Relevance to tourism	Barriers to implementation	Measures to remove barriers
'Soft' coastal protection	Many valuable tourism assets at growing risk from coastal erosion	Lack of credible options that have been demonstrated and accepted	Demonstration of protection for tourism assets and communities
Enhanced design, siting standards and planning guidelines	Many valuable tourism assets at growing risk from climate extremes	Lack of information needed to strengthen design and siting standards	Provide and ensure utilisation of targeted information
Improved insurance cover	Growing likelihood that tourists and operators will make insurance claims	Lack of access to affordable insurance and lack of finance	Ensure insurance sector is aware of actual risk levels and adjusts premiums
Shade provision and crop diversification	Additional shade increases tourist comfort	Lack of awareness of growing heat stress for people and crops	Identify, evaluate and implement measures to reduce heat stress
Reduce tourism pressures on coral	Reefs are a major tourist attraction	Reducing pressures without degrading tourist experience	Improve off-island tourism waste management
Desalination, rainwater storage	Tourist resorts are major consumers of fresh water	Lack of information on future security of freshwater supplies	Provide and ensure utilisation of targeted information
Tourism activity/ product diversification	Need to reduce dependency of tourism on 'sun, sea and sand'	Lack of credible alternatives that have been demonstrated and accepted	Identify and evaluate alternative activities and demonstrate their feasibility
Education/awareness raising	Need to motivate tourism staff and also tourists	Lack of education and resources that support behavioural change	Undertake education/ awareness programmes

Source: Becken, S. and Hay, J. (2007)

An important element of adaptation strategies for small islands and coastal destinations is the planning of tourism activities under the Integrated Coastal Zone Management (ICZM) approach. As it is recommended by the Barbados Plan of Action for SIDS; 'Small Island Developing States should be supported to develop integrated coastal zone management plans, including measures for responding adaptively to the impacts of climate change and sea level rise'. [478]

> **Box 14 Impacts and adaptation in the Caribbean** [479, 480, 481]
>
> **Tourism destination and situation:** Caribbean Region.
>
> **Climate change impact:** Seasonality changes, climate extremes and increased frequency of hurricanes.
>
> **Adaptation strategy/strategies:** Marketing and advertising campaign promoting the Caribbean as a four-season destination and 'Blue Chip Hurricane Guarantee', which provides a replacement stay of the same duration or equivalent value as the one originally booked.
>
> **Organization implementing the adaptation strategy:** Caribbean Tourism Organization and Sandals Resorts.

Box 15   Climate change adaptation in Fiji [482, 483]

UNWTO and UNEP are working with the Fiji Ministry of Tourism on a project to reduce tourism's vulnerability from climatic impacts by implementing adaptation initiatives. The project will contribute to the long term viability and sustainability of tourism in Fiji. A Global Environmental Facility (GEF) funded feasibility study was undertaken in 2006. This involved participants from key Government agencies, industry representatives, research organisations, NGOs and aid agencies. A full proposal for a 3-year project was submitted to GEF, which makes Fiji a key pilot destination to produce knowledge and experience about adaptation to climate change. This project is paralleled by a similar project in the Maldives. The aim of both projects is to further develop and demonstrate adaptation initiatives that will reduce the vulnerability of the tourism sector, as well as its natural and human resource base, to the impacts of climate variability and change.

The Fiji project covers the full spectrum of adaptation, from community and business level to national policy and planning. A specific focus of the project is to build and utilize the capacity of Fiji to integrate responses to concerns related to climate variability and change into a broader risk management framework, strategy and plan for the tourism sector.

The following existing policies serve as a baseline to the project:

• Pacific Climate Change Framework 2006–2015 and the National Climate Change Policy;

• Pacific Disaster Risk Reduction and Disaster Management Plan: Framework for Action 2006–2015 and the Fiji National Disaster Risk Management Plan;

• National Building Code;

• Coastal Tourism Development Guidelines;

• Environmental Management Act;

• Affirmative Action Program (to support ecotourism projects);

• National Biodiversity Strategic Action Plan.

The barriers that were identified so far in the feasibility study related to low awareness, especially among industry stakeholders, lack of coordination between government agencies, lack of integration of climate change aspects into existing legislation (e.g., building code), insufficient enforcement (e.g., Environmental Impact Assessment), and poor environmental practices (and insufficient funds to make larger investment, such as sewage systems).

Figure 9.14 Coastal erosion and sea wall protection on a beach in Fiji

Photo credit: Becken, S.

9.2.6 Adaptation in Natural and Cultural Heritage Destinations

The range of adaptation measures available to natural and cultural heritage destinations overlap somewhat with those already outlined in Sections 9.3.1 to 9.3.5 of this Chapter. Particularly those suitable for natural heritage destinations (mountain regions, coastal zones and small islands) make up a significant number of those destinations that could be classed as containing natural heritage assets. However, there are also strategies which are specific to heritage sites; and adaptive and preventive measures which can be taken at the local level of World Heritage sites (Table 9.5).

Table 9.5 Summary of possible adaptation strategies for natural and cultural heritage destinations

- Master plans and response plans: e.g., water supply planning (in drought susceptible destinations), risk assessment and preparedness strategies, and implementation of early warning systems (e.g., flooding).

- Scientific monitoring survey programmes to assess changes and necessary protection (e.g., levels of endemic species Cape Floral, South Africa; flood protection Thames Barrier, London; glacial lake levels to prevent outburst flooding, Sagarmatha National Park, Nepal).

- Reconstruction and stabilization of historic assets such as architecturally rich buildings and archaeological sites using a combination of traditional materials and skills (to preserve their historic aesthetics and attraction), and modern engineering techniques to enhance their longevity.

- Product diversification; for example: opening up new 'micro' destinations and attractions within an adjacent to an already popular heritage site.

- Translocation; a final strategy for species such as flowering plants that will not survive in their current location involving safer wild habitats or storing the genetic resources in gene or seed banks.

- Protected area re-design/redefinition; i.e., zoning certain areas, protecting a larger area, creation of migratory corridors to allow threatened species to more easily find new geographic ranges and alleviate the effects of climate change.

- Combining traditional materials and skills with modern engineering when reinforcing, stabilizing and renovating historic sites.

- Education and awareness raising on minimising external stresses; increasing the profile and knowledge base of users and stakeholders of the undermining nature of external stresses to a destination struggling to deal with the impacts of climate change.

- Reduction or removal of external stresses such as overuse, pollution and in the case of marine resources, agricultural run-off.

Source: UNESCO-WHC (2007)

For example, a range of strategies are being taken in the cases of glacial areas visited by tourists that are being impacted by climate change, such as the glacial lake of Tsho Rolpa in Sagarmatha (Mt. Everest) National Park, Nepal. Sagarmatha Park is populated by the Sherpa people, and receives over 20,000 tourists a year. Almost 67% of the glaciers in the park have retreated in the past decade and local communities, animal populations and tourists suffer from the threats of glacial lake outburst floods, reduced water supply and changes in biodiversity. Adaptation strategies include: artificially lowering the water level in the glacial lake of Tsho Rolpa by 3 metres in 2002 to reduce the threat of flooding [484]; as well as implementing an effective monitoring and early warning system within a risk preparedness strategy. [485]

To adapt to the impacts of climate change on the popular Cape Floral Region in South Africa, one of the world's biodiversity hotspots with a level of over 30% endemism, different stakeholders are assessing the implementation of various adaptation strategies. Monitoring and risk assessment studies have been conducted [486], programmes to reduce or remove external sources of stress have been implemented to increase resilience, risk preparedness strategies for wildfire management are being considered by national and regional agencies [487], the redefinition of protected area design to allow threatened species to shift geographic ranges, and finally the translocation of exceptionally threatened species to safer habitats or seed banks. Water supply planning and a tailored scientific monitoring programme were implemented as adaptation measures in the Ichkeul National Park, Tunisia, which successfully increased the resilience of the national park, a stopover for migrating birds and tourist destination for bird watchers.

The much-visited city of Timbuktu in Mali has suffered both from flooding and from desertification as a result of climate change over recent years. Adaptation measures at this cultural heritage site include the improvement of drainage systems, the creation of buffer zones, the removal of sand in the vicinity of the most visited buildings such as mosques, as well as the restoration of mosques and damaged historic houses. The success of these measures led the World Heritage Committee to withdraw Timbuktu from the List of World Heritage in Danger. [488]

More ironic, revenue generating adaptation strategies include attracting visitors to sites endangered due to the impacts of climate change. The 'see it whilst it's still here' or 'see climate change in action' travel marketing concepts seem not have taken off fully with tour operators as yet. However, Conde Nast, the popular travel magazine, has featured articles listing 'endangered wonders' that travellers were recommended to visit before they disappear. [489] Sites that fall into this category include the Belize Barrier Reef, Waterton-Glacier International Peace Park, Australia's Great Barrier Reef and the snows of Kilimanjaro.

9.3 Adaptation Policy

There are only few examples of governments developing adaptation policies specifically for tourism, however, more generic climate policies have evolved considerably over the last decade and many of these affect tourism. The National Adaptation Programs of Action (NAPA) financed by GEF aim to address urgent and immediate needs and concerns related to adaptation to the adverse effects of climate change for less developed countries. Tourism is a major economic sector in many of these countries, although NAPA does not specifically address tourism issues. The NAPA in Samoa is one which has addressed tourism, recognising the importance of the sector to the Samoan economy, assessing impacts of climate change and climate variability on the loss of beaches, inundation, and degradation of the coastal ecosystems, saline intrusion and damage to critical infrastructure and the loss of attractiveness of coral due to bleaching. Activities have included awareness raising and training activities for tourist operators and employees on issues such as cyclones and flood prone areas, and the development of a national Sustainable Tourism Environmental Policy. Three roles have been identified for climate policy: a) to control atmospheric concentrations of greenhouse gases (GHG), b) to reduce the negative consequences of changes in climate, and c) to address development and equity issues. [490] While poverty and gender inequality are not the primary concerns of climate change policy, it is increasingly recognised that effective implementation of climate policy addresses these issues as well. UNWTO is collaborating for the implementation of the Nairobi Work Programme on Impacts, Vulnerability and Adaptation to Climate Change, lead by UNFCCC. The programme has a strong focus on cross-sectoral integration, and therefore represents a good opportunity to build policy linkages for a better involvement of the tourism sector in international and national adaptation activities.

It is now recognised that regardless of the emissions reduction efforts, there will be a need to adapt to unavoidable changes in climate. International climate policy generally accepts that developed countries will support developing countries in their climate change adaptation efforts. [491] To assist the process and implementation of adaptation several international organisations have prepared tools or guidelines. For example, the United Nations Development Programme (UNDP) has prepared a comprehensive Adaptation Policy Framework, a users' guidebook, a series of technical papers, case studies and related tools and resources designed to provide technical guidance to key national players for developing and assessing climate change adaptation policies and measures. The four guiding principles that underpin the framework are [492]:

- place adaptation in a development context;

- build on current adaptive experience to cope with future climate variability;

- recognise that adaptation occurs at different levels – in particular, at the local level;

- recognise that adaptation will be an ongoing process.

The Asian Development Bank developed framework and a set of guidelines to facilitate the implementation of adaptation policies in developing countries (Figure 9.15). While these are not tourism-specific they are highly relevant for the tourism sector. The framework aims to enhance the adaptive capacities of these countries and their resilience to climate change and climate variability, including extreme events. [493] The overarching goal of the risk-based approach to climate change adaptation is to manage both current and future risks associated with actual and potential climate hazards. Case studies have been reported on highlighting the range of levels at which adaptation takes place and the linkages between them. Two cases studies illustrate how and why reducing climate-related risks is an integral part of sustainable development. The process included a climate risk profiling for the sites and stakeholder analysis. The case studies identified three levels of adaptation activity: project/community level, sector level (e.g., tourism), as well as policy and planning at regional/national levels. 'Climate proofing' policy decisions proved to be effective: case studies involving infrastructure projects (e.g., roads) and strategic development plans in Micronesia indicated that many of the costs of damage attributable to climate change were avoided if 'climate proofing' was undertaken at the design stage of the project.

Figure 9.15 Guidelines for adaptation mainstreaming

A. Guidelines relating to the principles underpinning the mainstreaming of adaptation

Guideline 1:   Manage climate risks as an integral part of sustainable development

Guideline 2:   Ensure intergenerational equity related to climate risks

Guideline 3:   Adopt a coordinated, integrated and long-term approach to adaptation

Guideline 4:   Achieve the full potential of partnerships

Guideline 5:   Adaptation should exploit the potential of sustainable technologies

Guideline 6:   Base decisions on credible, comparable and objective information

Guideline 7:   Maximize the use of existing information and management systems

Guideline 8:   Strengthen and utilize in-country expertise

Guideline 9:   Strengthen and maximize use of existing regulations, codes, tools

B. Guidelines relating to enhancing the enabling environment for adaptation

Guideline 10:   'Climate proof' relevant legislation and regulations

Guideline 11:   Strengthen institutions to support the 'climate proofing' of development

Guideline 12:   Ensure macroeconomic policies and conditions favor 'climate proofing'

Guideline 13:   Ensure favourable access to affordable financing of 'climate proofed' development initiatives

C. Guidelines relating to the process of mainstreaming adaptation

Guideline 14:   Characterize climate-related risks that require sustained attention

Guideline 15:   Replicate the knowledge, motivation and skills that facilitate successful adaptation

Guideline 16:   Enhance the capacity for continuous adaptation

Guideline 17:   Ensure 'climate proofing' activities complement other development initiatives

Guideline 18:   A Process of continual improvement in adaptation outcomes

Source: Asian Development Bank (2005)

The Stern Review [494] highlighted that it is more economical to take measures that are proactive rather than reactive and also to favour no-regrets measures. 'No regrets', preventive measures, whilst they may not be sufficient on their own, are consistent with sound environmental management and wise resource use, and are thus appropriate responses to natural hazards and climate variability, including extreme events. Proactive, no-regrets measures are beneficial and cost effective, even in the absence of climate change. They are also in line with the precautionary principle. Examples of proactive measures include:

- raise awareness and educate tourists and operators of potential hazards and what to do in the case of an extreme event (rather than dealing with stranded passengers, damage control and negative media coverage);

- analyse potential changes in tourist flows and adapt products, marketing and positioning (rather than waiting for arrival numbers to decline);

- strengthen the enabling environment for tourism adaptation measures (e.g., provide incentives for investment into adaptation or facilitate administration);

- 'climate-proof' tourism policies and regulations (e.g., distance of buildings from the shoreline, building standards, food hygiene, staff training);

- integrate the tourism sector into other government policies, for example in the area of environmental impact assessment, disaster management or land use planning (to ensure best fit of these policies with tourism's needs);

- include disaster and adaptation responses in tourism training curricula;

- locate new tourist facilities in low-risk areas to avoid the negative impacts of a disaster and also the risk of poor investment;

- promote environmental management practices to protect natural ecosystems, and use efficiently scarce natural resources;

- strengthen relations between tourism facilities, operators and local communities, to collaborate in preventive and mitigating actions and response to extreme events.

Box 16: Facilitating adaptation in the tourism community

Awareness of climate change adaptation among local tourism operators has generally been found to be relatively low. [495, 496, 497, 498, 499, 500, 501, 502, 503] Consequently, there is a real need for effective communication between the climate change science community and tourism operators at the regional and local scale. The South West Climate Change Impacts Partnership in England developed an outreach brochure that explained to tourism business owners how climate change affects their business and provides a checklist for planning for climate change impacts. [504] Similar regionally specific initiatives, perhaps in conjunction with climate change adaptation workshops, would be highly valuable in many other tourism destinations.

Examples of adaptation measures and their potential barriers are shown in Table 9.6.

Table 9.6 Adaptation measures in relation to tourism policy and barriers

Adaptation measures	Barriers to implementation	Measures to remove barriers
Mainstreaming adaptation in tourism planning and policy	Lack of information on which to base policy initiatives The transversal and fragmented nature of the tourism sector makes coordination difficult (e.g., inter-ministerial, public-private- community relationships)	Improve targeted information (e.g., climate-risk profile for tourism, special climate information and weather forecasting services and products for tourism operators)
Include climate risk in tourism regulations and codes	Lack of information on which to base regulatory strengthening Lack of enforcement of regulations	Improve information, such as climate-risk profile for tourism, integrate climate risk factors in licensing criteria (e.g., location of facilities, water resources), streamline licensing and inspection processes through improved coordination between authorities
Institutional strengthening and capacity building to coordinate climate responses across tourism-related sectors	Lack of clarity of the institutional strengthening required to improve sustainability of tourism	Assess options and implement the most appropriate strategies
Education/awareness raising, motivate and mobilise tourism staff and also tourists	Lack of education and resources that support behavioural change Lack of finance	Undertake education/awareness programmes

Source: Becken, S. and Hay, J. (2007) and Simpson, M. C. (2008 – in press)

While much adaptation policy is undertaken at an institutional level (e.g., international organisations, national governments or communities), tourism businesses, entrepreneurs, investors can also improve their management of climate change risks. This includes managing vulnerabilities to direct impacts from climate change, and those to changes in the resource or customer bases. For example, business planning might benefit from an understanding of which markets might react most strongly to the negative perception of air travel, as discussed above. Climate change risk management should be integrated into business practices relating to revenue and cost, assets and liabilities, and the wider supply chain.

> "If only the risks are communicated without communicating adaptation options, people will probably react by avoidant maladaptive responses like denial of risk."
>
> Grothmann and Pratt (2005: 209)

9.4 Conclusion

This Chapter illustrated that climate change has far-reaching consequences for tourism businesses and destinations. At the destination level, the magnitude of the impact of climate change will depend upon the importance of tourism in the regional economy, the characteristics of climate change and its effect on the natural environment, the adaptive response of the tourism sector, and how the impacts of climate change interact with other long-term influencing variables in the tourism sector, including: globalization and economic fluctuations, fuel prices, aging populations in industrialized countries, increasing travel safety and health concerns, increased environmental and cultural awareness, advances in information and transportation technology, environmental limitations. No destination should assume they will not be affected by climate change. The fate of individual destinations in particular markets will also at least partly depend on the fate of its competitors.

Table 9.7 provides a qualitative assessment of the tourism destinations that are most at-risk to major types of climate change impact by the mid- to late-21st century. This assessment takes into consideration the available scientific information on climate change impact relevant to tourism, the relative adaptive capacity of nations and regions as summarized by the IPCC, and the importance of tourism to national economies. Figure 9.7 integrates this information to identify regional vulnerability 'hotspots' where clusters of major impacts are anticipated to occur and adaptation assistance is likely to be needed by nations and destinations. Due to the very limited information available on the potential impacts of climate change in some tourism regions (Table 9.8 and Figure 9.16), this qualitative assessment must be considered with caution. Until systematic regional level assessments are conducted, particularly in Africa, South America, and Asia (Table 9.8) a definitive statement on the most vulnerable tourism regions and the net economic and social impacts in the tourism sector will not be possible.

Table 9.7 Tourism vulnerability hotspots [a]

Warmer summers	Warmer winters	Extreme events	Water scarcity
Mediterranean and Middle East	European Alps	Caribbean	Mediterranean and Middle East
Southern USA and California	Northeast-Midwest USA/ Eastern Canada	USA Gulf of Mexico coast	Southwest USA
Caribbean	Australian Alps	Polynesia/Micronesia	Australia
South Africa	Rocky Mountains	East China Sea coast	North and Sub-Saharan Africa
North Queensland	Pyrenees Mountains	Northern Australia	Small island nations

Land biodiversity loss	Marine biodiversity loss	Sea level rise	Disease
South Africa Cape Region	Polynesia/Micronesia	Maldives and other Indian Ocean islands	Sub-Saharan and Southern Africa
Mediterranean Basin	Australia	Florida	Western Europe
Polynesia/Micronesia	Caribbean and South America	Polynesia/Micronesia	South USA
Central America-Costa Rica	South China Sea	Gold Coast	Mediterranean
South America Amazon Basin	Maldives islands	Coastal China	Northern Australia

Travel cost increase from mitigation policy	Political destabilization
Australia	Middle East and Sub-Saharan Africa
New Zealand	Southern Africa
Seychelles/Maldives	Caribbean
Sub-Saharan and South Africa	Southeast Asia
Polynesia/Micronesia	Bangladesh-India-Pakistan

(a) Based on independent evaluations of: Gössling, S. and Hall, C. M. (2006); IPCC (2007b), *Sumary for Policymakers*, and estimation of the authors.

Considering that the direct and indirect impacts of climate change on tourism destination are for the most part very negative, it is in the industry's interest to contribute actively to both adaptation and mitigation. The sector is more exposed than many others to climate change impacts, and it has the opportunity to set a compelling example of leadership in taking actions which contribute to mitigation and adaptation that contributed to reducing the overall vulnerability of communities to climate change.

Figure 9.16 Geographic distribution of major climate change impacts affecting tourism destinations

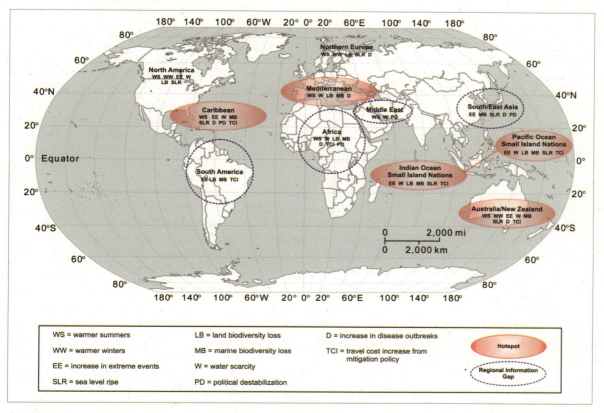

Table 9.8 Relative level of regional knowledge on climate change and tourism (a)

Region (as defined in IPCC AR4)	Relative level of knowledge on climate change impacts
Africa	Extremely poor
Asia	Japan – Poor Southeast Asia – Extremely poor Middle East – Extremely poor Central Asia – Extremely poor
Australia and New Zealand	Moderate
Europe	Moderate
Latin America	South America – Extremely poor Caribbean – Extremely poor
North America	Moderate
Polar Regions	Poor
Small islands	Poor – Moderate

(a) Based on independent evaluations of: IPCC (2007b), *Sumary for Policymakers*; Hall, C. M. (2008-submitted), *Tourism and Climate Change: Knowledge Gaps and Issues*; and Report of the Authors.

"It is vital for tourism destinations [...] to anticipate the coming changes and to draw their consequences, starting now. (Adaptation) is a long-term project that must be anticipated and carefully prepared beforehand; it is not easy to see this through successfully, because it entails, all at the same time, modifying economic circuits, introducing new technologies, carrying out intensive training, investing in the creation of new products, [...] changing the minds of public authorities, entrepreneurs, host communities and tourists."

Francesco Frangialli, *UNWTO Secretary-General* (2007)

A number of adaptation measures are currently employed in the tourism sector. Relying on past experience is not likely to be adequate in many destinations, as the future climate and environmental conditions are going to be sufficiently different as to require further adaptation. An important lesson learned from Hurricane Katrina and the extremely warm winter of 2006–2007 in the European Alps is that adaptations can be overwhelmed by events unexpected and beyond the range of experience of the tourism sector. Such events should be anticipated under climate change, and consequently there is a critical need for the tourism sector to evaluate the effectiveness of current adaptations under projected climate conditions.

Knowledge of the capacity of current climate adaptations utilized by the tourism sector to cope successfully with future climate change is rudimentary at this time. Furthermore, the available studies that have examined the climate change risk appraisal of tourism operators [505, 506, 507, 508, 509, 510, 511, 512, 513] have consistently found low awareness of climate change and little evidence long-term strategic planning in anticipation of future changes in climate. Consequently, the incorporation of adaptation to climate change into the collective minds of private and public sector tourism decision-makers ('mainstreaming') remains several steps away.

There will undoubtedly be costs of climate change and costs of adaptation. [514] The causes of climate change are global, however impacts are also experienced locally and as such these costs cannot just be borne by those affected, especially as those worst affected are likely to be those less able to take action to mitigate the changes (e.g., developing countries and local tourism SMMEs). Therefore these costs also need to be addressed by governments and international organisations. International climate policy generally accepts that developed countries have obligation to offer assistance to less develop countries in order to enhance their adaptive capacity to climate change. The UNFCCC Article 4.1 stipulates commitments for all countries in terms of formulating, cooperating and considering the impacts of climate change in social, economic and environmental policies and actions, and also requires Parties to cooperate, exchange and communicate information related to the implementation of adaptation measures. Articles 4.3, 4.4, 4.5, 4.7, 4.8 and 4.9 specifically address obligations to assist developing countries (including SIDS and LCDs) in meeting various commitments of Article 4.1 through various funding mechanisms. This commitment to assist developing countries does not go as far as providing a formal or informal process for deciding how the burden of funding should to be shared and how (and to whom) adaptation funds should to be distributed. [515] Wider issues relate to decisions as to who defines risk and vulnerability, who 'deserves' aid and at what level it is given – national, regional, local, institutional/organisational, community – and also who is 'responsible' for paying, remain critical questions for the international community to resolve. The tourism sector should ensure that it has a voice in the adaptation agenda dialogue that will only intensify in the decades ahead.

Chapter 10

Implications of Climate Change
for Tourism Demand

The influence of climate change on tourism demand patterns will be shaped by the response of tourists to the complexity of the impacts on destinations as discussed in Chapter 9. Climate, the natural environment, and personal safety are three primary factors in destination choice, and global climate change is anticipated to have significant impacts on all three of these factors. Climate is also a principal driver of seasonality in demand, which has been described as one of the most problematic features of the tourism industry. [516, 517] Climate change will alter seasonal tourism demand by creating, deteriorating or improving climatic conditions at destinations and in source markets. As indicated, tourists have the largest adaptive capacity in the tourism sector, because of their ability to respond to climate change impacts by substituting the place, timing and type of holiday; even at very short notice. Tourists are expected to adapt to the impacts of climate change by 'voting with their feet,' with potentially profound implications for patterns of tourism demand at the local and regional scale. Currently there is a very wide choice of destinations and travel experiences on offer and climate factors will play an increasing role in the travel decisions of tourists.

Understanding and anticipating the potential geographic and seasonal shifts in tourism demand is of keen interest to the tourism industry and is the subject of this Chapter. Because the impacts of climate change on destinations and tourism demand are so closely interlinked, and to facilitate cross-connections with Chapter 9, this Chapter is similarly structured to examine the potential influence of four major types of climate change impacts on tourism demand:

* direct impacts of a changed climate;

* indirect impacts of environmental change;

* mitigation policy and tourist mobility; and

* societal change (economic growth and social-political stability).

Illustrative examples of projected changes in tourism demand are drawn from around the world, including mountain, islands and coastal areas, and natural-cultural heritage areas.

10.1 Consumer Response to a Changing Climate

A number of lines of evidence demonstrate the intrinsic importance of weather and climate for tourist decision making and the vacation experience. Weather and climate are of universal importance in defining destination attractiveness and a central motivator in the selection of a holiday destination and the timing of holiday travel. [518, 519, 520, 521, 522, 523, 524, 525, 526, 527] Warmer temperatures and greater sunshine have been found to influence travel patterns (proportion of domestic and international holidays) [528, 529, 530] and tourism expenditures in some temperate nations. [531] There is also evidence that the weather conditions experienced at the destination have important influence on overall holiday satisfaction. [532] As climate is an important resource sought after by tourists, projected changes in the distribution of climate resources are anticipated to have important consequences for tourism demand.

10.1.1 Changes in Global Demand Patterns

Simulation models have been used to explore the potential impact of climate change, in conjunction with population growth and per capita income and other variables included in the IPCC SRES scenarios, on aggregate international tourism demand, and generate scenarios of the potential geographic redistribution of tourist departures and arrivals. These models are necessarily highly simplified and have important limitations (see Box 19). [533, 534, 535] The general geographic patterns of projected changes in tourism flows are summarized below in Tables 10.1 and 10.2.

Anticipated impacts include a gradual shift in preferred destinations to higher latitudes and to higher elevations in mountainous areas. Tourists from temperate nations that currently dominate international travel (e.g., Northern Europe) are expected to spend more holidays in their home country or nearby, adapting their travel patterns to take advantage of new climatic opportunities closer to home. This shift in travel patterns would have three important implications: proportionally more demand for temperate nations, proportionally less demand for warmer nations which are now highly frequented by tourists from temperate regions, and a net reduction on the total number of international tourists. In warmer countries, the reverse would occur, as these nations would attract less tourists from temperate regions and would have increased outbound travel.

Table 10.1 Ranking of countries with highest and lowest proportional change in tourist arrivals with climate change in 2025 *

Highest proportional increase in arrivals	Lowest proportional increase in arrivals
Canada	Mauritania
Russian Federation	Mali
Mongolia	Bahrain
Iceland	Qatar
Finland	Senegal
Zimbabwe	Kuwait
Norway	Niger
Zambia	United Arab Emirates
Sweden	Gambia
Republic of Korea	Chad

* Data for 1995 arrivals and departures for the 207 nations included in the study were derived from World Resources Database 2000–2001. World Resources Institute, Washington, DC. These data are not necessarily consistent with UNWTO data used in this report (Chapter 9 and 11). Population and economic growth scenario data are taken from the 17 region IMAGE 2.2 model implementation of the SRES scenarios. The climate change scenarios for the IPCC SRES emission scenarios were derived with the FUND (Tol 1999) and COSMIC (Schlesinger and Williams, 1998) models, and represent the average-minimum-maximum of 14 GCMs.

Source: Hamilton, J. M. et al. (2005b)

The macro-economic effects of these broad changes in geographic patterns were assessed with a general equilibrium model. A net negative macro-economic impact have been found for three regions: the 'European Union'; the 'Energy Exporting nations' group, which include many Arab nations; and the 'Rest of the World' category of nations, which includes the Caribbean. China and India were expected to be largely unaffected, though with slightly positive changes in tourist numbers. Net gains were projected for North America, Australasia, Japan, Eastern Europe and the former Soviet Union. The aggregate global economic impact of a climate change-induced change in tourism demand was concluded to be quite small in 2010, but by 2050 could become a non-negligible loss under higher emission scenarios. [536]

Table 10.2 Regional changes in international departures and arrivals in 2050

Region	Arrivals	Departures	Macro-economic impact
USA	Decline (–)	Decline (+ +)	Increase (+)
EU	Decline (– –)	Decline (+ +)	Decline (–)
EEFSU	Increase (+)	Decline (+ +)	Increase (+ +)
JPN	Decline (–)	Decline (+)	Increase (+)
RoA1	Increase (+ +)	Decline (+ +)	Increase (+ +)
EEx	Decline (– –)	Increase (– –)	Decline (– –)
CHIND	Decline (–)	Decline (+)	Increase (+)
RoW	Decline (– –)	Increase (– –)	Decline (– –)

Region abbreviations: [EU] European Union, [EEFSU] Eastern Europe and Former Soviet Union, [JPN] Japan, [Rest of Annex 1 Nations – developed nations, including Canada], [EEx] Energy Exporters, [CHIND] China and India, [RoW] Rest of World – developing nations, including Caribbean]

Source: Berrittella, M. et al. (2006)

These aggregated results mask many sub-regional changes, such as the anticipated redistribution of tourists from southern to middle-northern Europe and from southern to middle-northern North America, as well as the potential restructuring of tourism seasons, such as a strengthening of current shoulder seasons in the Mediterranean or other regions where peak summer months might be considered uncomfortably hot * by a majority of tourists in the future (see Box 17).

Box 17   Will the Mediterranean be too hot for tourism? Sorting out the science from the science siction

A number of media stories [537, 538, 539, 540, 541, 542, 543] have foretold the major threat that increased future summer temperatures poses for tourism in the Mediterranean. Indeed some stated that "The likelihood [is] that Mediterranean summers may be too hot for tourists after 2020" [544] and that "[…] by 2030, the traditional British package holiday to a Mediterranean beach resort may be consigned to the 'scrap-heap of history'." [545, 546, 547]

Little is known about what tourists perceive to be 'too hot' for any particular tourism destination. The limited information on what tourists define as optimal temperatures for beach holidays [548] however indicates that the daily maximum temperatures in many Mediterranean destinations are currently near the optimal range in July and August (Figure 10.1). Under the lower range of warming scenarios for 2071–2100 (+3° C) warming, average daily maximum temperatures at four of the destinations in Figure 10.1 would only exceed the optimal perceived temperature for a beach holiday by about 1–2° C, which is unlikely to significantly deter visitation. It is possible however, that media coverage of extreme heat waves may have a greater impact on perceptions of climate suitability for tourism in the Mediterranean (see Box 17).

At the higher end (+6° C) there is a notable departure between the perceived optimal temperatures for a beach holiday and the projected maximum summer temperatures at all five destinations in Figure 10.1. Importantly, no such summer warming scenarios are projected until the later decades of the century and only under high emission scenarios. [549] Furthermore, the projected number of weeks with heat waves (temperatures of over 35° C) increased by one or two through mid-century. Whether this increase is sufficient to alter tourist perceptions of the Mediterranean is uncertain. Improved summer climate conditions in major source markets for Mediterranean tourism (i.e., Northern Europe) may have a greater impact on travel patterns than climatic changes at Mediterranean destinations

---

*   For a critical discussion of the role of 'temperature' as a weather parameter see: Gössling, S., and Hall, C. M. (2006), *Uncertainties in Predicting Tourist Travel Flows Based on Models.*

by mid-century. A more imminent climate change threat to tourism in parts of the Mediterranean is likely to be a diminishing water supply and increasing risk of forest fires.

Figure 10.1 Average July-August daily maximum temperatures and preferred beach holiday temperatures

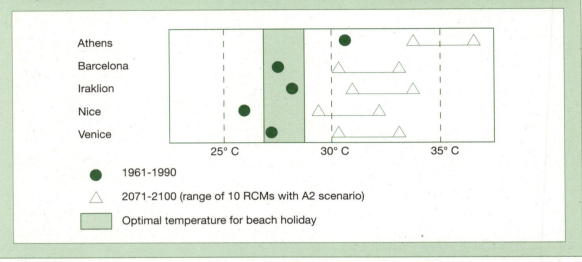

Box 18 The impacts of the 2003 summer heat wave on tourism in France

During the first two weeks of August 2003, France was struck by the most severe heat wave since 1873. The heat wave was not only exceptional by its temperatures (15% of meteorological stations recorded temperatures exceeding 40° C), but also by its length. It was associated to serious, though not exceptional drought, in spring and the beginning of summer (causing forest fires) and to a lack of wind towards its end. The best known impact was the rise in mortality (nearly 15,000 deaths) [550], but it also had consequences for economic activities including tourism.

Shifts in destinations were noted; some of which have been documented by tourism statistics. The hotels on the northern and northwestern shores benefited from additional customers, while the opposite occurred in the Mediterranean and the southwest. The central mountains accommodated holiday makers leaving the southern shores – camping sites with shade and swimming pools were most favoured. Attractions such as caves also benefited from increased visitation. The heat was also detrimental to urban tourism. There were some modifications in consumption habits across the whole population: more light meals, more mineral water (+18%), more soft drinks (+13%), more ice creams (+14%) and less clothing sold. [551]

There were impacts on environmental resources that were detrimental to tourism: access was denied to forests (risk of fire) or to some mountain sites, some streams dried and the quality of recreational water deteriorated; fishing was forbidden over large parts of the country, so was canoeing and sometimes bathing. Restrictions on the use of water were severe (irrigation of lawns, swimming pools, etc.). Other vulnerabilities were discovered in the transportation and accommodation sectors. The number of trains arriving on time dropped from 87% to 77% often because their cooling systems broke down. The refrigerating systems at one quarter of the food trade (restaurants and markets) enterprises proved insufficient to cope with such heat. A very significant portion of accommodation proved uncomfortable, whereas the increased need for space cooling was confronted by difficulties in the production of electricity and by breakdowns in the network due to excessive heat. [552] Though no catastrophic failures in the power grid occurred, the situation was considered very critical and it would certainly have been worse if more tourist accommodation had been equipped with space cooling.

If institutional holiday flexibility were to increase in the future (e.g., moving to a year-round school schedule with interspersed holidays), the overall impact of climate change may reduce demand seasonality by evening out visitation levels across a larger number of months. Europeans, for instance, would be able to extend their demand over a longer period, with holidays in spring and autumn concentrating on the Mediterranean region and that in the summer months concentrating on the more northerly regions. If the institutional context for holidays remains largely the same as today, the geographic redistribution of tourism is likely to be intensified, because the temporal redistribution of tourists is restricted. Destinations would become uncomfortably hot in the peak summer travel season could experience decreased visitation, with little or no compensation in the shoulder seasons. The countries that would experience better summer conditions, on the other hand, could benefit from large increases in visitation, without being able to shift some of this additional demand to the shoulder seasons which are also climatically improved for tourism. [553]

Box 19 The challenges and uncertainties of long-range global scale demand modelling

Statistics-based models (used to explain or predict travel flows) express the behaviour of tourists as a function of a given set of variables, such as 'average temperatures at destination', 'travel costs', etc. While these models can be indicative of travel behaviour, they may also have large error margins, as there are potentially many aspects that can influence holiday decision-making, while models usually account for only a few. Such models also forced to generalize to a great extent, as databases may not always differentiate between different climate zones in one country, business- and leisure-travellers, or travel motives (say a beach holiday, urban sightseeing-shopping trip, ecotourism holiday to see polar bears, or visiting friends- and relatives) which may require different climatic conditions or be less influenced by climate-related variables. Moreover, there are scientific uncertainties regarding the role of perceptions in decision-making (i.e., to which extent a change in a given parameter like temperature will really result in travel behaviour adaptation). Some of these aspects are discussed in more detail below.

Data on tourism demand: According to the UNWTO/United Nations Recommendations on Tourism Statistics, 'Tourism' is defined as "[…] the activities of persons travelling to and staying in places outside their usual environment for not more than one consecutive year for leisure, business and other purposes not related to the exercise of an activity remunerated from within the place visited" The use of this broad concept makes it possible to identify tourism between countries as well as tourism within a country. 'Tourism' refers to all activities of visitors, including both 'tourists (overnight visitors)' and 'same-day visitors'. UNWTO collects, on a regular basis, data on several indicators of tourism demand including: international visitors arrivals (including overnight visitors, i.e tourist, same-day visitors and cruise passengers), as well as number of guests and overnights stays in accommodation units both for inbound and domestic tourism. Nonetheless, despite the considerable progress made in recent decades, international tourism statistics are often not uniform, because definitions and methods of data collection tend to differ.

Temperature and weather information: Temperature is often assumed to be the most important weather parameter in the analysis of tourism flows, because outside a certain temperature range, weather perceptions become unfavourable and problems of discomfort arise. While it is not to question that temperature is a very important weather parameter, there is evidence that other weather parameters are also important, sometimes equally as important as temperature, including wind, rain or hours of sunshine. [554] These parameters are not necessarily correlated to temperature which thus cannot be considered as a satisfactory proxy. It is also uncertain of when temperatures are perceived as being 'too hot' by the majority of tourists. The representation of climate within such models is admittedly crude; often using the temperatures of capital cities to represent entire nations (i.e., Washington, DC represents Florida and California) or annual average temperatures, so that no shift in seasonal visits can be accounted for.

Weather extremes: Many weather parameters are predicted to change slowly over time. However, while such averages can be measured and incorporated into models, it is less straightforward to assess the consequences of weather extremes, such as heat- and cold waves, prolonged periods of rain or drought. Experiences with such phenomena in Europe in recent years suggest that extremes can have a substantial influence on travel patterns.

Terrorism, war, epidemics, natural disasters, environmental change: All of these could have impacts on travel behaviour. Immediately after the terrorism attacks of 11 September 2001, many tourist reservations were cancelled and international tourism was diminished for months to follow. The second Iraq war is an example of military conflicts impacting on tourism demand. SARS, as an example of an epidemic, had substantial influence on tourist flows in Asia and Canada in 2003, and the tsunami hitting South Asia in December 2004 cost hundreds of thousands of human lives, and has had devastating consequences for tourism destinations involved, at least in the short-term. Environmental change leading to altered landscapes, changes in biodiversity, the spread of diseases (Malaria, Lyme-disease, etc.), or organisms perceived as disturbing (ticks, mosquitoes, algae, various insects) are also likely to influence the perception of destinations (Chapter 9). For example, Iceland is projected to be one of the biggest tourism 'winners' as a result of a changed climate (Table 10.1), but this cold water island has seen substantial tourism growth because the combination of glaciers and volcanoes makes this island so attractive. If the glaciers diminish substantially or disappear, the attractiveness of the landscape and this destination may be irrevocably altered, while projected warming will hardly make Iceland the new Majorca.

Weather anomalies: Heat- and cold waves could have a considerable and unpredictable influence on tourism in the future. The summer of 2007 showed largely varying weather patterns deviating substantially from previously observed long-term averages. This included, for instance, prolonged periods of drought in Southern Europe, and periods of intense rainfalls and flooding in Central and Northern Europe. Swedish media reported on tourists being stuck in their rented summerhouses, as heavy rainfall made it impossible to leave houses. In Seychelles, prolonged periods of rainfall in the supposedly driest month (July) impacted on tourist's satisfaction. Diving conditions deteriorated, as visibility in coastal waters was reduced to a few metres.

Costs of transport: Mobility is a precondition for tourism and worldwide. According to UNWTO's data some 45% of all international tourist arrivals are now by air. Air travel consumes large amounts of fuel, and is thus partially dependent on the availability of oil resources as well as on rather stable world market prices for fuel. Oil prices are currently high and are anticipated by many experts to generally increase in the years and decades ahead as so called 'cheap' oil supplies are conservatively expected to peak within the next 40 years [555] and post-Kyoto Protocol policies on GHG emissions may also indirectly increase oil prices.

10.1.2 Changes in Regional-local Demand Patterns

The possible response of tourists to changing climate conditions and the implications for demand has also been assessed for a range of specific tourism sub-sectors at the regional and local scale.

Visitation to national parks

Illustrative of the expanded opportunities associated with an improved and expanded warm-weather tourism season in temperate regions is projected nature-based tourism in Canada's system of national parks. Tourism in many of the parks in Canada and the northern USA is constrained by winter conditions, except where skiing operations exist. Assuming that other socio-economic factors that influence park visitation (e.g., desire to interact with nature, travel costs, amenity requirements) remain relatively constant, Canada's national parks are anticipated to have higher visitation under a warmer climate. Assuming little change in visitation patterns, with an extended warm weather tourism season, total annual visits to the national parks analyzed were projected to increase by approximately 6 to 8% over the next thirty years. [556] Annual visits by mid-century could increase between 9 and 29%. With further warming by the end of the century, the number of people visiting these parks is projected to increase 10 to 41%. Of course, demographic change (population increase) or socio-economic change (increased or decreased desire to interact with nature, travel costs to parks or other alternate holiday destinations for both domestic and international tourists) would also influence visitation patterns in the decades ahead. The interaction of these factors remains an important area of analysis to better understand how tourism demand may evolve under climate change.

Although visitation to Canada's national parks is projected to increase system-wide under climate change, there are important regional and seasonal differences in the projected magnitude of increase. Parks on the Atlantic Ocean (Prince Edward Island and Cape Breton Highlands) were projected to experience the largest increases, with visitation levels potentially doubling in late century under the warmest climate change scenarios. Most of the parks are projected to experience the largest increases in visitation during the spring (April to June) and fall (September to November) shoulder seasons, with minimal increase during the traditional peak months of July and August Banff National Park, for instance, is projected to experience average spring increases in visitation of 19% and average fall increases of 16% under the warmest climate change scenario compared to an average increase of only 5% during July and August (Figure 10.2). Changes in the seasonal timing of increases in visitation will influence a range of management issues, including user-fee collection, environmental operations and staffing needs.

The projected increase in visitation (an additional 1 to 4 million visitors annually by mid-century) would generate substantial growth in park revenues and the economies of nearby communities. Increased visitation could also exacerbate visitor-related ecological pressures and crowding issues at popular park attractions in high visitation parks. Under a changed climate, more intensive visitor management strategies may be required to support sustainable tourism in these parks and prevent the degradation of visitor experience.

Figure 10.2 Change in average monthly visitation to Banff National Park (Canada) in mid-century

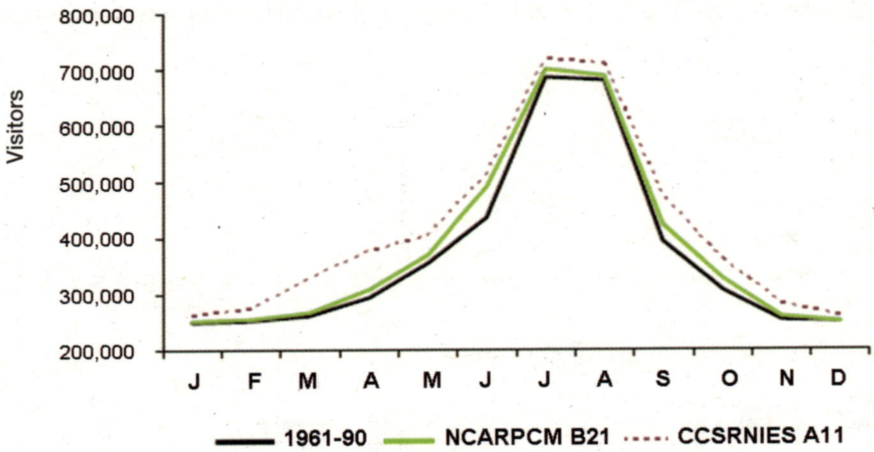

Source: Scott, D. and Jones, B. (2005)

Climate change implications for golf tourism

The golf industry is economically [557, 558] one of the largest recreation sectors in the world and an increasingly important tourism sector. Golf is projected to be highly influenced by climate change because it will alter the length of the operating season, influence seasonal and total golf demand, require increased turf management (i.e., irrigation, turf grass selection and turf disease and pest management), and threatens some of the world's historic coastal courses through sea level rise and erosion. [559, 560, 561, 562]

Climate change has been identified as an important issue by leading golf organizations around the world. Drawing on the input of over 250 golf industry stakeholders, the Golf Course Advisory Panel at the Royal and Ancient Golf Course of St. Andrews (Scotland) identified climate change as one of six strategic issues facing the golf industry over the next twenty years. [563] More recently, the World Rules and Golf Development Committee of the Royal and Ancient Golf Club of St. Andrews stated, "Every national governing body and golf facility should be finding out more about climate change predictions for their region, and starting to anticipate the effects on golf." [564]

Currently there remains limited information on the potential impacts of climate change on the golf industry. A survey of golf course managers in the UK found that 69% believed their course is facing serious threat from erosion and/or flooding in the next 50 years. [565] In Canada, climate change was projected to have a positive impact on the length of the golf season and on overall golf demand. In two important golf holiday destination areas, the golf season was projected to lengthen considerably by mid-century: 25 to 86 days longer north of Toronto (Great Lakes Region) and 28 to 56 days longer in the Province of Prince Edward Island (Atlantic Coast). Assuming that other socio-economic factors that influence golf demand (e.g., social popularity of golf, travel costs and playing fees, demographics, golf course supply) remain relatively constant, by mid-century, annual rounds played in these two locations were projected to increase by 27% to 61% and by 48% to 74% respectively (Figure 10.3). As illustrated in the pattern of daily rounds played in Figure 10.3, much of this growth was expected in the shoulder seasons. Assuming little change in other factors that affect demand patterns, changes in the season length and increased annual demand, these two locations are likely representative of the types of changes that can be expected throughout central and eastern Canada as well as major golf markets in northern US states in the New England and Mid-West regions. Longer golf seasons in these regions would alter competitive relationships between major golf destinations in the south, diminishing the 'push factor' to winter golf tourism destinations in the southern United States (e.g., Myrtle Beach, Palm Springs, Phoenix and Las Vegas). Golf has the potential to offer greater possibilities for proximity leisure in the future, which may be important in a era of higher travel costs for sports tourism.

Figure 10.3 Climate change impacts on golf demand in Canada (annual and seasonal increases) (a)

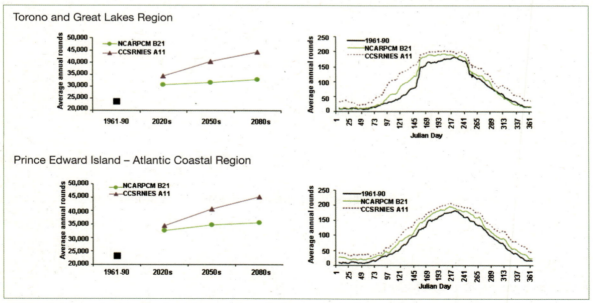

(a) The analysis was conducted with two global climate models (NCAR-PCM – from the National Center for Atmospheric Research in the USA and CCSRNIES from Japanese Centre for Climate Research Studies) each run with different GHG emission scenarios (B2 – lower emissions and A1 – higher emissions), so as to represent the full range of climate futures in each of the study areas.

Source: Scott, D. and Jones, B. (2006a)

Climate change would also pose challenges for the operation of golf courses, particularly under the warmest climate change scenario. As the climate warms, there will be increased demand for irrigation to keep turf grass in optimal playing condition. This increased demand for water is likely to create or intensify water allocation conflicts in tourism regions with limited water resources, such as the southwest US, Mediterranean, Australia. Indeed, the golf industry in Las Vegas has already opposed planned water restrictions, arguing that 3 in 10 tourists to the city spend time golfing and that the restrictions would impact the entire tourism economy. Aspects of pest and disease management could also be impacted by projected changes in the climate, posing challenges to the maintenance of playing conditions. Insect pests that currently have only one life cycle in some regions could begin to have two life cycles under warmer conditions. Similarly, turf grass diseases and pests currently limited to southern latitudes could also expand northward and require management interventions, although there are other pests whose burden could diminish in some regions (e.g., fusarium patch, snow scald, red thread, typhula blight). [566]

Figure 10.4 Climate change might favour some regions for golf tourism development, and constrain others

"The golf industry's significant sensitivity to weather will make it one of the first to feel the impacts of increasing weather uncertainty due to climate change. As a result, we anticipate the industry to be impacted in the near-term as the old paradigm of business and financial planning around predictable and cyclical weather patterns may be disrupted by an increasingly volatile climate. [...] certain geographic markets are already facing these challenges [...]."

WeatherBill Inc. (2007)

Winter sports

As identified in Chapter 9, winter sports tourists are faced with the prospect of less natural snowfall and shorter, more variable ski seasons in the future. A critical question for the future of the ski industry and closely associated tourism operators is how tourists might respond to these changed conditions and what will happen to overall demand in the tourism marketplace. Insight into these questions comes from several nations.

Marketplace surveys with skiers have been conducted in Australia [567] and Switzerland [568] to determine how skiers would change their skiing patterns if climate change conditions were realized (described as poor snow conditions existing over five years). In Australia, 25% of respondents indicated they would continue to ski as often in Australia, while 31% said they would ski less often, but still in Australia. An even greater portion of skiers would be lost to the Australian ski industry, with 38% of respondents indicating they would substitute destinations and ski overseas (mainly in New Zealand and Canada) and a further 6% would quit skiing altogether. With 44% of the ski market potentially lost and 31% skiing less often, the implications of climate change for Australia's ski industry appear ominous. [569] Whether the remaining skiing demand would be sufficient to sustain the ski industry in Australia remains an important uncertainty. A similar investigation with Swiss skiers found that 58% would ski with the same frequency (30% at the same resort and 28% at a more snow reliable resort at higher elevation).

Almost one-third (32%) of respondents indicated they would ski less often and 4% would stop skiing altogether. [570] No similar surveys have been conducted in other European nations, so it is uncertain whether these results can be generalized to the European ski market.

An assessment of the national ski industry in Japan (61 ski areas) estimated that reduced snowfall at ski areas resulting from a 3° C warming scenario would reduce overall skier visits by 30%. [571] Ski areas in southern regions were considered the most vulnerable, with skier visits falling by 50%. Conversely, the impact of climate change on skier demand was projected to be negligible in some northern high altitude ski areas.

In eastern North America, a climate change analogue approach has been used to understand the potential response of the ski tourism marketplace to future climate change. The winter of 2001–2002 was the record warm winter throughout much of the region and approximated the normal temperatures expected in mid-century under a mid-range warming scenario (approximately +4.5° C). Skier visits during this record warm winter were consistently lower than in the previous climatically normal winter of 2000–2001: –11% in the Northeast ski region of the US, –7% in Ontario, and –10% in Quebec. [572] Although this finding is not surprising considering the ski season was approximately 20 days shorter in the record warm winter, what is somewhat surprising is how small the reduction in skier visits was during this climate change analogue season. It was observed that utilization levels at ski areas increased, as many skiers in the region adapted by skiing more frequently than in a normal year (i.e., skiing every weekend, instead of every two weeks). Notably, skier visits declined the least at larger ski areas, suggesting that skiers may have adapted by selecting ski areas that generally have greater snow-making capacities and diversified tourism products. It is uncertain whether this same pattern of adaptation would occur if consecutive years of poor snow conditions occurred. Future analogue events may provide insight into this question.

10.2 Demand Implications of Climate-induced Environmental Change

It is important to emphasize that it is the holistic impact of climate change on tourism environments that tourists will respond to, not just changes in climatic conditions. [573, 574] Tourism demand at the regional scale will also be affected by the range of environmental impacts brought about by global climate change. Environmental change is a particular risk for destinations where nature-based tourism is a primary tourism segment and ecosystems are highly sensitive to climatic change. This Section focuses on two such destination types: coral reefs and alpine landscapes.

Coral reefs

Recent coral bleaching events and the imperilled future for many coral reefs under climate change [575] are a cause for concern for diving and other related tourism. Unfortunately, there is limited information about how tourists responded to the severe coral bleaching that occurred in many reef systems around the world in 1998.

A case study from El Nido, Phillippines does provide some insight into the response of different tourist market segments to coral bleaching and degraded reef environments. [576] In El Nido and nearby islands, severe coral bleaching in 1998 led to 30–50% coral mortality and a typhoon that same year (also linked to El Niño) caused further damage to local reefs. Whether divers or not, most tourists (95%) coming to El Nido have at least some interest in the local marine environment. However, general awareness of coral bleaching among tourists was found to be low (44%). The bleaching event did not impact budget tourist arrivals, but fewer budget tourists went diving during their stay. The impact at resorts, some of which cater to the high-end dive market, was much worse. The annual economic losses were estimated to be US$ 6–7.4 million over the next ten years, concurrent with coral recovery timeframe. If however there is no significant coral recovery or a bleaching event reoccurs, the economic losses increased to between US$ 15–27 million.

Another study [577] found that there may be large differences between dive destinations. In this case study of Mauritius, it was found that the state of coral reefs was largely irrelevant to dive tourists and snorkellers, as long as a certain threshold level was not exceeded. This threshold level was defined by visibility, abundance and variety of species, the occurrence of algae or physically damaged corals, and was not exceeded in the case study, despite the fact that considerable damage had already occurred. However, this will probably depend upon the type of divers attracted by a destination. Experienced divers making conscience decisions for certain dive sites can be assumed to be more critical about climate change related damage of coral reefs than holiday divers partaking in diving as sideline activities.

In other coastal locations, the impact of climate change was also projected to adversely affect tourist preferences for these destinations. In Bonaire and Barbados, more than 75% of tourists were unwilling to return for the same holiday price in the event that coral bleaching or reduced beach area occurred as a result of climate change. [578]

Although the climatic conditions for tourism in northern Germany are projected to improve, [579] a survey of tourists found that when presented with scenarios that described potential impacts of climate change on the coastal areas and marine life on the German coasts of the North and Baltic Seas, respondents were less likely to intend to spend their main vacation at these destinations. [580]

Box 20   Coral bleaching and Great Barrier Reef tourism

The Great Barrier Reef has experienced several mass coral bleaching events in the past decade (1998, 2002, 2006). During the 1998 global mass bleaching event about 50% of Great Barrier reefs suffered bleaching; 87% of inshore reefs and 28% of mid-shelf and offshore reefs. Overall, about 5% of reefs were severely damaged by this bleaching event. [581] The Great Barrier Reef suffered the largest mass bleaching event on record in 2002, when 60% of reefs were bleached. [582] The response of tourists to these bleaching events remains unknown and an important area for future market research. A survey of tourists in Cairns (North Queensland, Australia) asked if they would visit the region if they knew that there had been a recent bleaching event – 29% were uncertain and 35% indicated they would not. [583]

Figure 10.5 Coral bleaching in the Great Barrier Reef

Photo credit: Great Barrier Reef Marine Park Authorities

Increases in surface water temperatures are projected to occur more frequently in the future under climate change scenarios. Coral bleaching events are likely to increase in frequency and severity and are therefore thought to be one of the most serious long-term threats to the Great Barrier Reef and its massive tourism industry. The increasing threat of coral bleaching under projected climate change scenarios triggered the Great Barrier Reef Marine Park Authority to prepare a Coral Bleaching Response Plan [584], with the objectives to:

- improve ability to predict bleaching risk;

- provide early warnings of major coral bleaching events; measure the spatial extent of bleaching;

- assess the ecological impacts of bleaching;

- involve the community in monitoring the health of the Reef;

- communicate and raise awareness about bleaching; and

- evaluate the implications of bleaching events for management policy and strategies.

Alpine landscapes

The perceived quality of the alpine environment is an important attraction for tourism in mountain regions and there have been repeated warnings about the potential negative effects of environmental change to reduce the attractiveness of the mountain landscapes to the extent that tourism may be adversely impacted. [585, 586, 587] The limited knowledge of how tourists might respond to changes in sensitive mountain landscapes comes from the Rocky Mountain region of North America.

When presented with hypothetical scenarios of how the landscape might be affected by climate change over the next 30–50 years, the responses of tourists in three national parks (Rocky Mountain National Park – USA, Glacier-Waterton Lakes International Peace Park – USA and Canada, and Banff National Park – Canada) were remarkably consistent. When asked how the specified changes in the mountain environments would have affected their intension to visit that park, the majority of visitors indicated that they would not change their visitation patterns. In Rocky Mountain National Park, visitor response to the environmental changes resulted in a 10 to 14% increase in annual visitation under scenarios of moderate warming, while the 'extreme heat' scenario would cause a 9% decline in visitation. [588] The environmental change scenarios constructed for the early and mid-decades of the 21st century were also found to have minimal influence on the intention to visit Glacier-Waterton International Peace Park or Banff National Park, with almost all visitors still intending to visit the parks and 10% indicated they would visit them more often, presumably due to improved climatic conditions. [589, 590] There is also the potential that media coverage of melting glaciers might motivate more people to visit these parks over the next 20–30 years to personally see or show children the glaciers before they disappear and in order to witness the impacts of climate change on the landscape. This market trend is already being observed in some areas of Alaska, including Kenai Fjords National Park, where the chief range has described climate change as one of the new major themes for the park. [591] If such an increase in visitation is realized, it would require adaptation to accommodate larger numbers of visitors and provide new public education about the changes in natural heritage that are occurring.

In the studies that attempted to look at the potential impacts of greater environmental change, an important threshold was reached for many visitors to Glacier-Waterton International Peace Park and Banff National Park in scenarios that might occur by the end of the 21st century. A substantial number of tourists (19% in Glacier-Waterton and 31% in Banff) indicated they would not intend to visit the parks if the specified environmental changes occurred. The projected loss of glaciers in the region was noted as a significant heritage loss and the most important reason cited for not intending to visit the park in the future. Another 36–38% of tourists indicated they would plan to visit less often. Visitors most likely to be negatively affected by climate-induced environmental change were long-haul tourists and ecotourists, motivated by the opportunity to view pristine mountain landscapes and wildlife. As such, the impact of environmental change was more pronounced in Banff National Park, which has a much greater number of international tourists. If realized, such impacts would require these destinations to adapt to very different impacts of climate change.

Of course the findings from the aforementioned North American studies cannot be generalized to other mountain regions, and similar research on visitor responses to environmental change needs to be conducted in mountain regions around the world, particularly in developing nations where tourism is a vital component of local or regional economies.

It seems, overall, that despite concerns that climate-induced environmental change may adversely impact the aesthetics and hazards in mountain tourism destinations, [592, 593, 594] the temporal scale of these changes are such that, with the exception of a few high profile tourism attractions (e.g., well known glaciers or snow capped peaks like Mt. Kilimanjaro) or some key tourist market segments (e.g., expert mountaineers), the eventual impact on visitation to mountain parks and mountain destinations more broadly may actually be minor as the frame of reference of mountain landscapes evolves in future generations of tourists. The perception of some contemporary visitors that the landscape would be degraded from a former state if the specified environmental changes occurred, may not be shared by a visitor born in the 2040s who has no experience with the former condition. It therefore remains uncertain if the stated behavioural intentions of contemporary visitors would translate similarly to visitors a generation from now, who may have never experienced the attributes that current visitors used to define the quality of these mountain landscapes for their tourism experience. Arguably the 20th century offers some historical analogues for visitor perceptions of changing mountain landscapes. For example, ice caves in Glacier National Park, the US portion of Waterton-Glacier International Peace Park, were an important tourist attraction in the 1930s, but melted decades ago so that contemporary tourists have no experience with these ice caves or any perception that the park landscape is less attractive than that of a previous more pristine state. More generally, glaciers have been melting and vegetation responding to warmer temperatures throughout the European Alps and North American Rocky Mountains over the last half of the 20th century and these environmental changes have had no known impact on visitation levels to these regions. Contemporary visitors still value these mountain landscapes and the recreation opportunities they provide, even though they are different than in previous decades. [595] This interpretation is of course debateable, as others might argue that landscape values and preferences are relatively stable between contiguous generations.

Box 21 The importance of tourist perceptions of climate impacts

The perceptions of future impacts of climate change are likely to play the central role in the decision-making of tourists and tourism investors alike, as perceptions of climate conditions or environmental changes are just as important to consumer choices as the actual conditions. Perceptions of climate change impacts in a region are often heavily influenced by the nature of media coverage. For example, market surveys found that media coverage of the three hurricanes that hit parts of Florida in August and September 2004 had created an impression that the entire state was heavily damaged. Reservation cancellations went up sharply and one in four tourists were less likely to plan to visit Florida between July and September in the following years. [596] Tourists were unable to distinguish between areas that had been damaged and those that were unaffected by the hurricanes. The drought and resulting wildfires in the state of Colorado (USA) in 2002 provides a similar example of perceptions based on media coverage being as damaging for tourism as actual impacts of the climate event. Media coverage of major fires in some parts of the state and a misstatement by a senior government official who sail that "it felt like the whole state was on fire" had a significant impact on summer tourism, with visitor numbers 40% lower in some areas of state, even well away from fire affected areas. [597] In both Florida and Colorado, the state governments and tourism industry spent millions of dollars on marketing campaigns to inform consumers that the climate impacts were isolated. Similar effects have been observed as a result of wildfires in Portugal, Spain and France in recent years.

The impact of extreme events such as storms, drought and wildfires on tourist perceptions of a destination are likely to be short-lived and thus the recovery period relatively quick. Other climate change impacts are likely to be more enduring in the minds of consumers and may over time widely alter the perceived attractiveness of a destination. The expansion of geographical areas susceptible to the transmission of vector-borne diseases, such as malaria and dengue [598], to popular tourism destinations where these diseases are not now prevalent is one such example. How would travellers respond if required to take malaria medication to go to the Azores, South Africa, Cuba or Mexico in the future? Traveller response to media coverage of regional outbreaks and perceived changes in disease risk could have important implications for travel patterns and remains an important area for further research. Similarly, in the absence of credible information and recurrent exposure to messages that the Mediterranean is or will soon become too hot for comfortable holidays may eventually lead some consumers to accept this notion, especially if it is combined with education campaigns on the increased risk of skin cancer. While the effectiveness of public relations and marketing campaigns to avoid or correct consumer misperceptions about climate impacts is uncertain, this is likely to be an indispensable adaptation strategy for the tourism industry and governments alike.

10.3 Demand Implications of Mitigation Policies and Tourism Mobility

National or international mitigation policies – that are policies that seek to reduce greenhouse gas emissions – have an impact on tourist behaviour in two ways. First, policies, especially market-based instruments, will lead to an increase in the costs of travel. Second, policies can foster environmental attitudes that lead tourists to change their travel patterns.

Tourism transport providers and especially the airline industry seek to improve their fuel efficiency to reduce their costs and offer more competitive prices. At the same time climate change initiatives such as carbon trading are likely to increase transport costs and this may well outweigh economic savings achieved through efficiency gains. [599] Recognition should also be given to the manner in which various transport sectors are approaching mitigation, either through their own initiative or via mandatory participation in incentive-based systems. Notwithstanding regional and unilateral efforts, such as the proposed inclusion of aviation in the EU ETS, which would require certain emission targets for all aircraft operating within and to the EU to be met, industry groups such as ICAO and IATA have called for more global measures that would act outside of incentive-based mitigation schemes. [600]

A number of studies have analysed the price sensitivity of air passengers, and the results vary considerably. [601] Overall, it appears that leisure travellers are more price sensitive than business traveller), and short-haul travellers are more sensitive to price increases than those on long-haul trips. The reason for this is that there are more choices and possibilities for substitution for shorter trips compared with long ones. [602] Also, tourists who can afford long-distance holidays are likely to be wealthier than average. Research also found that tourists are more likely to adjust their behaviour (i.e., travel less by air) in response to higher prices in the longer term rather than immediately. This means that an increase in airfares may not have an immediate effect (i.e., tourists cannot change their plans quickly), but over time tourists may learn to avoid the pricier option of air travel and become more savvy in alternative transport options (e.g., trains).

The perception of transport, and in particular air travel, in relation to its carbon footprint is possibly more important than tourists' responses to price changes. Recently, there has been substantial media coverage on this topic, for example:

- 'What is the Real Price of Cheap Air Travel?', *The Observer,* 29 January 2006

- 'It's a Sin to Fly, Says Church', *The Sunday Times,* 23 July 2006

- 'Flugreisen als Klima-Killer', *Abendblatt,* 6 July 2004

- 'Flight or Fright?', *The Listener*, 3–9 March 2007

- 'Climate Conscious May Ditch Air Travel', *New Zealand TV One*, 9 April, 2007

- '100% Pure not Enough for Green Future', *Stuff.co.nz*, 17 May 2007

- 'The Plane Truth', *Guardian Unlimited*, 20 July 2007

- 'Eco-friendly Flyers Buy Carbon Offsets', *The Calgary Herald*, 1 August 2007

The growing awareness of the potential environmental impacts of air travel is reflected in a number of opinion polls. [603, 604, 605, 606] A British survey found that the proportion of respondents that believed 'air travel harms the environment' increased from 62% in 2002 to 70% in 2006. [607] The same survey found that 64% agreed that that 'the price of a plane ticket should reflect the environmental damage that flying causes, even if this make air travel a bit more expensive.' However, support dropped to 47% when the inclusion of environmental damage 'makes air travel much more expensive' (33% disagreed). The British Social Attitudes Survey from 2003 to 2005 also found consistently low support (15–18%) for unlimited air travel if it harms the environment. Notably support for unrestricted air travel increased to 78% if 'damage to the environment was limited'. [608]

Public opinion polls have also identified varied 'willingness to pay' to offset the environmental consequences of air travel. The aforementioned British survey found 69% would be willing to pay some additional charge to reflect environmental costs, with 52% stating a willingness to pay an extra 20%. [609] In a recent survey of Canadian travellers, 76% reported that they would pay C$ 10 or more for every C$ 1,000 spent on airfares to offset carbon emissions when travelling by air, while 18% would be willing to pay C$ 40 or more. [610] Similarly, TripAdvisor, the world's largest travel community, recently surveyed more than 1,000 (largely eco-) travellers worldwide: 24% of respondents said that air travel should be avoided to help preserve the environment; 38% of travellers surveyed were willing to pay more to take an eco-friendly flight and 26% were willing to pay a premium of up to 10%. Only 3% of travellers surveyed, however, have actually purchased carbon credits. [611] These uncertainties about the 'willingness to pay' to offset greenhouse gas emissions from travel are important and reveal the need for further market research to understand the real potential for mitigation through off-setting and the impact of other forms of mitigation policies on future air travel.

The growing media and consumer awareness of the environmental impacts of air travel and in some cases a willingness to pay to offset or reduce impacts are a signal that customer behaviour may be about to change, and the tourism industry and tourism ministries need to begin to put in place measures to reflect this concern and take actions to help shaping the tourism market to reduce climate change impacts from which the sector suffers itself, and to lead by example.

One way of reducing the footprint of a destination is for tourists to travel less and stay longer when travelling, an option that has been featured by the tourism and travel media. For example Mark Ellingham, the founder of Rough Guides, and Tony Wheeler, who created Lonely Planet, encourage tourists to 'fly less and stay longer' and donate money to carbon-offsetting schemes. They urge their readers to: "[…] join to discourage 'casual flying'". This may mean that tourist destinations have to revisit their tourism forecasts, marketing strategies and targeted markets in the light of these new trends. It remains to be seen at this point in time if tourists' attitudes translate into actual changes in behaviour, for example reducing the number of flights or the widespread use of carbon offsetting schemes.

Long-haul destinations are particularly concerned about impacts on tourism demand. The Australian government and Australian Tourism Export Council, for example, have expressed concern that 'growing guilt over the impact of jet flights on global warming' could adversely impact the nation's tourism economy. [612] Similar concerns about the impact of 'anti-travel' sentiments in Europe and the costs of carbon taxes or other mitigation policies have been expressed in other Asian and Caribbean long-haul destinations as well. [613, 614] Tourism destinations are currently seeking to position themselves and address growing concerns over air travel. The New Zealand tourism minister said at the 2007 tourism trade show: "We must develop a sustainable tourism proposition so compelling all our visitors continue to feel good about travelling here." The Caribbean Hotel Association and Caribbean Tourism

Organization, while supporting initiatives to achieved reductions in GHG emissions that would reduce the negative impacts on the climate system, propose that "[…] every effort must be made to ensure that future consumer movements and government action in the EU to address climate change […] do not deter potential European travellers from taking vacations in the Caribbean", as this could jeopardize the sustainable livelihood of a large proportion of the region's population. [615]

Box 22   Cutting down GHG emissions means reshaping demand: a 'factor four' scenario for France [616]

The scenario shows that under a constraint of complying with a 75% reduction of GHG emissions nationwide by 2050, maintaining widespread access to holidays and to some extent to long-haul leisure travel are feasible. The scenario accepts a small increase in individual distance travelled per year (12% to 2050), added to the growth in the number of trips resulting from increased population. This choice reflects the positive values related to tourism (contacts between people, economic development, etc.), which are preserved in the scenario. Nonetheless, a reduction of the environmental impacts and a compliance with other dimensions of sustainable development (equity of access to holidays for the less wealthy) imply that such results can only be reached through a considerable redistribution of mobility between the types of trips, transport modes and categories of tourists. For example, overseas travel by air is globally maintained almost at the same volume as in 2000 in this scenario, whereas it would grow at a fast pace in a 'business-as-usual' scenario. Another difference is that long-haul trips are more fairly shared: one intercontinental trip a year for 10% of households in 2000 is replaced in 2050 by one intercontinental trip every seven years for 70% of households. The scenario accepts a fall of 20% in the mean distance of trips as long distance mobility diminishes. This is largely a consequence of the level at which intercontinental mobility is maintained, and related to the assumption that exoticism will remain more attractive than traditional European resorts. An increase in outings compensates for the fall in long distance mobility. Leisure near the home is another manner to compensate and this type of mobility doubles by 2050.

In summary, the two main factors in this scenario are a change in tourism/leisure behaviour and habits, and a change in the modal share. Compared to 2000, when train and bus had only 14% of the market shares (in pkm), these two transport modes represent 51% in 2050. Aviation is limited to 19% (pkm) under this scenario to achieve the necessary GHG emission reductions.

10.4 Demand Implications of Climate-induced Societal Change

The economic scenarios of the Stern Review [617] have not been systematically interpreted for the tourism sector, and interpretation of the socio-economic scenarios that are the basis of the IPCC SRES scenarios has also been limited. [618] Although, these are useful resources for tourism, considering the obvious affects of climate change impacts on the economy. When the long-range IPCC SRES scenarios for global population and GDP are considered (Table 10.3), the importance of interpreting the socio-economic scenarios associated with these alternative development pathways in any future long-range tourism forecast like *Tourism 2020 Vision* [619] is unmistakable. Stabilisation scenarios (see Chapter 8) offer another field of research which is largely unexplored. Setting emission goals for GHG such as reducing by a factor 3 or 4 emissions from tourism in developed countries by 2050 and examining the means to reach them (see Box 22), inevitably leads to drastic changes in demand and tourism patterns since progress in technology and management currently appear likely to be insufficient.

Tourism depends on economic prosperity and socio-political stability. Following the conclusions of the Stern Review on the Economics of Climate Change [620], in the long-term the negative impact of climate change on global economic growth would reduce the discretionary wealth available to consumers for tourism. Tourists are averse to political instability and social unrest [621, 622] and the negative tourism demand repercussions for the climate change security hotspots of Sub-Saharan Africa, Southern Africa, Caribbean, Southeast Asia, and Bangladesh-India-Pakistan are very evident. [623]

Table 10.3 Socio-economic characteristics of IPCC SRES scenarios (2000) *

	1990 Baseline	2100			
		A1fi	A2	B1	B2
Global population (in billions)	5.3	7.1	15.1	7.0	10.4
Global GDP (in trillions US$)	23.0	525.0	243.0	328.0	235.0
Income ratio between developed and developing nations	16.1	1.5	4.2	1.8	3.0

* A description of these socio-economic futures is provided in Box 2 in Chapter 8 and additional details, including regional breakdowns of each indicator, can be obtained in the SRES report from the IPCC.

Source: IPCC (2000)

10.5 Conclusion

With their capacity to adapt to the effects of climate change by substituting the place, timing and type of holidays in their travel decision, tourists will play a pivotal role in the eventual impacts of climate change on the tourism industry and destinations. The evidence available suggests that the geographic and seasonal redistribution of tourism demand resulting from changes in climate may be very large for individual destinations and countries by late-century. The direct affect of climate change might be significant enough to alter major intra-regional tourism flows where climate is of paramount importance, including Northern Europe to the Mediterranean, North America to the Caribbean, and to a lesser extent Northeast Asia to Southeast Asia. However, the net effect of a change in climate on tourism demand at the global scale may be limited, as there is no evidence to suggest that a change in climate will directly lead to a significant reduction of the global volume of tourism. Similarly, the indirect impacts of global climate change, including environmental change and social change, are anticipated to have an important impact on tourism demand for specific destinations, but not affect it at the regional or global level, unless, as some economic analyses indicate [624], global economic growth were to be adversely affected by climatic change.

Information on tourist climate preferences and key thresholds (i.e., 'what is too hot for a beach holiday') and tourist perceptions of the environmental impacts of global climate change at destinations (i.e., perceptions of coral bleaching, diminished or lost glaciers, degraded coastlines, reduced biodiversity or wildlife prevalence) remain important knowledge gaps that need to be addressed if potential long-range shifts in tourism demand are to be more accurately projected. There is also limited understanding of how climate change impacts will interact with other longer term social and market trends influencing tourism demand, including: aging populations in industrialized countries, increasing travel safety and health concerns, increased environmental and cultural awareness, advances in information and transportation technology, as well as shifts toward shorter and more frequent holidays.

Chapter 11

Emissions from Tourism: Status and Trends

This Chapter is the first attempt to estimate CO_2 emissions from both international and domestic tourism and thus the contribution of tourism to human-induced climate change. The Chapter provides an overview of CO_2 emissions and radiative forcing for 2005 and a 'business-as-usual' scenario for 2035, using an approach specifying different tourism activities (transport, accommodation, and other activities *). The goal is to provide a first baseline for the discussion on tourism's contribution to climate change, as well as the identification of strategies to reduce emissions from this sector (see Chapter 12).

The reported amount of CO_2 emissions attributed to tourism varies considerably, depending on, among others, the definition of what constitutes 'tourism'. The share of radiative forcing caused by tourism activities varies even more depending on the greenhouse gases included apart from CO_2 emissions. According to UNWTO's definition, 'tourism' refers to "[…] the activities of persons travelling to and staying in places outside their usual environment for not more than one consecutive year for leisure, business and other purposes not related to the exercise of an activity remunerated from within the place visited", thus including international and domestic tourism, overnight and same-day trips, for all purposes of visit (leisure, business, and other). For the purpose of tourism statistics and in conformity with the Basic References on Tourism Statistics [625], visitors (international and domestic ones) are classified as a) tourists (overnight visitors) and b) same-day visitors.

Existing data on tourism demand (international and domestic) present several constraints for emission inventories. For that reason, UNWTO prepared for the purpose of this report a specific set of tables with approximations of consistent worldwide tourism volumes for the baseline year of 2005 based on the various indicators in its own database and on air transport data from ICAO and IATA. These tables contain a mix of hard data, estimations – missing data are extrapolated or derived from similar countries – and approximations – where only little data are available (see Annex 1).

Global warming is often expressed as a change in average surface temperatures, resulting from changes in the planetary radiative balance, and determined by the concentration of greenhouse gases in the atmosphere (Chapter 8). In this Chapter, the contribution of tourism to global warming is assessed using two metrics: CO_2 emissions and radiative forcing (RF). While CO_2 is the most important greenhouse gas from human activities, other greenhouse gases also make significant contributions to global warming. This is particularly relevant for the impacts of aviation, which, at cruise altitude, has an additional impact on global warming (see Box 23). For most non-carbon greenhouse gases it is possible to calculate a carbon dioxide equivalent, i.e., a factor that allows for comparison of the warming caused by CO_2 and non-CO_2 greenhouse gases. This is not possible for aviation, as most additional emissions are not well-mixed in the global atmosphere nor long-lived. [626, 627] For this reason, radiative forcing is used for the purposes of this report as the second metric to calculate aviation's contribution to global warming. Radiative forcing measures the extent to which emissions of greenhouse gases raise global average temperatures (see Box 23). CO_2 emissions and RF are estimated for the year 2005 (see Section 11.1). Based on projections of tourism growth, the results are then used to build a 'business-as-usual' emission scenario for the year 2035 (see Section 11.3). Supporting methodological information can be found in detail in Annexes 1 and 2.

---

* From the perspective of the tourist and many tourism researchers, tourism is divided into transport, accommodation and activities. From a business perspective all tourism related activities are determined as 'activities', thus including transport and accommodations. Therefore we designated all those activities that do not comprise the return transport to the destination nor accommodation 'other activities', including local transport, all local leisure activities, business activities (meetings, conferences), visits to restaurants, bars, cafes, excursions in the destination region, etc.

> **Box 23 Understanding the contribution of aviation to climate change**
>
> Carbon dioxide is the most important greenhouse gas (GHG), accounting for 77% of global anthropogenic warming [628], but is not the only GHG contributing to anthropogenic climate change. [629] The warming caused by GHG emissions other than CO_2 is usually expressed in CO_2 equivalents to allow for comparison of the contribution of various GHG emissions, measured over a period of 100 years. This implies that CO_2-equivalents can only be calculated for GHG with a lifetime of more than ten years. [630] Consequently, the comparison of emissions from aviation – including nitrogen oxides forming ozone and methane as well as water vapour forming contrails (the white condensation bands often visible behind aircraft) and cirrus clouds – is difficult, as these emissions are short-lived and not well mixed in the atmosphere. An alternative parameter to assess the contribution of aviation to climate change is the radiative forcing index (RFI) [631], which is the ratio of all radiative forcing caused by aviation since 1945 and the radiative forcing caused by CO_2 emissions from aviation over the same period. The RFI can however only be applied to calculate accumulated radiative forcing, and not for emissions occurring in any single year. In 2000, the radiative forcing caused by non-carbon emissions from aviation was estimated to be almost equal to the accumulated warming effect of all aviation-related CO_2 emissions since 1945, i.e., corresponding to an RFI of 1.9. [632] However, there is considerable uncertainty regarding the impact of contrail-induced cirrus clouds, and 1.9 may be seen as the confirmed minimum, with a possible RFI of up to 5.1. Note that the RFI is not a constant, as it develops over time as a function of the growth rate of aviation-related CO_2 emissions in comparison to the overall RF – i.e., the development of emissions in other sectors. The future RF is thus dependent upon the development of aviation as well as development in other sectors. A RFI can thus not be used as an 'uplift' factor for CO_2 emissions.

11.1 Current CO_2 Emissions and Radiative Forcing from Tourism

11.1.1 Introduction: Global Tourism Demand

The tourism industry uses energy in several activities – for transport to and from, as well as within the destination, in accommodation establishments and in a range of other tourism activities, the latter including for the purpose of this report local transport within the destination. Most energy use in tourism, as in many other economic sectors, is based on fossil fuels, with only a fraction of energy being generated through renewable energy sources. Calculations of the contribution of tourism to climate change have so far focused mainly on international tourism due to limited availability of comprehensive data on domestic and same-day tourism demand. For the purpose of this publication, UNWTO prepared an approximation of domestic tourism based on the limited data available in order to include this in the calculation of emissions.

Tourism demand (overnight and same-day; international and domestic) is estimated to have accounted for about 9.8 billion arrivals in 2005. Of these, 5 billion arrivals are estimated to be from same-day visitors (4 billion domestic and 1 billion international) and 4.8 billion from arrivals of visitors staying overnight (tourists) (4 billion domestic and 800 million international). Taking into account that an international trip can generate arrivals in more than one destination country, the number of trips is somewhat lower than the number of arrivals. For 2005 the global number of international tourist trips (i.e., trips by overnight visitors) is estimated at 750 million. This corresponds to 16% of the total number of tourist trips, while domestic trips represent the large majority (84% or 4 billion).

Table 11.1 presents an overview of the worldwide approximate numbers of arrivals and trips (both same-day and overnight) for international and domestic tourism broken down by transport mode. Data in the table show that the share of trips using air transport is relatively small (17% of tourist trips, 1%

of same-day trips) as compared to the total volume of trips, exception made for interregional travel – i.e., between Europe, the Americas, Asia and the Pacific, Africa and the Middle East – where air travel accounts for 92% of all tourist trips. Nonetheless, it is important to note that globally, these long-haul interregional trips account for no more than 3% of all tourist trips (130 million vs. 4.75 billion trips).

Table 11.1 Approximate tourism volumes, 2005 [a]

(billions)	Total	of which:		of which:	
		Domestic	International	Intraregional	Interregional
Total trips	9.75	8.00	1.75		
Same-day	5.0	4.00	1.00	1.00	0.00
over land/water	5.0	4.00	0.99	0.99	
by air	0.05	0.04	0.01	0.01	
by air (%)	1	1	1	1	
Tourist					
Arrivals	4.80	4.00	0.80	0.65	0.15
Trips [b]	4.75	4.00	0.75	0.61	0.13
over land/water	3.93	3.52	0.41	0.40	0.01
by air	0.82	0.48	0.34	0.22	0.12
by air (%)	17	12	46	35	92

(a) Green: estimated volumes based on UNWTO country data or other sources; yellow: approximate volumes (as only little data are available);

(b) Trip volumes are derived from available arrivals data as one trip can produce more than one arrival (see Annex 1).

Source: UNWTO 2007c (see Annex 1)

11.1.2 Transport Emissions

It is a complex task to determine CO_2 emissions from tourism transport worldwide. For air transport at least figures on overall traffic are available, such as the estimated number of trips (860 million) and the number of passenger kilometers (4 trillion). However, assumptions have to be made in order to reasonably subdivide this into the various categories of trips (same-day and overnight, domestic, intraregional, interregional) and regions. Surface transport is quite more complicated as only very scarce data are available on distances travelled for tourism purposes.

Several attempts have been made to analyse tourism transport and its contribution to emissions in individual nations or regions. [633, 634, 635, 636] These studies indicate, for instance, that for all citizens of the then EU25 plus Norway and Switzerland, emissions of CO_2 for domestic and international tourism (by car, train, coach and air) amount to 250 million t CO_2. [637] It also indicates that 55% of tourism transport emissions by Europeans are caused by the 20% of trips based on air transport (see Box 24). Transport volumes are forecasted to grow by 122% between 2000 and 2020, while the number of trips is forecasted to increase by 57%, thus mirroring a considerable increase in average trip length. Consequently, CO_2-emissions from tourism transport in Europe are expected to increase by 85% between 2000 and 2020. Detailed data are also available for tourism by the French (*Suivi de la Demande Touristique**, a regular survey of 20.000 citizens). Analyses of the data show that passengers arriving by air account for only 11% of all tourist nights, but represent 46% of all tourist transport emissions.

---

*   See http://www.tns-sofres.com/sofres/secteurs/sesame/souscription-suivi-demande-touristique.php for general information and http://www.tourisme.gouv.fr/fr/z2/stat/memento/memento_2007.jsp for detailed data (chapter 5 for France).

A common challenge faced by previous analyses of CO_2 emissions has been data limitations. An ideal data set would include information on the origin and destination of tourists, the routing, transport mode and operational factors, such as occupancy rates (load factors), as well as information on engine types. No such systematic information exists for worldwide tourism, and the following analysis is thus based on multiple data sets, including the set of tables and approximations of consistent worldwide tourism volumes developed by UNWTO for this report (see Annex 1).

One procedure for measuring CO_2 emissions is to multiply average emissions per passenger kilometre (pkm) with travel distances. CO_2 emissions per pkm vary substantially among different transport modes. Table 11.2 provides emission factors for transport in the EU, showing that:

- coach and rail have the lowest factor, 0.022 kg CO_2/pkm and 0.027 kg CO_2/pkm, respectively; the difference between coach and rail is mainly caused by occupancy rates (see Table 11.2); in terms of per seat kilometre emissions, rail is much lower (0.016 kg/skm) than coach (0.020 kg/skm);

- in the mid-range, are emissions from cars (0.133 kg CO_2/pkm) and from flights of 1,000 or more km (0.130 kg CO_2/pkm);

- flights of less than 500 km have the highest emission factors (0.206 kg CO_2/pkm), as take offs and climb-outs consume disproportionately high amounts of fuel.

The following Sections provide a discussion of global tourism emissions from air and ground transport, as well as estimates of the total transport emissions from international and domestic tourism.

Table 11.2 Emission factors for tourism transport modes in the EU context

Mode	CO_2 factor (kg/pkm)	Occupancy rate/load factor (%)
Air < 500 km	0.206	–
500-1,000 km	0.154	–
1,000-1,500 km	0.130	–
1,500-2,000 km	0.121	–
> 2,000 km	0.111	–
Air world average [a]	0.129	75
Rail	0.027	60
Car	0.133	50
Coach	0.022	90

(a) This value is calculated in Section 11.1.2.1.

Source: Peeters, P. et al. (2007b)

Box 24 CO_2 emissions from European Union tourism transport

While there is no comprehensive analysis of global emissions from tourism transport, a detailed EU study [639, 640] has provided some insight into the importance of emissions from different tourism transport modes and market segments. Several tourism data sets were combined to develop a comprehensive origin-destination table for five transport modes and including international (i.e., intercontinental) and domestic tourism from and within the then 25 member states of the EU plus Switzerland and Norway. Based on the number of trips and the average trip distances between origin/destination for the various transport modes, total distances travelled as well as emissions of CO_2 and other pollutants were calculated. In 2000, most trips were made by car, while air travel represented the major share of passenger kilometres travelled as well as the largest source of CO_2 emissions (Figure 11.1). As a consequence, air transport, though accounting for 20% of all trips, causes 55% of all CO_2 emissions and an even higher share of radiative forcing. The projected increase in the share of trips and passenger kilometres means that the proportion of CO_2 emissions from air transport is expected to increase to approximately 72% in 2020, while the share of trips by air will rise to 29%. With the increased RF of aviation emissions at high altitude taken into account, the relative contribution of air travel to global warming in this analysis would actually be much higher.

Figure 11.1 Trips, mobility and CO_2 emissions of all tourism trips by EU25 citizens (including domestic, intra-EU25 plus Switzerland and Norway, and intercontinental) in 2000 and a forecast for 2020 (%)

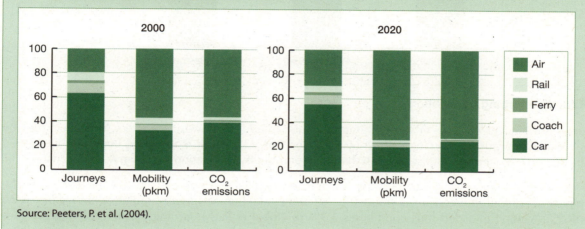

Source: Peeters, P. et al. (2004).

11.1.2.1 Aviation

The tourism share of aviation-related CO_2 emissions can be estimated from the well documented contribution of commercial aviation, which includes all passenger traffic and freight transport. Emissions from all commercial aviation are estimated to be in the order of 640 Mt CO_2 in 2005 [641], with a share of tourism-related emissions of 80.5% (see Annex 2.2.2). Consequently, the tourism-related share of aviation emissions is 515 Mt CO_2. Given global distances of about 3,980 billion pkm travelled by air (i.e., the total distances covered by air transport as shown in Table 11.3), a global emission factor for passenger transport can be derived, which is 0.129 kg CO_2 per pkm.

Figure 11.2 shows the estimated distribution of air transport regarding the number of trips, transport volume (in billion pkm) and CO_2 emissions. The most important finding is eventually that though international tourist trips by air (intra- and interregional) stand for about 45% of all international tourist trips (see Table 11.1), they represent 87% (321 Mt CO_2) of emissions of international tourist trips (371 Mt CO_2 – see Table 11.3).

Figure 11.2 Tourist air transport: trips, passengers and CO₂ emissions, 2005

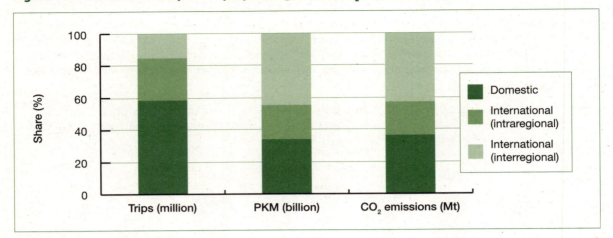

Radiative forcing by aviation

Emissions caused by aviation at flight altitude cause an additional warming effect. This effect may be 2–5 times the radiative forcing caused by CO_2 (see Box 23), and it is therefore important to make a distinction between CO_2 emissions and the total contribution of aviation to radiative forcing (RF).

The radiative forcing caused by aviation is estimated to have contributed 0.053 W/m² (excluding the impact of contrail-induced cirrus clouds) [642, 643] to the total human-induced radiative forcing of 1.6 W/m². [644] Aviation transport thus contributes 3.3% to global radiative forcing, not considering contrail-induced cirrus clouds (note that the IPCC assumes a range of 2–8% as aviation's contribution to global RF; see also Box 23). The share of tourism travel in global aviation is estimated to be of 73% (for calculations see Annex 2.2.2), and the corresponding RF for tourism related air transport would thus be 0.039 W/m² or 2.5% (excluding cirrus) and up to 6.1% if the maximum estimate for cirrus-related radiative forcing is considered.

11.1.2.2 Road and rail

The most important land-based tourism transport mode in industrialized countries is the car. [645, 646] Other transport modes, such as rail and coach, as well as water transport are less important in terms of global passenger volumes, and even less so with respect to CO_2 emissions, due to their relatively high energy efficiency.

The CO_2 emissions from rail, coach and water-borne transport are more difficult to calculate because data on the number and length of trips are more scattered and only available for a limited number of countries. In this analysis, global emissions from international and domestic tourism are calculated for each surface-based mode of transport by multiplying an estimated average distance travelled per trip by the total number of trips and the emission factor per pkm (emission factors can be found in Table 11.2; see Annex 2.2.1 for further details). To facilitate calculations, an average emission factor for coach and rail (0.025 kg/pkm) was used. Further assumptions were made regarding average trip distances and the modal split between car and other transport modes (including coach and rail; see Annex 2.2.1). The results show that all tourism transport other than aviation, are estimated to have caused emissions of **465 Mt CO₂,** the bulk of this, 420 Mt CO₂ is estimated to be attributable to travel by car– Table 11.3).

Of all emissions by surface traffic, 122 Mt CO₂ corresponds to the 5 billion same-day trips (of which 4 billion are estimated to be domestic and 1 billion international, see Table 11.1). The 3.5 billion domestic tourist trips (surface transport) account for 293 Mt CO₂ and the 410 million international tourist trips (surface transport) to 49.5 Mt.

11.1.2.3 Overview of all transport emissions

Table 11.3 summarizes the CO_2 emissions from international and domestic tourism transport. Total CO_2 emissions from tourism transport are estimated to be in the order of **980 Mt CO$_2$,** 52% of these is estimated to be caused by air travel (515 Mt CO_2), 43% by car (420 Mt CO_2), and 5% by other means of transport – coach, rail and water borne – (45 Mt CO_2). Simultaneously, from the 982 Mt CO_2 emissions, 86% originate from tourist trips (i.e., from overnights visitors) and the remaining 14% from same-day tourists. Within emissions generated by tourists (850 Mt CO_2), 56% comes from domestic tourist trips and the other 44% from international tourist trips. Nonetheless, it is important to stress that emissions per trip vary substantially. While 4 billion domestic tourist trips generate 479 Mt CO_2 emissions (120 kg per trip), 750 million international tourist trips are responsible for almost the same level of emissions (371 Mt CO_2 or 494 kg per trip).

Table 11.3 Overview of estimated number of trips, distances and CO$_2$ emissions from tourism related transport, 2005

	Total	Same-day visitors (domestic and international)	Tourist trips (overnight)		
			Domestic	International		
				Total	Intraregional	Interregional
All tourism						
Total number of trips (million)	**9,750**	5,000	4,000	750	615	135
Passenger kilometres (billion)	**9,147**	1,237	4,832	3,077	1,313	1,763
Average return distance (km)	**938**	247	1,208	4,102	2,135	13,063
Total CO$_2$ emissions (Mt)	**982**	133	478	371	153	218
CO$_2$ kg per km	**0.107**	0.107	0.099	0.121	0.116	0.124
CO$_2$ emissions (kg/trip)	**101**	27	120	494	248	1616
Air						
Total number of trips (million)	**870**	50	480	340	215	125
Passenger kilometres (billion)	**3,984**	60	1,340	2,585	833	1751
Average return distance (km)	**4,580**	1,200	2,791	7,602	3,875	14,012
Total CO$_2$ emissions (Mt)	**515**	11	185	321	104	217
CO$_2$ kg per km	0.129	0.177	0.138	0.124	0.125	0.124
CO$_2$ emissions (kg/trip)	**592**	212	385	945	484	1737
Surface						
Total number of trips (million)	**8,880**	4,950	3,520	410	400	10
Passenger kilometres (billion)	**5,162**	1,177	3,493	492	480	12
Average return distance (km)	**581**	238	992	1,200	1,200	1,200
Total CO$_2$ emissions (Mt)	**465**	122	294	49	49	1
CO$_2$ kg per km	**0.090**	0.104	0.084	0.101	0.101	0.079
CO$_2$ emissions (kg/trip)	**52**	25	83	121	121	95

| | Total | Same-day visitors (domestic and international) | Tourist trips (overnight) | | | |
| | | | Domestic | International | | |
				Total	Intraregional	Interregional
of which:						
Car						
Total number of trips (million)	**5,956**	3,641	2,028	287	282	5
Passenger kilometres (billion)	**3,354**	892	2,117	344	338	6
Average return distance (km)	**563**	245	1,044	1,200	1,200	1,200
Total CO_2 emissions (Mt)	**420**	115	259	46	45,0	0.8
CO_2 kg per km	**0.125**	0.129	0.122	0.133	0.133	0.133
CO_2 emissions (kg/trip)	**71**	32	128	160	160	160
Other (train, coach, ship, etc.)						
Total number of trips (million)	**2,924**	1,309	1,492	123	118	5
Passenger kilometres (billion)	**1,809**	285	1,376	148	142	6
Average return distance (km)	**619**	218	922	1,200	1,200	1,200
Total CO_2 emissions (Mt)	**45**	7	34	4	4	0.2
CO_2 kg per km	**0.025**	0.025	0.025	0.025	0.025	0.025
CO_2 emissions (kg/trip)	**15**	5	23	30	30	30

Sources: Approximations by UNWTO based on UNWTO, ICAO and IATA (see Annex 1), and estimated emissions, surface transport modal split and average distances by the expert team (see Annex 2).

As seen, the modal split of trips and emissions varies substantially between international and domestic tourism, as well as regarding transport modes. Figure 11.3 illustrates the dominance of domestic trips in all transport modes. Figure 11.5 shows the split of CO_2 emissions between domestic and international travel by transport mode. In international tourist trips, air travel causes 87% of CO_2 emissions (321 Mt CO_2), while in domestic tourism the car is the most important contributor to emissions, accounting for 54% (259 Mt CO_2). With regard to radiative forcing (Figure 11.6), air travel is the major contributor both domestically and internationally. It causes approximately 67% of the overall contribution of tourist transports to climate change. Note that 'other transport' is used in an estimated 1.6 billion tourist trips (overnight), i.e., more than one third of all trips, but causing just 3% of the radiative forcing.

Figure 11.3 World tourism transport volume by mode of transport, 2005

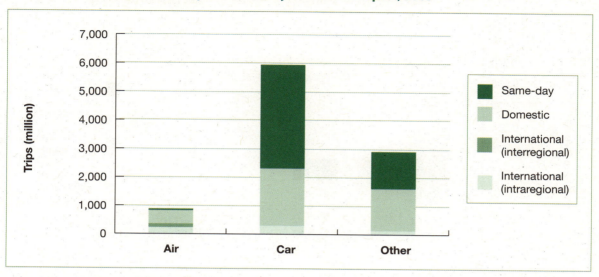

Figure 11.4 World tourism passenger kilometer volume by mode of transport, 2005

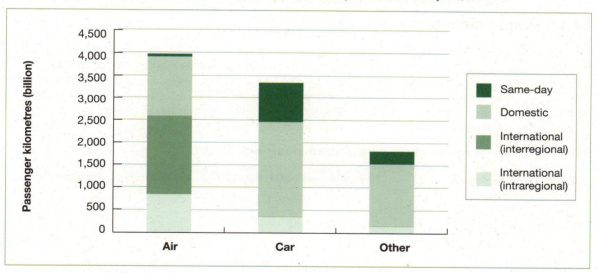

Figure 11.5 CO_2 emissions by tourism transport, 2005

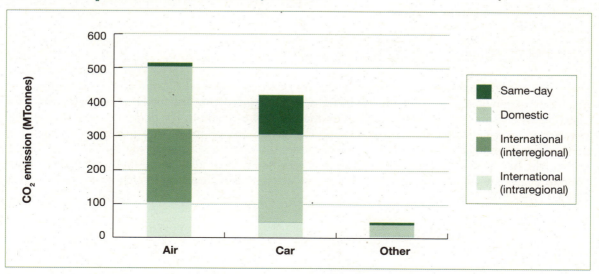

Figure 11.6 Radiative forcing by tourism transport (excluding impacts of cirrus), 2005

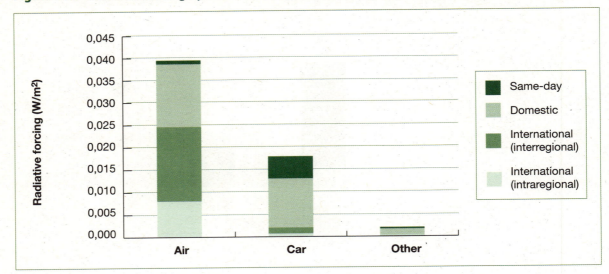

11.1.3 Accommodation

Internationally, more than 80 different accommodation categories can be identified, including hotels, hostels, motels, pensions, bed and breakfast, self-catering accommodation, bungalows, vacation homes, holiday villages, campsites and farms, to give just some examples. Energy use in the different types of accommodation includes heating/cooling, cooking, illumination, cleaning, and, in tropical or arid regions, the desalination of seawater. Average energy use has been found to vary substantially by type of accommodation (Table 11.4).

Table 11.4 Average energy use by type of accommodation[647]

Type of accommodation	Energy use per guest night (MJ)	Emissions per guest night (kg CO_2)
Hotels	130	20.6
Campsites	50	7.9
Pensions	25	4.0
Self-catering	120	19.0
Holiday villages	90	14.3
Vacation homes	100	15.9
Estimated average	**98**	**15.6**

The calculation of emissions from accommodation can be achieved by multiplying the number of tourists by length of stay and an emission factor (CO_2 per guest night). The total number of international guest nights is estimated by UNWTO to be in the order of 6.1 billion. For domestic tourism, the total number of guest nights is estimated at 13.7 billion. While an average of 19 kg CO_2 per international guest nights is estimated, the emissions for domestic tourism are assumed to be at 11.5 kg CO_2 per guest night, because of lower emission levels in accommodation used by domestic tourist in developing countries (see Annex 2.2.3). Total CO_2 emissions associated with accommodation are estimated at **274 Mt** (see Table 11.5).

Table 11.5 Overview of estimated number of trips, guest nights and CO$_2$ emissions from tourism accommodation, 2005

		Total	Domestic	International
Tourist trips (overnight)	bn			
total		4,7	4,0	0.75
in hotel and similar (H & S)		1,7	1,3	0.37
other CE & private		3,0	2,7	0.37
tourists in H & S (%)		36	33	50
Guest-nights	bn			
total		19,8	13,7	6,1
in hotel		5,9	3,8	2,2
other CE & private		13,9	9,9	4,0
Room-nights in H & S	bn			
total		3,9	2,5	1,4
avrg person per room		1,5	1,5	1,5
Average nights	nights			
total		4,2	3,4	8,2
in hotel		3,5	2,8	5,8
other CE & private		4,6	3,7	10.6
CO$_2$ emissions				
total CO$_2$ emissions (Mt)		274	158	117
average CO$_2$ per night (kg)		13,8	11,5	19,0
average CO$_2$ emissions (t/trip)		0,058	0,039	0,156

a) H & S: hotel and similar establishments

b) CE: collective establishments, except for hotel and similar, this includes campsites, rented apartments, bungalows, etc.

c) Green: data estimated from UNWTO country data or from external sources; yellow: approximated data

d) Half of domestic guest nights is assumed to be from developing source markets and half from high income source markets, which are assumed to have produced 4 kg of CO$_2$ and 19 kg of CO$_2$ per guest night respectively. The term 'high income' is used for the group of countries designated by the World Bank as 'high income economies' (see http://go.worldbank.org/K2CKM78CC0).

11.1.4 Other Tourism Activities

Tourists visit attractions and participate in a wide range of activities at the destination. Emissions caused by these activities vary widely between various categories of attractions, such as museums or theme parks, outdoor-oriented activities and events (e.g., sport events or concerts) or shopping. Data on energy use and emissions caused by these tourist activities are rarely available, except for some larger attractions like theme parks or ski areas. One exception is a study of the energy use and emissions related to tourist activities in New Zealand. [648]

With no systematic international data on tourism activities being available, an average energy use of 250 MJ of energy for 'other activities' during an average international trip was estimated at about 40 kg of CO$_2$ emissions.[649] This calculation includes local transport. While 250 MJ may be a suitable estimate for international leisure tourists, shorter and less activity-oriented business trips are likely to be less energy-intense, and are here assumed to be one fifth of this value (50 MJ per trip). For visit friends and relatives (VFR) tourism, a value of 100 MJ per trip is assumed, as less energy-intense, family-related activities will be the focus of this segment. The breakdown of travel purposes for international tourism was based on UNWTO, [650] with 50% arrivals estimated in 2004 for leisure purposes, 26% for VFR, health, religion and other and 16% for business. The weighted average energy consumption for tourist activities is thus estimated to be 170 MJ per trip, corresponding to emissions of 27 kg of CO_2 per trip. These numbers are valid for international tourists. For domestic tourists in high income economies the international per day emissions have been multiplied with the average length of stay to calculate the per trip emissions for activities. This means 11 kg per domestic trip in high income economies. For domestic tourists in developing countries we again assume the amount of energy associated with tourist activities to be one quarter of the amount consumed by tourists from high income economies and thus used 2.7 kg per trip. Extrapolated to all 4.75 billion tourist trips in 2005, emissions from tourist 'activities' are estimated to be in the order of **48 Mt CO_2.**

11.1.5 Total CO_2 Emissions and RF from Global Tourism in 2005

Table 11.6 shows the estimated contribution of tourism to global warming (including transport, accommodation and other tourism activities) in terms of CO_2 emissions as well as of radiative forcing (RF). The contribution of aviation to RF was derived from existing research. [651] For other means of transport, for accommodation, and other tourism activities, the RF was calculated proportionally to these sectors' contribution to emissions of CO_2. To do so, the authors have assumed that the growth rate of emissions from aviation has been equal to that of all other tourism sectors since 1945, as the calculation of RF is based on accumulated emissions of CO_2.

Table 11.6 Estimated emissions [(a)] **from global tourism (including same-day visitors), 2005** [(b)]

	CO_2		Contribution to RF (W/m2) [(c)]	
	Mt	Share in tourism (%)	Excluding cirrus	Including maximum cirrus impact
Air transport	515	40	0.0395	0.0979
Car	420	32	0.0176	0.01973
Other transport	45	3	0.0021	0.0021
Accommodation	274	21	0.0116	0.0116
Other activities	48	4	0.0020	0.0020
Total tourism	**1,302**	**100**	**0.0734**	**0.1318**
Total world [(d)]	**26,400**	–	**1.6**	**1.7** [(e)]
Share of tourism in total world (%)	4.9	–	4.6	7.8

(a) Estimates include international and domestic tourist trips, as well as same-day visitors (base year 2005).

(b) Colours represent the degree of certainty with respect to the data and underlying assumptions. Green represents a degree of uncertainty of +/–10%, blue +/–25% and red +100%/–50%.

(c) The share of tourism in total radiative forcing is lower than in CO_2 emissions alone because the global CO_2 emissions account just for the year 2005, while radiative forcing gives the impact of all CO_2 emissions accumulated in the atmosphere since the industrial revolution. The contribution for aviation and tourism started to become significant only after 1945, and thus accumulated over a much shorter timespan.

(d) Annual fossil carbon dioxide emissions (including those from cement production), according to IPCC (2007a), *The Physical Science Basis.* [652]

(e) This value is higher to account for the impact of cirrus.

As shown in Table 11.6, estimates for CO_2 and RF excluding cirrus are rather good, with an error margin of up to 25%. Taking into account the respective calculation's uncertainty, this means that tourism's contribution to global CO_2 emissions is estimated to range between 3.9% and 6.0%, while the contribution for RF ranges from 3.7% to 5.4%. Including the maximum contribution of cirrus would result in a share of between 4.4% and 9.0% (see Figure 11.7).

Figure 11.7 Estimated contribution and uncertainty ranges of tourism (including same-day tourism) to global CO$_2$ emissions and radiative forcing, 2005

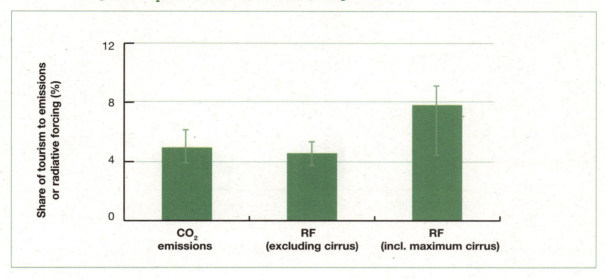

Figure 11.8 shows that tourism transport to and from the destinations accounts for 75% of all emissions of CO$_2$ emissions from tourism, while accommodation stands for 21% and other tourism activities for 4%. For radiative forcing, the transport share increases to 81% (excluding cirrus) and up to 90% if a maximum cirrus impact is included.

Figure 11.8 Estimated share of tourism activities to tourism CO$_2$ emissions and radiative forcing (including same-day visitors), 2005

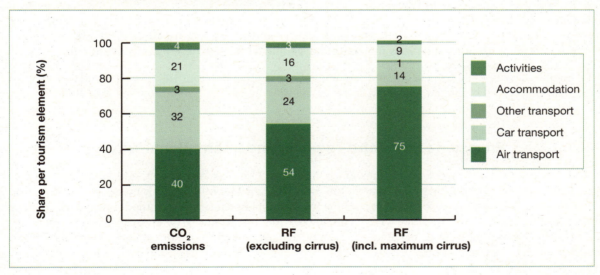

Figure 11.9 Estimated contribution of tourism activities to CO$_2$ emissions (including same-day visitors)

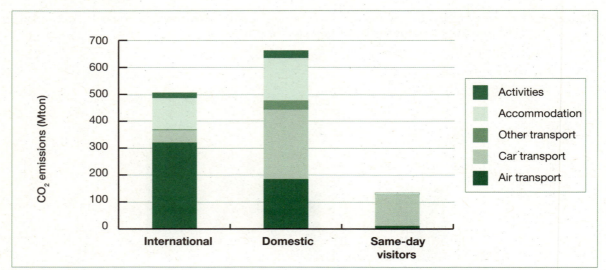

Figure 11.9 presents a breakdown of CO$_2$ emissions for all tourism activities and forms of tourism. Most emissions are caused by domestic tourism. However, due to the far higher number of domestic trips (4 billion vs. 750 million international), there is an important difference in per-trip emissions: these are estimated at 0.678 t CO$_2$ per trip for international trips, 0.258 t CO$_2$ per trip for domestic trips in the high-income markets, and 0.074 t CO$_2$ per trip for domestic trips in the developing countries (these figures include accommodation and activities and thus are larger than those given in Table 11.3).

As outlined, calculations in this report only consider energy throughput. As the construction of hotels, airports and aircraft, cars and roads all consume considerable amounts of energy, a lifecycle perspective accounting for all energy 'embedded' in tourism would be better suited to assess tourism's contribution to climate change. However, this would demand a detailed calculation of energy used for construction, and the energy embodied in the various goods, products and materials used in the various tourism activities. Another issue not considered here is indirect energy use, as tourism accounts, for instance, for considerable amounts of freight, such as transport of food and other goods for tourism. Small destinations, and in particular island destinations may import a significant part of these by ship or aircraft.

Taking into account all lifecycle and indirect energy needs related to tourism, it is expected that the sum of emissions would be higher, although there are no specific data for global tourism available.

11.1.6 CO$_2$ Emissions from Intra-regional and Interregional Travel

From table 11.6 it followed that air transport contributes a bit over half of CO$_2$ emissions attributed to tourism transport (not considering radiative forcing), i.e., 515 Mt of 981 Mt. Air transport's contribution is not so much higher because of a high per km emission, but because of the comparatively long average travel distances. In fact, from Table 11.2 it can be seen that the average CO$_2$ emissions per kilometre for air travel (0.129 kg/person km) is about equal to the average emission of a private car when used by two persons (0.133 kg/person km).

In order to understand better the contribution of the various travel modes and also to better identify the mitigation potential, it is useful to know more about origin and destination of trips. Table 11.7 shows an assessment based on data by UNWTO, ICAO and IATA of the number of international tourist trips within and between regions, and the related travel distances and emissions.

Air transport accounts for an estimated total of 870 million trips from a total of 9.8 billion trips (domestic and international, same-day and overnight). Of these trips by air, the bulk, 820 million (94%), are overnight trips and some 50 million are same-day trips. Given the travel time needed, travel distance for same-day trips is limited with an estimated average return distance of 1,200 km. Given the comparatively small number of same-day trips by air and the short distance, the overall contribution to CO_2 emissions is estimated to be fairly small (11 Mt).

Table 11.7 Approximation of trip volume and tourism transport emissions by region of origin and destination, 2005

| | Total | | By air | | | | | |
| | Trips (million) | CO₂ emissions (total Mt) | Trips (million) | km (billion) | km (avg return) | CO₂ emissions | | |
						Total Mt	kg/km	T/trip
Total	9,750	981	870	3,984	4,600	515	0.129	0.59
Same-day (dom. and int.)	5,000	133	50	60	1,200	11	0.177	0.21
tourists	4,750	848	820	3,924	4,800	506	0.129	0.62
within regions	4,615	630	695	2,173	3,100	289	0.133	0.42
domestic	4,000	478	480	1,340	2,800	185	0.138	0.39
Europe			66	122	1,900	17	0.138	0.26
Americas			272	888	3,300	123	0.138	0.45
Asia and the Pacific			127	303	2,400	42	0.138	0.33
Middle East			8	14	1,700	2.0	0.138	0.24
Africa			6	11	1,800	1.5	0.138	0.25
international within own region	615	153	215	833	3,900	104	0.125	0.48
Europe	366		126	313	2,500	39	0.125	0.31
Americas	96		37	178	4,900	22	0.125	0.61
Asia and the Pacific	117		41	318	7,800	40	0.125	0.97
Middle East	18		7	14	2,100	1.8	0.125	0.27
Africa	16		5	10	1,900	1.2	0.125	0.24
between regions	135	218	125	1,751	14,000	217	0.124	1.74
short-haul	30	11	20	77	3,900	10	0.125	0.32
long-haul, predominantly from-to	104	208	104	1,674	16,000	208	0.124	1.99
high income-developing	40	79	40	639	16,000	79	0.124	1.99
developing-developing	5	9	5	76	16,000	9	0.124	1.99
developing-high income	24	49	24	392	16,000	49	0.124	1.99
high income-high income	35	70	35	567	16,000	70	0.124	1.99

Sources: Approximations by UNWTO based on UNWTO, ICAO and IATA (see Annex 1) and estimated emissions and surface transport modal split and average distances by the expert team (see Annex 2).

Intra-regional travel (within regions)

The vast majority of tourists travelling by air, move within their own region, either on domestic trips (480 million) or on international trips (215 million). Depending on the geographical characteristics of the regions, the mix of domestic and international traffic varies considerably. In the Americas and in Asia and the Pacific, a comparatively big share of traffic is domestic, owing to large countries with large populations such as United States, China, India or Brazil. In Europe on the other hand, a comparatively large share is international, due to relatively large number and small size of the countries. Most of the intraregional trips will be short- and medium-haul, although a limited part of it represents long-haul travel within regions, such as between North America and South America or between North-East Asia and Oceania.

With regard to CO_2 emissions, the largest contributions related to intra-regional air travel can be attributed to, in decreasing order, domestic travel within the Americas (123 Mt), domestic travel within Asia and the Pacific (42 Mt), international traffic within Asia and the Pacific (40 Mt), international travel within Europe (39 Mt), international travel within the Americas (22 Mt) and domestic travel within Europe (17 Mt).

It is interesting to note that air traffic flows within Africa are only very small, with some 6 million domestic air travellers and 5 million international air travellers, together accounting for less than 1% of CO_2 emissions (3 Mt) by intra-regional air travel. The contribution of the Middle East is also fairly small, with 8 million domestic air travellers and 7 million international air travellers within the region, generating a bit over 1% of all CO_2 emissions (4 Mt) by intra-regional air travel.

Interregional travel (between regions)

A comparatively large share of passenger flight kilometres, and thus emissions, corresponds to air travel between the various UNWTO regions (Europe, Americas, Asia and the Pacific, Middle East and Africa). An estimated 125 million of trips by air are to another region. Of these trips, some 20 million are actually to short- or medium-haul destinations bordering the region of origin, for instance from Europe to North Africa (11 million) or to the Middle East (11 million), from the Middle East to Europe (2 million), from the Middle East to South Asia (0.3 million) or from South Asia to the Middle East (estimated at 3.5 million, i.e., some 70% of travel from Asia and the Pacific). Some 104 million trips can be considered interregional long-haul trips, generating an estimated 1,674 billion passenger kilometres and 208 Mt CO_2 emissions (40% of air transport emissions).

Although data on a country to country base are only available for the largest flows, UNWTO has developed a matrix (see Annex 1) allowing for a breakdown of trip volumes by regions of origin and (sub)regions of destination. Based on this matrix an assessment has been made of the flows between high-income and developing countries *. It should be taken into account that those flows are categorised by the predominant direction, as high-income or developing source markets or destinations can not always be isolated, for instance in North-East Asia, though considered predominantly developing, some high-income countries are included, such as Japan.

A third of long-haul trips, corresponding to some 40 million, are from predominantly high-income economies to destinations in developing countries, with as most significant flows:

- from Europe and Americas to North-East, South-East and South Asia, respectively 15 million and 8 million trips;

- from Europe to sub-Saharan Africa (5 million trips);

- from Europe to the Caribbean, Central and South America (9 million).

---

*   This divison is based on the World Bank Country Classification by Income Group where developing countries are all countries from the low to upper middle income categories (see http://go.worldbank.org/K2CKM78CC0)

Some 35 million long-haul trips take place from high-income to high-income countries, mostly travel between Europe and North America:

- from Europe to North America (15 million);

- from Americas to Europe (18.5 million trips, predominantly from North America but including some from Caribbean, Central and South America).

Some 24 million long-haul trips originate from developing countries heading to high-income countries, with as most significant flows.

- from Asia and the Pacific to Europe (13 million) and North America (8.4 million);

- from Africa to Europe (2.2 million) and North America (0.3 million);

- from the Middle East to North America (0.2 million).

Some 5 million long-haul trips take place between developing countries in different regions, with as most significant flows:

- from Asia and the Pacific to the Middle East (1.5 million, i.e., excluding some 70% of arrivals from South Asia that are considered short- and medium-haul);

- from the Middle East to North-East and South-East Asia (0.5 million);

- from Asia and the Pacific to Africa (1 million);

- from Africa to North-East, South-East and South Asia (0.8 million);

- from Asia and the Pacific to the Caribbean, Central and South America (0.6 million).

Those trips are for all purposes, including leisure, business, visiting friends and relatives, health, pilgrimage and other. Worldwide and for all modes of transport, just over half of all international tourist arrivals were motivated by leisure, recreation and holidays (51%), business travel accounted for some 16% and 27% represented travel for other purposes, such as visiting friends and relatives (VFR), religious reasons/pilgrimages, health treatment, etc., while for the remaining 6% of arrivals the purpose of visit was not specified (see Annex 1). No detailed data are available on the mix of purposes for the various interregional flows, but anecdotal evidence indicates that a proportionally large share of trips are for the purposes of business and for visiting family and friends, due the internationalisation of business and trade and to international migration patterns.

Figure 11.10 Tourist trips and CO$_2$ emissions by air transport, 2005

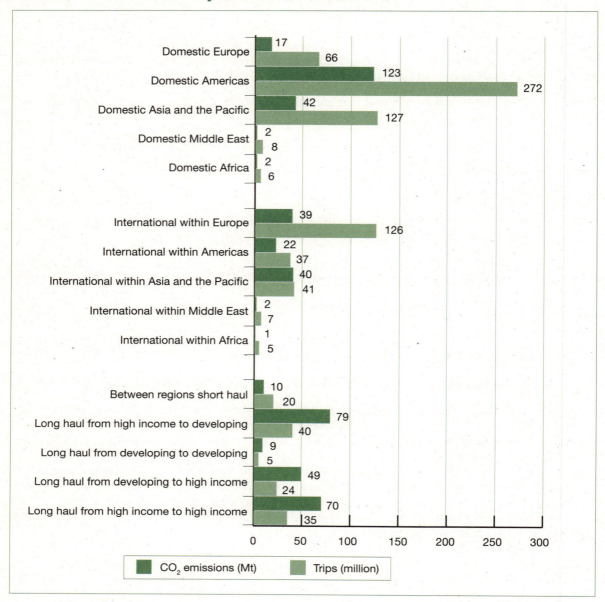

Based on ICAO and IATA data the overall number of passenger kilometres are estimated for interregional flights (i.e., between regions), however, no precise information is available for distances flown for each traffic flow. For this reason, the average return distance flown is assumed equal for all four long-haul flows to about 16,000 km. With respect to CO$_2$ emissions, this results in a total of 79 Mt for travel from high-income source markets to destinations in developing countries, 70 Mt for travel from high-income source markets to high-income destinations, 49 Mt for travel from developing source markets to destinations in high-income countries and 9 Mt for travel from developing source markets to destinations in developing countries. This is of interest, as it confirms that long-haul travel from the high-income source markets causes a relevant share of emissions and the highest per trip emissions at an average of 2.0 ton per trip. However, it should not be overlooked that a considerable part of this traffic is to destinations in developing countries, where tourism receipts are a vital source of subsistence and development.

11.2 Emissions Related to Individual Holidays

Section 11.1.5 has shown that CO_2 emissions from tourism are significant, even though they may seem to appear small in comparison to other economic sectors. Results also show that trip distance is an important variable, with long-haul international air travel being a comparatively major contributor to overall emissions. Given still considerable growth in tourism demand, a perspective only focused on the global contribution of tourism to climate change may thus be misleading. As global emissions from tourism are the sum of individual trips, a perspective on these is provided in this Section. This is of particular importance in the context of mitigation strategies (see Chapter 12).

Emissions vary widely between trips. A fly-cruise to Antarctica, for instance, may entail emissions 1,000 times larger than those of a domestic cycling holiday. Figure 11.11 illustrates this for a number of journeys. These figures were found by using the great circle distances for the specific trips, the average emissions per pkm as given in Table 11.2 and the average emissions for accommodation and other tourism activities as used for all calculations for tourists from high income economies. According to UNWTO estimates, an average tourist trip lasts 4.15 days (for all international and domestic tourist trips – see Annex 1) and causes emissions of 0.25 t CO_2.* The vast majority of trips produce lower emissions, but a small share is highly emission-intense. For instance, a 14-day holiday from Europe to Thailand may cause emissions of 2.4 tonnes of CO_2, and a typical fly-cruise from the Netherlands to Antarctica produces some 9 t CO_2.[653] Even holidays said to be eco-friendly, such as dive holidays, will cause high emissions in the range of 1.2 to 6.8 t CO_2 (see Box 25). These figures show that emissions caused by a single holiday can vastly exceed annual per capita emissions of the average world citizen (4.3 t CO_2), or even the average EU citizen (9 t CO_2). However, many holidays cause comparably low emissions, only marginally increasing overall per capita emissions. Figure 11.12 illustrates this by breaking down annual emissions to per-day emissions for various examples of holidays. Emissions will largely depend on the choice of transport mode, with air transport generally increasing emission levels substantially. Other factors of importance for per day emissions are the distances travelled as well as the length of stay, the accommodation chosen or the activities carried out at the destination. Destination choice has thus a considerable impact on the ecological impact of various journeys.[654]

Figure 11.11 Annual per capita CO_2 emissions and emissions caused by various journeys (emission factors as for 2005 technology)

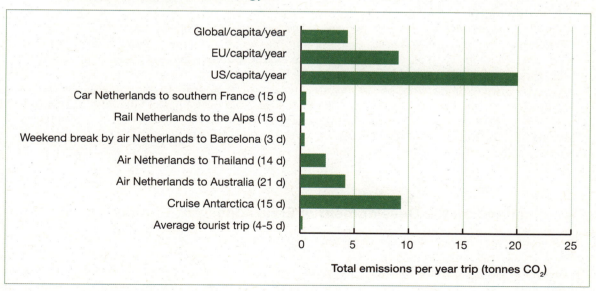

*   This number is found by dividing all emissions from Table 11.6 minus the emissions from same-day tourism by all tourist trips in Table 11.3 = (1308-107) Mt / 4.75 billion).

Figure 11.12 Daily average emissions per person and emissions per tourist-day for various journeys (emission factors as for 2005 technology)

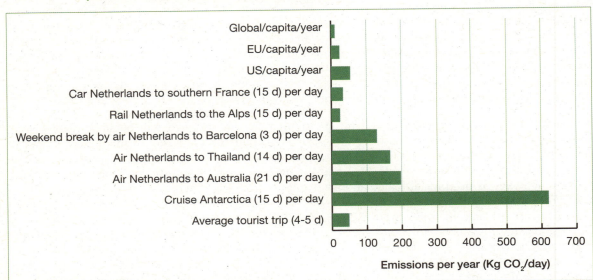

Box 25 Dive tourism emissions

Visiting popular dive sites usually involves a flight, as many popular dive sites are located in warm or tropical destinations. [655] To exemplify emissions caused by a dive holiday, imagine return distances of 7,000 pkm, corresponding to a trip from the UK to Egypt, and 30.000 pkm, corresponding to a trip from the UK to Australia. These would cause emissions of 0.8 t and 4.8 t CO_2. [656] If divers carry on diving equipment, this might add on the weight of the aircraft and lead to higher fuel use. On the distance from the UK to Australia, 1 kg of additional weight will lead to additional fuel use of approximately 0.7 kg (return flight), corresponding to emissions of almost 6 kg CO_2-equivalent per kg of baggage.

At the destination, divers will cause additional emissions through their stay in various accommodation establishments, using various means of transport and developing other activities (including dive trips). Depending on how energy is generated, corresponding emissions will be in the order of up to 120 kg CO_2 per bed night. Dive trips mostly cause emissions from the boat trip. Emissions caused by Australian tour boat operators for example are in the order of about 60 kg of CO_2 per trip if the boat uses a diesel engine or 27 kg CO_2 if the boat uses a petrol engine. [657] Overall, a dive holiday may thus cause emissions of between 1.2 t and 6.8 t CO_2. This can be compared to globally 'unsustainable' emissions of about 4.3 t CO_2 per person per year.

11.3 Scenario on the Development of Emissions from Tourists

CO_2 emissions from tourism have grown steadily over the past five decades to its current estimated level of 5% of all anthropogenic emissions of CO_2 (Section 11.2.5). In this section a projection is provided on the development of emissions for tourist activities only (thus excluding same-day visitors). The reason for excluding same-day visitors is that the current numbers of same-day visitors are the least certain part of the data. There are no time-series available to base any growth of same-day visitor trips on, nor is there any projection in the literature available, and finally, the current share of same-day in emissions is low and expected to stay relatively low. The future growth of tourists' emissions will depend upon three major trends:

- **Growing tourism demand:** the number of tourist trips is for the purpose of this report projected to grow exponentially over the coming three decades. According to UNWTO's *Tourism 2020 Vision* [658], the number of international tourist arrivals is forecast to reach 1.6 billion by 2020. an increase of nearly 100% over 2005 (803 million). It is unclear how domestic tourist volumes will develop, but rapid growth can be expected in many markets as well, and in particular in developing countries like India and China. Current growth rates in domestic tourist trips in India and China have been in the order of 10% per year in recent years. [659, 660]

- **Increased long-haul travel:** according to *UNWTO's Tourism 2020 Vision,* the share of long-haul tourism is projected to increase from 18% in 1995 to 24% in 2020 [661], which, given the overall growth in tourism, implies that the number of long-haul trips will more than triple between 1995 and 2020. Furthermore, average trip distance is also increasing. In the EU, the number of trips is projected to grow by 57% between 2000 and 2020, while the distances travelled are expected to grow by 122%. [662]

- **More frequent holidays:** there is a trend of more frequent holidays over shorter periods of time. Consequently, guest night numbers are likely to grow at a slower pace than the number of trips, distances travelled and corresponding CO_2 emissions.

In the framework of this report, we developed several scenarios considering different mitigation options, in order to estimate how emission of global tourist activities might be mitigated in the future (see Chapter 12 for the results of these scenarios).

These scenarios are based on a 'business-as-usual' scenario projection. This was built to the year 2035, in order to provide an estimate on how emissions might evolve when actions are not taken in a comprehensive manner at an appropriate scale in the tourism sector. This scenario is based on projected tourism demand growth rates, as well as distances travelled by various means of transport. These projections also take into account that the number of arrivals is expected to grow faster than the number of guest nights due to the trend of reduced length of stay (see Table 11.8 for the assumptions and Table 11.9 for the references used).

Emissions also depend on changes in energy efficiency. For air transport, estimates of high efficiency gains [663] were assumed (Table 11.10). For cars, efficiency improvements were assumed to be moderate in the developed world and somewhat higher in the developing world, as strong economic growth in many regions will result in a comparably new car fleet (Table 11.10). For other means of transport, a 1% increase in efficiency was assumed. Energy efficiency per tourist night was assumed to be constant, as efficiency gains in this sector are likely to be outpaced by higher standards (e.g., concerning room size) in accommodation. Other activities can also be expected to become rather energy-intense, even when the average length of stay declines and efficiency measures are taken. This is primarily because there is a recent trend towards motorised activities (Table 11.10).

Table 11.8 Model assumptions: tourist arrivals and travel distance growth rates average annual growth (%/year) between 2005 and 2035

	Air transport (distance)	Car transport (distance)	Other transport (distance)	Accommodation (number of nights)	Tourism volume (number of trips)
International	5.3	2.3	2.0	4.0	4.5 [a]
Domestic	11.1	7.5	3.7	5.3	6.3

(a) UNWTO forecasts a 4.1% annual growth of international tourist arrivals until 2020. The figures in this table, including the 4.5% growth of international tourist arrivals until 2035 is based on estimation carried out by the expert author team of this report. However, UNWTO assumes that the growth might even slow down due to a number of factors, for example the maturing and saturation of main tourism markets.

Table 11.9 Model assumptions: references for tourist arrivals and travel distance growth rates

	Air transport (distance)	Car transport (distance)	Other transport (distance)	Accommodation (number of nights)	Tourism volume (number of trips)
International	Boeing [664]	MuSTT study [665]	Expert estimate	MuSTT study	Expert estimate
Domestic	Boeing	MuSTT study	MuSTT study	MuSTT study	Expert estimate

Table 11.10 Model assumptions: efficiency changes (%)

	Air transport (overall reduction between 2005 and 2035)	Specific energy use car transport (change per year)	Other transport (change per year)	Accommodation (change per year)	Activities (change per year)
International	-32	-1	-1	0	+1
Domestic (developed world)	-32	-1	-1	0	+1
Domestic (developing world)	-32	-2	-1	+2	+2

The results of the 'business-as-usual' scenario, based upon the expert's extrapolation of UNWTO's *Tourism Vision 2020* are shown in Figure 11.13. The number of tourist trips is projected to grow by 179%, while guest nights would grow by 156%. Passenger kilometres travelled is expected to rise by 223%, while CO_2 emissions are estimated to increase at somewhat lower levels (161%) due to efficiency improvements. The share of aviation-related emissions would grow from 40% in 2005 to 52% by 2035 (Figure 11.13). Within the accommodation sector, emissions are forecast to increase by 170%, while for other tourism activities, growth is expected to be at 305%.

Figure 11.13 Comparison of current emissions caused by tourist trips (overnight) and projections of emissions for the year 2035 under the assumptions of a 'business-as-usual' scenario (%)

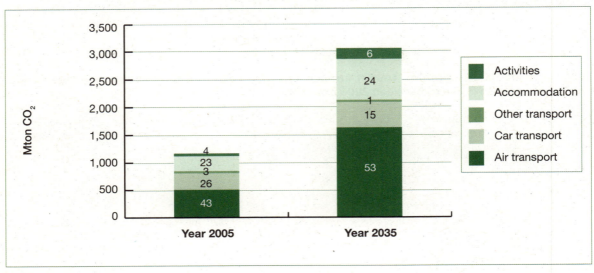

The latest global emissions projections by IPCC * show a 30 year (2000–2030) change in overall emissions of at best a reduction by 6% up to an increase by 88%. This is much lower than the 161% growth seen here for emissions generated through tourist trips. This development of CO_2 emissions from tourism is also in stark contrast to emission reduction needs. Tourism-related CO_2 emissions will reach 3,057 Mt by 2035 under the 'business-as-usual', up from 1,167 Mt in 2005 (this figure excludes same-day visitors emissions). Box 26 illustrates the implications of such developments with regard to aviation in the EU.

Box 26 Emission reduction goals and the development of aviation emissions in the EU

The upper two curves in Figure 11.14 shows the maximum amount of annual emissions of CO_2 in the EU in a +2° C warming scenario, as agreed upon by the EU as the maximum temperature change acceptable to avoid 'dangerous interference with the climate system'. [666] The lower curves show the projected levels of emissions from aviation for a range of scenarios in the European Union, under mixes of optimistic and pessimistic assumptions about technical efficiency improvements and aviation growth. The Figure shows that in a 'business-as-usual' scenario, emissions from aviation alone would in several cases correspond to the maximum amount of emissions that can be emitted within the EU by 2050. The implication is that a 'business-as-usual' growth scenario for aviation is not feasible, if the EU 2° C maximum warming scenario is to be taken seriously

Figure 11.14   EU emission reduction targets and aviation emissions

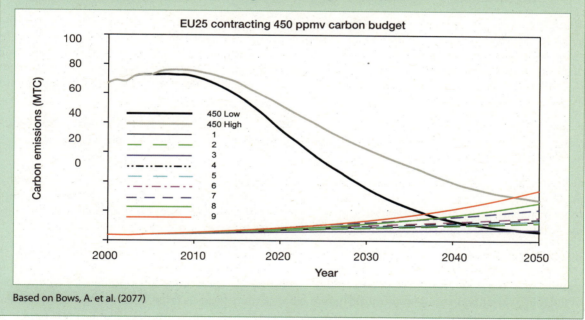

Based on Bows, A. et al. (2077)

In terms of radiative forcing, tourism's contribution to global warming will grow even faster, given an increase of RF in the order of 192% (excluding cirrus) to 209% (including maximum cirrus), corresponding to 0.198 W/m² (without cirrus) and 0.387 W/m² (including maximum cirrus). Figure 11.15 shows a breakdown of CO_2 emissions and RF for tourism by 2035. According to this 'business-as-usuals' scenario, aviation would be responsible for 53% of the total tourist trips emissions (CO_2 only) from an estimated 40% in 2005 and even higher shares for RF (compare for 2005 in Figure 11.8).

---

*   30-year growth projections for 2000-2030. IPCC (2007c), figure SPM 4 on page 7.

Figure 11.15 CO_2 emissions and radiative forcing shares of different tourism sectors by 2035 (excluding same-day visitors)

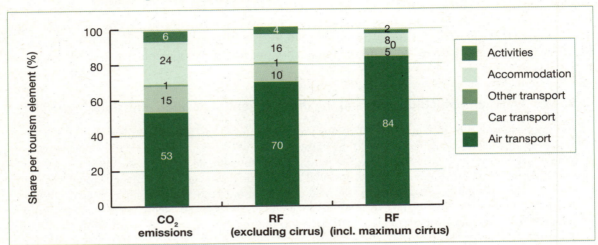

11.4 Conclusion

This Chapter represents the first detailed attempt to assess the global share of CO_2 emissions attributable to tourism, which is here estimated to be around 5% (within a range of 3.9% to 6.0%). Measured in radiative forcing, the contribution of tourism to global warming is estimated to be 4.6% (excluding cirrus-related effects), with a range from 3.8% (excluding cirrus-related effects) to a possible maximum of 9.0% (including maximum cirrus-related effects). The ranges reflect the uncertainty associated with current assessments.

It should be noted that results are based on a number of assumptions, and it remains an important task for the future to further develop worldwide comprehensive tourism demand data on transport, accommodation and other activities.

Furthermore, it is important to start a more complete assessment of the use of various forms of accommodation and average emissions per accommodation type and class. The same is true for other tourism activities. The latter should also include local transport at the destination and specifically address the issue of touring that can comprise significant amounts of travel and consequent emissions.

Regarding CO_2 emissions by sector, it is clear that transport generates the largest proportion of emission (75%). In terms of radiative forcing (contribution to 2005 climate change) the share of transport is significantly larger and ranges from 81% to 89%, with air transport alone accounting for 54% to 75% of the total. Variation in emissions from different types of tourist trips is large, with the average domestic tourist trip generating 0.12 t CO_2 and the average international tourist trip 0.49 t CO_2. Long-haul and very luxury cruises can however generate up to 9 t CO_2 per trip (i.e., 18 times the emissions caused by an average international tourist trip). The majority of tourist trips cause only small amounts of emissions, though. For instance, international tourist trips (i.e., overnight tourist trips) by coach and rail, which account for an estimated 16% of international tourist trips, stand only for 1% of CO_2 emissions generated by all international tourist trips (transport emissions only). In contrast, a small number of energy-intense trips is responsible for the majority of emissions, i.e., the air-based passenger transport (17% of all international tourist trips) is estimated to cause about 40% of all tourism-related CO_2 emissions and 54–75% of the radiative forcing. Likewise, long-haul travel between the five world regions stands for only 2.2% of all tourist trips (excluding same-day tourism), but contributes around 16% to global tourism emissions (including accommodation, activities, overnight and same-day tourism).

The 'business-as-usual' scenario developed for 2035 shows that there will be considerable growth in CO_2 emissions and RF in the tourism sector, if systematic mitigation measures are not implemented. As a consequence, a comprehensive strategy is required to reduce tourism-generated emissions. Chapter 12 provides a discussion on the range of technological, behavioural, managerial and policy measures and initiatives that can bring tourism on are more sustainable emission pathway.

Chapter 12

Mitigation Policies and Measures

Climate change mitigation relates to technological, economic and social changes, as well as substitutions that lead to emission reductions. Mitigation poses a challenge when significant reductions in emissions cannot be achieved by technological restructuring alone, but also requires behavioural and structural changes. Tourism-related emissions are growing rapidly, but mitigation policies need to address a number of dimensions, such as the need to stabilize the global climate versus people's desire to rest, recover and explore; or the need to reduce long-haul emissions versus tourism's role in development and poverty alleviation. Climate change mitigation policies within tourism have to find a balance between such potentially conflicting objectives. Clearly, decisions on climate change and tourism have implications for local, national and global, as well as inter-generational equity and all these aspects need to be taken into account to arrive at an effective policy mix.

Emission reductions should thus ideally combine various instruments, such as voluntary-, economic-, and regulatory ones. Instruments are more effective when targeted at different stakeholder groups, including tourists, tour operators, accommodation managers, airlines, manufacturers of cars and aircraft, as well as destination managers. Instruments could also be applied with different emphasis in different countries, so as not to jeopardize the development and poverty reduction opportunity offered by tourism to developing countries.

It is clear that for those actors being pro-active in addressing climate change, mitigation offers a range of business opportunities. Given current societal trends, it seems that there will be new markets for environmentally oriented tourists and opportunities to develop new low-carbon tourism products.

Four major mitigation strategies for addressing GHG emissions from tourism can be distinguished: [667]

- **Reducing energy use** (i.e., energy conservation): this can for example be achieved by changing transport behaviour (e.g., more use of public transport, shift to rail and coach instead of car and aircraft, choosing less distant destinations), as well as changing management practices (e.g., videoconferencing for business tourism).

- **Improving energy efficiency:** this refers to the use of new and innovative technology to decrease energy demand (i.e., carrying out the same operation with a lower energy input).

- **Increasing the use of renewable or carbon neutral energy:** substituting fossil fuels with energy sources that are not finite and cause lower emissions, such as biomass, hydro-, wind-, and solar energy.

- **Sequestering CO_2 through carbon sinks:** CO_2 can be stored in biomass (e.g., through afforestation and deforestation), in aquifers or oceans, and in geological sinks (e.g., depleted gas fields). Indirectly this option can have relevance to the tourism sector, considering that most developing countries and SIDS that rely on air transport for their tourism-driven economies are biodiversity rich areas with important biomass CO_2 storage function. Environmentally-oriented tourism can play a key role in the conservation of these natural areas.

Mitigation can be achieved through various mechanisms, including technological improvements, environmental management, economic measures, and behavioural change. Policy can support all of these mechanisms. The following Section will set out with a discussion of mitigation options in the transport sector. This will be followed by an overview of mitigation options for tourism establishments. Policy options to support mitigation will be provided within each Section. Finally, tourist behaviour that is relevant to climate change mitigation will be discussed.

12.1 Transport

As outlined in Chapter 11, transport accounts for 75% of the total GHG emissions caused by tourism. Aviation and the private car are the major contributors to tourism transport emissions. Current trends show a strong growth of air transport at the expense of car, coach and rail in the developed world, while in the developing world, both car and air transport grow to the disadvantage of public transport (bus, rail). The challenge for tourism transport is to increase fuel efficiency of all transport modes, and to facilitate a modal shift towards rail and coach. Furthermore, the growth in distances travelled demands strong attention.

12.1.1 Air Transport

Fuel is now a major cost for airlines at about 20–25% of direct operational costs, [668] which should be a compelling argument for aircraft manufacturers to design fuel-efficient aircraft. Space and the weight that can be carried are both limited on board of an aircraft, and high fuel consumption is thus also a factor negatively affecting maximum payload-range, take-off and landing capabilities.

Fuel-efficiency of aircraft has been improved for jet aircraft introduced in the 1950s (Figure 12.1). The IPCC expects future emission reduction potentials from combined improved engine and airframe technology in the order of 20% between 1997 and 2015 and 30–50% between 1997 and 2050. [669] Several advanced technologies have to be combined to reach this Figure (Box 27). At the moment it is thought that the ultimate reductions of fuel consumption per pkm that can be achieved through technological change are in the order of 50%. However, these are for economical reasons not likely to be achieved. Furthermore, it should be noted completely new aircraft configurations like the blended wing body or a propulsion system based on fuel cells and hydrogen* have a large temporal lag of several decades between the conception of a new technology and the full operational use of it in the total fleet.

Based on actually achieved energy efficiency in the history of jet aircraft (up to 1997), a regression curve has been constructed. From this curve it has been calculated the expected reduction between 2000 and 2050 will be less than 40%. [670] Note that the new Boeing B787 Dreamliner fits neatly in the regression curve.** The A380 is even some 10% above this curve. [671]

---

*   See for example technology break-throughs proposed by Masson, P. J. et al. (2007), *HTS Machines as Enabling Technology for All-electric Airborne Vehicles.*

**   The Dreamliner is 20% more fuel efficient than its competitors, that all entered service in the 1990s. The curve shows the same 20% for this eleven-year period to 2008, the year of market introduction planned for the B787.

Figure 12.1 Historic and expected future trends in fuel efficiency for aircraft

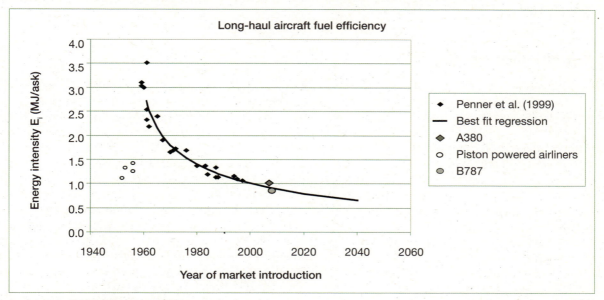

Source: Peeters, P. and Middel, J. (2006)

> ## Box 27 Engine and airframe technology
>
> The expected advances in engine and airframe technology to date are: [672, 673, 674]
>
> - development of gas turbine engines with a higher bypass and pressure ratios;
>
> - optimisation of the balance between increasing fuel efficiency (i.e., through higher temperatures and pressure ratios) and reduced NOx emissions (by optimised combustion chambers and combustion control);
>
> - higher lift-to-drag ratios by increasing wing-span, using, wing-tip devices, increased laminar flow on the wings and advanced airframe skin designs (e.g., riblets);
>
> - structure weight reductions;
>
> - new aircraft configurations for example the blended wing body.

Alternative fuels

Various aircraft using alternative fuels have recently been discussed. For instance, hydrogen powered aircraft would use a clean source of energy. However, neither Boeing nor Airbus are currently developing such an aircraft, and it should also be noted that hydrogen is a secondary energy, rather an energy carrier; i.e., unless it is produced from carbon-neutral primary energy sources there will be no global reduction in GHG emissions. Producing hydrogen from renewable sources is also constrained by lack of infrastructure, considerably higher costs, and competing uses of renewable energy. Furthermore, using liquid hydrogen in conventional turbojets would eliminate CO_2 and particle emissions but not reduce the problem of NO_x-emissions, and it would also lead to the release of larger quantities of water vapour (about 2.6 times). Both would cause additional radiative forcing (see Box 23, Chapter 11).

Currently available biofuels are not suitable for use in aviation, except in a very low mix ratio with jet fuel. Aviation fuels must stay liquid at low temperatures, and also have a high energy content by volume. Fuels such as biodiesel or ethanol do not match these requirements well. However, a biofuel tailored for aviation could possibly be developed in the future. Virgin Atlantic in partnership with Boeing aims to develop such a fuel within the next five years. Nevertheless, several problems remain unsolved regarding biofuels. These relate to the sustainability and efficiency of production and increasing competition over land, especially arable land area (see Box 29).

Air traffic management

Fuel reductions of up to 10% can be expected from improved operations and air traffic management (ATM), mainly by reducing congestion and optimising flight paths. Optimisation of air traffic management will be facilitated through new navigation systems such as the Galileo satellite navigation system being developed in Europe. [675] The primary factor in optimization of ATM in Europe is overcoming the political hurdles in getting a common system, such as realigning FIR boundaries. Also, achieving higher load factors would decrease the emissions per pkm. Currently, load factors typically vary between 70–75% on international routes (and up to 90% for charter planes). Fuel use also depends on the density of the seating, as more people carried in the same space will increase the overall weight of the aircraft, but reduce per capita fuel use. Seating density can vary substantially. Boeing, for example, offers the 777–300 with in between 368 to 500 seats. Low cost carriers and charter planes typically have the highest seat densities, which can result in fuel reductions per seat kilometre of up to 20–30%. In contrast, flying business-class (with ample space) is more carbon intense than flying economy class due to the lower number of passengers carried. A recent study found that emissions in business and first class are 133% and 250% higher, respectively, than those of economy class. [676] There is also a noteworthy recent trend towards small, executive aircraft (hired or owned), which are even more carbon intense than business- or first class.

Aircraft manufacturers pursue different concepts to improve service and fuel efficiency. Boeing is focusing on point-to-point connections; i.e., longer non-stop flights with medium-sized aircraft (200–250 seats). The use of advanced technologies means that Boeing's 787 Dreamliner (rolled out in July 2007) is 20% more fuel efficient at the same air speeds compared with today's commercial jets. In contrast, Airbus continues to build on the hub-and-spoke concept (i.e., the use of large aircraft from central airports, to which passengers have to travel from smaller airports). Their A380, a double-decker aircraft with an initial capacity on offer of 555 seats, has a non-stop range of 14,800 km to connect major hubs. Airbus however also offers smaller aircraft, such as the A350XB.

Wider initiatives by the airline industry

Corporate social responsibility is taken up by more and more airlines. Airlines try to be as fuel efficient as possible by continuously renewing their fleet, introducing fuel saving technologies; reducing engine–on time when on the ground; reducing operating empty weight by removing excess amounts of water, catering; choosing more efficient flight paths; etc. An increasing number of airlines also produce annual environmental reports. [677, 678, 679]

In their last Annual General Meeting in 2007, IATA outlines four challenges on their pathway to a 'zero emissions future'.

1.   **Air traffic management:** IATA calls for a Single Sky for Europe, an efficient 'Pearl River Delta' in China and a next generation air traffic system in the US, to be implemented by governments.

2.   **Technology:** IATA calls on the aerospace industry to build a zero emissions aircraft in the next 50 years. Basic research on a zero-emissions aircraft should be coordinated.

3.   **A global approach:** IATA asks the International Civil Aviation Organization (ICAO) and its 190 Member States to deliver a global emissions trading scheme that is fair, effective and available for all governments to use on a voluntary basis.

4.   **Green businesses:** IATA is developing 'IATA Project Green' to help airlines implement global best practice Environmental Management Systems.

12.1.2 Surface Transport

Car transport

The car is the most widely used mode of surface-bound transport for tourism. Most cars used by tourists are privately owned, but rental cars take an increasing share of car use at destinations. In this Section we describe the general technological developments with respect to the emissions of cars and give some examples of what destinations and fleet owners can do to reduce emissions.

In car transport, most vehicles still operate with traditional petrol or diesel based combustion engines. Improvements in fuel efficiency have been made through advanced engine technology (e.g., direct fuel injection) and more efficient transmission. In the last 15 years, however, the advances in energy efficiency have been counteracted by the development of more powerful, larger vehicles with more technological extras such as air conditioning. As a result, average fuel consumption has basically stagnated since the 1990s. [680] Consequently, the most substantial reductions in fuel use could be achieved by using smaller vehicles, based on the combination of lower weights, less power, and reduced speeds. In some countries, rental vehicle fleets are more efficient than the average vehicle as they tend to be newer and have smaller engines. [681] Tourism businesses could build on this leadership role and promote fuel-efficient vehicles.

Alternative engine technologies include electricity-powered vehicles, hybrid vehicles and the use of biofuels or hydrogen. Electric vehicles are very energy efficient and they have no tailpipe emissions of harmful pollutants (which makes them attractive for tourism), although the power plant producing the electricity will emit them,* unless renewable energies or nuclear power are used. [682] There are a number of down sides to electric vehicles, mainly related to battery capacity, battery loading and unloading energy losses, added weight and volume of batteries, as well as energy losses at power stations. Most of these disadvantages do not exist for electric trains, trams, metros and trolley busses that are directly coupled to the grid. Most batteries using electric vehicles have a limited autonomy and driving range of about 300 km, and recharging can take up to 8 hours. Notwithstanding this, electric vehicles have become popular in some destinations because they are quiet and non-polluting. Yosemite National Park is an example where electric buses were put into service for tourism purposes. Some cities use electric-powered buses, trolleys, and mini cars for tourists (Figure 12.2). However, these are exceptions in comparison to the majority of tourism transports.

Figure 12.2 Electric vehicle fleet for tourists in Werfenweng, Austria

Photo credit: Scott, D.

---

*   Emission abating is more effective at larger scale such as for electric power plants. Low emission technology (wind, solar) can be used directly and does not need inefficient energy transformation processes, for example to produce hydrogen.

Hybrid vehicles have two power sources, namely electricity and petrol or diesel. The hybrid vehicles differ from the original battery vehicles in that they recharge the battery using the petrol or diesel engine. Emission reductions of CO_2 can be in the order of up to 50% for hybrid cars compared with those only having combustion engines. Toyota's cumulative (across all years) sales of hybrid vehicles exceeded 1 million in 2007. [683] Of those, nearly 345,000 hybrids were sold in Japan, while 702,000 were sold abroad. Avis Portugal introduced 50 Honda hybrid cars in their fleet. In July 2007, Avis added more hybrid cars to its fleets. There are now 1,000 Toyota Prius in their fleet across different locations in the United States. Twenty hybrid cars will be available in Avis' fleet in London by summer 2007. Other rental car companies engage in similar 'green initiatives' (see also Box 28).

The carbon emissions from cars can also be reduced by using fuel cells in combination with hydrogen as fuel. This technology is theoretically ready for introduction, but main caveats are the distribution and production of hydrogen; the latter may even entail higher emissions of carbon dioxide if electricity for hydrogen production is generated in coal-fired power stations, but not if based on wind or solar energy.

Box 28 EV Rental Cars

EV Rental Cars started operations in 1998 in the United States with the goal to rent environmental vehicles and become the first rental vehicle company to offer an all-hybrid-electric vehicles fleet. Since then, EV Rental Cars' fleet has grown to more than 350 cars at 8 locations throughout the country. The company has won numerous environmental awards, including the 2000 Calstart Blue Sky Award and the Clean Cities Environmental Citizenship Award.

EV Rental Cars has prevented substantial amounts of greenhouse gas emissions and claims to have passed on to its customers more than US$ 1 million in fuel costs savings by acting environmentally.

There is increasing interest in biofuels as an alternative to petrol and diesel. Biofuels are already added to petrol and diesel (e.g., E85 is ethanol blended in petrol up to 85%). The advantage of adding ethanol to conventional fuel is that cars do not require changes in the fuelling system. Some rental car companies already use biofuel, for example Avis Scandinavia operates 400 ethanol-powered Saabs in its fleet.

The use of compressed natural gas (CNG) and liquefied petroleum gas (LPG) also reduces CO_2 emissions compared with traditional petrol or diesel engines. The gases contain less carbon, the recovery and processing are less energy intense, and other emissions (e.g., carbohydrates) are less toxic. [684] Fuel switching from diesel to CNG can reduce CO_2 emissions, but may lead to an increase in methane and NO_x emissions, thus reducing the overall benefit of lower GHG emissions. Another drawback is the inconvenience of accommodating heavy high-pressure tanks.

"Biofuels might play an important role in addressing GHG emissions in the transport sector, depending on their production pathway. Biofuels used as gasoline and diesel fuel additives/substitutes are projected to grow to 3% of total transport energy demand in the baseline in 2030. This could increase to about 5–10%, depending on future oil and carbon prices, improvements in vehicle efficiency and the success of technologies to utilize cellulose biomass."

IPCC (2007c:18), Summary for Policymakers

Box 29 Biofuels

Biofuels are based on biomass, either plant material or waste products from the food chain. All these raw materials have used carbon dioxide from the atmosphere to grow and are therefore considered renewable and of a low carbon footprint. However, the production of biofuels still causes significant CO_2 emissions, as it is usually based on the use of fossil fuels (e.g., transport, fertilizer). Emissions depend on the material used and the production process. Sugarcane based ethanol from Brazil, for example, has been found to be very efficient, whereas biofuel derived from corn in the United States is comparatively carbon intensive.

There are two basic types of biofuel. Biodiesel is made from vegetable oil or animal fat. It can be used in any diesel engine and can be mixed with mineral diesel in any percentage. Ethanol (an alcohol, like methanol) is the most common biofuel worldwide and it is used in petrol engines. It can be produced from sugar cane, wheat and corn and other biomass.

With an increasing interest in biofuels for transportation, the question arises whether large areas can be dedicated to the production of fuel, at the expense of other uses (such as forestry or food production). One scenario for 2020 shows that if all oil-based transport would be run on biofuels, area requirements would be in the order of 0.75 to 5.0 billion hectares, which can be compared to the current agricultural area of 1.5 billion ha, with another 3.5 billion ha being used for cattle grazing. [685] In addition to land use discussions, there is also concern that plantations will replace natural habitats (sugar cane or palms for oil). Thus, the production of biofuel can have huge implications for biodiversity and ecosystems in a wider sense (e.g., affecting global hydrological cycles). Sustainable land use for the production of biofuel crops has to be considered carefully. In the light of limitations to the production of biofuels, managing demand for energy remains central to achieving sustainable transportation.

Rail transport and busses

The main advantage of rail and coach is their high energy-efficiency compared to other transport modes. Rail and road mass transit systems using electricity from the grid can be made carbon neutral using renewable energy. Swedish Railways, for instance, have recently switched to renewable energy from wind- and hydropower. Swiss Railways run entirely on renewable energy sources and have done so many decades already by using their own hydroelectric plants. [686] Both Dutch and Austrian railways buy growing shares of renewable electricity.

It could be argued that railway and bus systems can offer advantages such as their central location in many cities, frequent departures, and punctuality. The actual operational energy consumption for trains depends among others on the speed, landscape relief (ups and downs) and the number of accelerations. [687] There are a number of technological developments that can improve the energy efficiency of trains, such as hybrid locomotives, regenerative breakage and kinetic energy storage systems. [688] Finally, railways may further increase load factors. For instance, the French double decker TGVs use almost the same amount of energy as the single deck ones, but can carry 40% more passengers. The main challenge for rail will be to reduce energy use for high-speed trains. Overall, railways have good opportunities to contribute to further reductions in emissions.

Urban public transport systems include light-rail transit and metro or suburban rail, and increasingly large-capacity buses. Bus Rapid Transit (BRT) systems have been developed in Curitiba, Brazil and are now in place in many South American cities. BRT offers the opportunity to provide high-quality, state-of-the-art mass transit at a fraction of the cost of other options. Bus Rapid Transit utilises modernised buses on segregated busways and incorporates such features as pre-board fare collection, safe and user-friendly transit stations, simplified transfers and routings, and superior customer service. Other destinations in the Asia, Australia, Europe, and North America have started to take up BRT as well.

Box·30: East Japan Railway Company [689]

The East Japan Railway Company operates over 13,000 rolling stock and 1,700 stations, and carries 16 million passengers. An annual 'Sustainability Report' is produced. The following goals (established in 1996) were achieved by 2002:

- 20% reduction of CO_2 emissions in general business activities;

- 80% of railcars are energy-saving cars, which consume about half the electricity of conventional railcars;

- 15% reduction in energy consumption for train operations in proportion to unit transportation volume;

- 60% reduction of NO_x emissions at a company-run thermal power plant;

- the promotion of environmentally friendly driving practices has lowered the instances of quick acceleration; this has reduced energy use and also accident rates by 38% over three years;

- implementation of specific environmental conservation activities (including tree planting) on an annual basis;

- the carbon efficiency of JR has improved from 94.5 to 71.5 tonnes of CO_2 per billion yen.

12.1.3 Modal Shift

As rail and coach transport have lower emissions than air and car transport (see Figure 12.3), a modal shift from air and car transport to rail and coach will help to reduce tourism transport emissions. Up to distances of about 1,500 km, rail and coach capture significant shares of the markets and thus are to some extend alternatives to air transport. The share of rail depends strongly on the rail travel time excess over the air trip. More than 50% of the rail-air market is captured by rail for times of up to 2.5 hours. If the rail travel time increases to over 5 hours the share reduces to below 10%. [690] High market shares can be captured by developing high-speed railway networks implying lower travel times. For instance, in the EU25, about one third of all tourist journeys by air cover less than 1,500 km and could theoretically be replaced by rail and coach, if high quality infrastructure is offered. This would correspond to emission reductions (CO_2) of about 8% of all EU tourism transport emissions. However, a modal shift of 100% of all air transport trips below 1,500 km one-way is not very likely to happen. Even 10% will require a strong incentive from the sector. This would just reduce emissions by less than 1%. A 20% shift from car to rail would result in a reduction in CO_2 emissions of 4–5%. This would require the entire EU to achieve the performance of the Swiss public transport system. Furthermore this shift has several other advantages in terms of traffic safety, noise, air quality, space use, congestion and space for parking at congested destinations.

Another option for short-haul travel is to shift from jet aircraft to turboprop aircraft. Though the variance between different regional aircraft types is large, it appears that regional turboprops are significantly (between 10–60%) more fuel efficient than regional jets. [692]

Figure 12.3 Relative carbon dioxide emissions for tourism transport modes at average seat occupation and different stage lengths; based on EU data

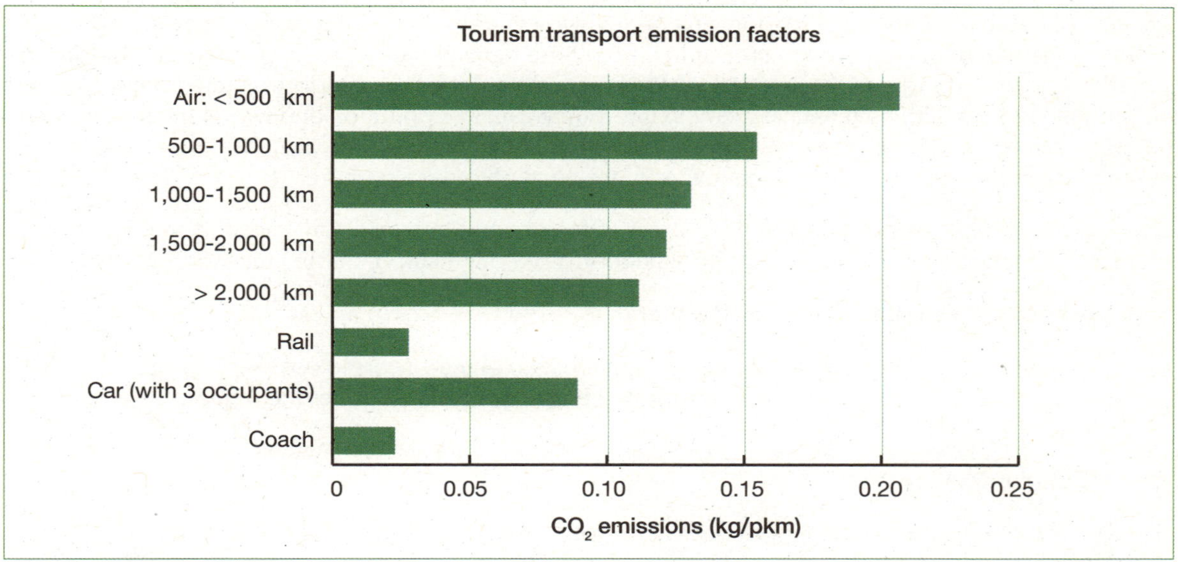

Tourism transport emission factors

Air: < 500 km	
500-1,000 km	
1,000-1,500 km	
1,500-2,000 km	
> 2,000 km	
Rail	
Car (with 3 occupants)	
Coach	

CO$_2$ emissions (kg/pkm)

Based on Peeters, P. et al. (2004).

High-speed trains have become important links between major European cities. Eurostar has proved to be a strong competitor and dominant market player in comparison with airlines (such as BA or Air France) on the London-Paris route. Similarly, other countries try to boost their high-speed rail network to substitute train for short-haul flights (e.g., in France on the Paris-to-Marseille route, Shikansen network in Japan, and the Madrid-Seville route in Spain). Overall, however, the participation in railway travel is comparatively small with the exception of Japan (see Box 29). The market share of train of passenger transport in Japan is 19.9%, while it is 6.1% in the EU, and 0.3% in the USA. For all intra-EU25 tourism transport in 2000 the share of rail is 5% and of coach 6.7% (in terms of pkm). But differences between countries are very large. The highest percentage is reached by the Swiss population at over 20% share, while countries as Ireland reach less than 3%.

Table 12.1 Modal mix for passenger transport (pkm) in selected countries for 2004 (billions)

	EU 25	EU 25 (%)	USA	USA (%)	Japan	Japan (%)
Passenger car	4,458	76.7	6,544	84.8	757	63.1
Bus/coach	502	8.6	226	2.9	86	7.2
Railway	352	6.1	(24) (b)	0.3	239	19.9
Tram and metro	75	1.3	(25)	0.3	(33)	2.8
Air	428 (a)	7.4	896	11.6	84	7.0

(a) Only intra-EU 25

(b) Values between parenthesis are from the 2005 version of the ERF dataset

Source: European Union Road Federation (2007)

12.1.4 Destination Mobility Management

There is increasing consideration of 'soft' measures to encourage a modal shift towards sustainable forms of transport. [693] Initiatives can range from destination-wide transport management (e.g., car-free resorts) to travel restrictions on certain routes, encouragement of public transport use, establishment of cycle paths or -networks, and other benefits offered at tourist attractions or accommodation to non-car users. Soft measures also involve improved information systems (for instance concerning departure times), better reliability of public transport systems, increased personal security, and improved transfer facilities to connect different types of public transport.

The role of urban planning is increasingly recognized as central to achieving sustainable cities (Wheeler, 1998). Since much tourism is taking place in cities, these developments are highly relevant for tourism. Wheller suggests a framework for sustainable cities, which includes compact, efficient land use; less automobile use yet with better access; efficient resource use, less pollution and waste; the restoration of natural systems; good housing and living environments; a healthy social ecology; sustainable economics; community participation and involvement; and preservation of local culture. [694]

There are a number of examples that illustrate different solutions for local transport management in tourism, indicating that it is possible to provide tourists with a chain of public transport options:

- **Copenhagen Free Bike Program (Denmark)**

  Between May and September, the city of Copenhagen offers visitors to use free bicycles all over the inner city. The 1,300 bicycles can be borrowed at 125 stations all over the inner city for a deposit of about   3. [695]

- **NETS (Europe)**

  A Europe-wide Network for Soft Mobility in Tourism. [696]

- **City of Málaga Tourist Mobility Management Plan (Spain)**

  This new plan includes the implementation of the following services: design of a new website for tourists, new tourist bus service, tourist maps and leaflets, funicular to the Gibralfaro castle, and the creation of the Metropolitan Transport Authority (MTA). [697]

- **United Kingdom's National Cycling Network**

  The network offers over 10,000 miles of walking and cycle routes on traffic-free paths, quiet lanes and traffic-calmed roads. An up-to-date map can be downloaded from the web. [698]

Destination management can also include a closer cooperation with destination marketers. Marketing campaigns could, in the future, take issues such as energy use and GHG emissions into account. [699] For instance, Sweden currently seeks to establish a massive inflow of Chinese tourists, despite strong growth in incoming tourism from European countries. This will substantially increase national emissions in both Sweden and China. Conversely, Norway decided to not focus on Chinese markets, in order not to increase national emissions. To assess the consequences of shifts in marketing more strategically, eco-efficiency could be used as a technique to guide tourism promotion strategies. [700]

Box 31 Sustainable mobility in the Alpine Pearls of the European Alps

In 2006, 17 Alpine towns in five nations (Austria, France, Germany, Italy, Switzerland) founded the Alpine Pearls Association (APA), and membership has grown to 20 communities in 2007. The objective of the APA was to 'break away from conventional tourist mobility' and emphasize sustainable mobility getting to holiday destinations and once there to take action on climate change. Travellers are guaranteed mobility without the use of a personal motor vehicle or airplane. Through the APA, several pre-existing initiatives in each community were combined to offer the traveller a brand of destinations and tourism operators that are committed to sustainable mobility options that comply with the following criteria:

- **Super-regional mobility:** Accessibility to/from each Alpine Pearl is provided via train or bus at minimum four times per day.

- **On-Site mobility:** When at an Alpine Pearl, guests can expect a mobility system to provide connections to the most important local tourist attractions with a maximum waiting time of 30 minutes each day from 9 am to 8 pm.

Each of the Alpine Pearls provides its own sustainable mobility options. For example, in Werfenweng, Austria, guests can utilize a fleet of electric vehicles. The 'Alpine-Flyer' electric Swiss bike is available in six of the Alpine Pearls. The 'Alpine Pearl Rail Pass' is also now available from OBB in Austria to connect passengers between APA member communities. Arosa (Switzerland) and Werfenweng (Austria) also offer a 'Neutral-Climate Holiday' package, where the unavoidable emissions resulting from rail access and local transportation are calculated with assistance from APA and offset by emission reduction initiatives in another location. Guests receive a certificate guaranteeing that their holiday journey is completely climate neutral.

These sustainable mobility projects have been very successful as demonstrated by the changes in Werfenweng (Austria) since it introduced its car-free resort programme. From 1999 to 2004 Werfenweng has seen:

- 38% increase in overnight stays in the winter season;

- 101% increase in overnight stays within the special interest offer 'holidays from the car';

- 31% increase in overnight stays in the summer season;

- increase in train arrivals from 16 to 25%, resulting in the reduction of 375 tonnes of CO_2 per year;

- tripling of passengers for the Werfenweng 'Dial-a-ride' shuttletaxi.

12.1.5 Transport Policies

General policies relevant for tourism transport

There is a general lack of tourism transport policies that address the specific issue of climate change (see also IPCC WG 3, which identified the lack of political will to address transport emissions as a major obstacle). Transport policies are often generic and do not distinguish between various travel motives. For instance, freedom restrictions to travel could be understood as unfair, and transport policies should be designed in a way to consider this in order to be supported by the public. Policies typically focus on transport security and an integration of different modes of transport into a transport network with convenient transfers for the tourist. In contrast, destination-based transport policies often focus on congestion, parking issues and local air pollution.

Transport policies (and as part thereof tourism) often seek further economic development – often in alignment with tourism plans – and as a result conflict with environmental policies, in particular those on climate change.

There are several initiatives at the supranational policy level to make tourism transport more sustainable. The 'Biofuels Directive', for example, is a European Union directive for promoting the use of biofuels in EU transport. The directive entered into force in October 2001, and stipulates that national measures must be taken by countries across the EU aiming at replacing 5.75% of all transport fossil fuels with biofuels by 2010. Currently, petrol and diesel specifications are being reviewed in order to lower both environmental and health impact, and to take into account the new EU-wide targets on biofuels and greenhouse gas emissions reduction. The EU, along with Japan, already has the most stringent fuel efficiency standards in the world (more information can be found on EurActiv.com).

Market-based instruments

Fuel use of international aviation, together with bunker fuels for shipping, is currently not included under the Kyoto-protocol and in national greenhouse gas inventories, which represents an underestimate of country's emissions up to 10%. [701] Instead, Article 2, paragraph 2 of the Kyoto Protocol states that the responsibility for limiting or reducing GHG emissions from aviation falls to the Annex I Parties, working through the International Civil Aviation Organization (ICAO). ICAO's geographic and policy ambit reflects its membership of 190 states, well beyond the 37 ratifying Annex I countries or even the 167 which have ratified the Protocol. While focusing on airframe/engine technology, air traffic management and operational practices, ICAO has also investigated the use of 'market-based' measures such as taxes, charges and emissions trading. Such economic instruments would have effects beyond aviation and tourism. ICAO has effectively ruled out taxes and charges, as well as 'closed' (intra-aviation) emissions trading, and is now grappling with issues of scope in 'open' emissions trading, on which discussion at ICAO's Assembly Session in September 2007 was expected to be seminal.

At present, the most likely market instrument to be implemented is emission trading. This approach is supported in principle by a number of airlines and aviation organisations. Emission trading is generally seen as an option that is more flexible than that of taxation. The EU proposal (see Box 32) is an important step towards a worldwide cap and trade scheme that is likely to reduce demand through higher ticket prices and encourage airlines to press the aircraft and engine manufactures to develop more efficient aircraft.

Table 12.2 Comparison of market-based instruments to reduce greenhouse gas emissions from aviation

Type of levy	Operational issues	Financing (in the EU)	Effect on emissions	Legal aspects
Charge on ticket	Simple and possible to introduce in the short-term; airlines could be responsible for collecting the charge.	Assuming a charge of 5% on the airfare, this charge could raise about € 10–16 billion annually.	Probably little effect on demand given estimated price elasticities; no incentive for airlines to reduce emissions.	Legally feasible.
Fuel tax	A tax could be added as a fixed amount per l of fuel sold or as a percentage of current fuel price; petroleum companies could collect the tax.	Assuming a tax of € 0.32 per l of kerosene a total of about € 14 billion could be expected.	Incentive for emission reductions; research into fuel-efficient technologies and operations.	Problematic, especially concerning the many bilateral agreements including tax exemption for fuel.
Emission tax	Complicated, given the many factors that determine overall radiative forcing. Estimates of emissions possible when considering aircraft type, engines, LTOs, and routings.	Assuming emission charges per l of kerosene of € 0.12 for CO_2, € 0.12 for water vapour and € 0.6 for NOx, the total amount would be around € 14 billion.	An emission tax would have the greatest impact on emission reductions and provides an incentive for technological and operational improvements for airlines.	Likely to be legally feasible unless the tax is closely correlated to fuel usage, because this could be seen as a hidden tax on kerosene.
Emission trading	Integration with existing trading schemes, for example EU ETS.	Depending on market price for CO_2	Directly controlled through the cap in the case of a cap-and-trade scheme.	Likely to be legally feasible.

Source: Becken, S. and Hay, J. (2007) [703]

Other market-based instruments include policies to establish additional charges on tickets, fuel taxes and emission taxes. A charge on tickets is the most straightforward and simplest option to internalise the climate-change costs of aviation (see Table 12.2). However, if the charge is low to moderate, demand will possibly continue to grow, and a ticket charge would also not provide an incentive for airlines to reduce their emissions. If the tax is clearly coupled to the emissions of the flight, long-haul flights will be significantly affected, eventually reducing the growth of the number of long-haul trips and possibly increase the length of stay for these trips (if people go, they will do so for a longer period to save on the cost of the trip per day).

Fuel taxes could be added on top of fuel prices, which would be of particular relevance given the current state of non-taxation of fuels for aviation in contrast to fuel used by surface-bound means of transport. For instance, the current price of one litre of fuel for cars is roughly one Euro higher in the European Union than the price of one litre of kerosene. At present, kerosene sells at about 0.31 per litre. This means that an increase by a factor of four for fuel costs would double ticket prices with major impacts on aviation volumes. Fuel taxes for aviation are difficult to implement legally, though, as there are a large number of bilateral agreements stating tax exemption for fuels. In contrast, emission charges target the source of the impact and theoretically it is possible to adjust the charge to the climate-effect of a particular flight. Legally, it is possible to introduce emission charges unless they are very closely correlated to fuel consumption. [702]

Irrespective of the policy instrument more research has to be carried out to determine the emissions of a particular flight, especially if non-carbon emissions were to be included. ICAO has started to develop a methodology for calculating emissions based on aircraft type, class of travel and route.

Box 32 Emission trading for aviation

Out of the various options to address emissions from aviation, emission trading is the only one that is in principle supported by a number of airlines and aviation organizations. Emission trading is favoured over the taxation of fuel or emissions, because it allows achieving emission reductions at the lowest cost, as well as putting caps on emission levels. The European Commission (EC) thus envisages including emissions from intra-European flights in the EU ETS from 2011 and all other aircraft flying into and out of the EU from 2012. However, this will mean to include aviation in the general trading system of the European Union, with the consequence that aviation will continue to grow. Several studies have shown air travel to be rather price-inelastic, [704, 705] and at prices of US$ 20 per ton of permit, ticket prices for aviation will become only marginally more expensive. For instance, a return-flight from the US to Europe (New York to Paris) would become US$ 24 more expensive. The aviation sector is thus likely to further expand in such a common trading system, while other sectors will have to achieve over proportionally large emission reductions.

Several publications have shown that emission reductions are cost-negative or – neutral, when companies implement measures to avoid low – or moderate amounts of greenhouse gas emissions. For instance, the IPCC WG3 Report [706] shows that emission reductions in the order of 15–30% are feasible at costs of up to US$ 20 per ton of CO_2-eq. However, further emission reductions become rapidly more expensive. Countries in the European Union are already struggling to achieve the 20% reduction goal agreed upon by 2020. As the 20% reduction goal only represents the first step in global emission reductions, with > 50% reductions needed by 2050, it is clear that there may be considerable problems in achieving further reductions in the medium-term future.

This has several implications with regard to the role of aviation. First, if aviation enters the EU ETS, pressure on other sectors to reduce emissions is likely to increase. This will have the consequence that economically feasible reductions (at < US$ 20 per ton of CO_2-eq.) will be more rapidly carried out in these sectors, and thus sooner lead to a situation where further reductions become more costly. For instance, there is already considerable debate by the Swedish industry that electricity will become more expensive because of aviation buying (scarce) emission rights. High electricity prices would in turn affect the costs of production. Note that the current trading system foresees only limited 'imports' of emission reductions generated through the CDM; i.e., reductions have to a large extent to be carried out within the European Union. Second, aviation is growing rapidly at the moment, with an increasing number of people in the European Union regularly using aircraft.

Such societal trends and the socio-cultural adaptation process going along with these are not easily reversed, and measures to regulate emissions from aviation could face growing resistance by part of the population in the future. In the light of this, it seems prudent to re-consider the implications of a common trading system.

An alternative is to include aviation in a trading scheme of its own. In such a system, aviation would have to reduce its own emission levels, and pressure on airlines would thus increase faster. The industry is currently opposed to such a system, as it is feared that this will limit the options for the aviation sector to grow and disrupt economic systems dependent on aviation. However, this problem could be dealt with by allowing moderate growth rates in the sector, which are reduced annually until emissions become constant (for instance, by 2015, when no further growth in global emissions of greenhouse gases is acceptable [707]). Economically, this would have the consequence that ticket prices will increase, as only a limited number of air miles can be sold. However, this would boost the profitability of the aviation sector, as prices for tickets can be increased despite stable costs of operating flights. At the same time, this will lead to a greater interest by the industry to invest in more fuel-efficient aircraft and to increase load factors.

12.2 Tourism Establishments

'Tourism establishments' include a variety of accommodation businesses, such as hotels, motels, bed and breakfast, camping grounds, holiday apartments, and second homes, as well as tourist attractions, such as entertainment facilities, historic buildings, recreational facilities, hospitality and information centres. The focus in the following will be on the commercial accommodation sector, which is of greater importance in terms of emissions than tourist attractions.

The accommodation sector represents, globally, approximately 21% of emissions from tourism (see previous Chapter on emissions). However, initiatives in this sector are important, as many hotels have considerable options to reduce energy use, which are usually economical. Initiatives such as the use of renewable energy or participation in certification schemes can have important repercussions for tourist perceptions of the importance of pro-environmental engagement in the tourism industry. The value of initiatives at the destination level thus also lies in their symbolic power for involving a larger number of tourists in environmentally proactive behaviour.

12.2.1 Technological Mitigation Options

Mitigation measures in tourism establishments focus largely on energy efficiency and renewable energy. The hotel sector is particularly well organised (especially the larger hotel chains) and there are a number of practical sources of information to help managers implement energy conservation and efficiency measures. One long-standing institution is the International Hotels Environment Initiative (IHEI), which was founded in 1992 to support and improve environmental performance by the hotel industry worldwide. IHEI provides benchmarking tools and publishes a quarterly magazine, the Green Hotelier. A similarly useful website is the Australian 'Twinshare: Tourism Accommodation and Environment'. In the following we will discuss energy conservation and efficiency measures in buildings, and provide an overview of renewable energy sources for tourist accommodation.

"The first step [for energy saving programs] is to build consumption history so you can see how you use energy. Understand what your costs are and where they are coming from."

Dan Gilligan, *Vice President of Utilities and Administrative Service, Accor* [708]

Energy conservation and efficiency in buildings

Energy use in the accommodation sector is usually a result of heating and cooling; i.e., hot water supply, central heating, cooling for fridges and freezers, air conditioning, and lighting. In warm holiday destinations, the single largest energy end-use is air conditioning. To address those key end-use areas, mitigation measures can be carried out in the following areas:

Room temperature

The key is to keep temperatures in guestrooms at comfortable levels, ideally between 20–25° C. For instance, the Hilton Seychelles has experimented with room temperatures, and the management reports that 25° C are accepted without any complaints by guests. Building design, including positioning, material and insulation can provide an important precondition for maintaining temperatures in the desired range and considerably reduce overall energy use (Figure 12.4). In a comparison of Scandic and Hilton hotels the differences in energy use between hotels may primarily be a result of hotel standard and management, with a higher standard leading to higher resource consumption. The study also shows that there are considerable options to reduce energy use through pro-environmental management, which often lead to cost savings. [709]

Figure 12.4 Air conditioning unit outside a tourist bungalow in Fiji*

Photo credit: Becken, S.

* The manager reported that because of the design (natural ventilation through windows) and the setting (ample of vegetation to provide shade), tourists only rarely use the air conditioning.

Technical options to reduce energy use include for instance thermostats, combined with a system to heat or cool rooms only shortly before they are used. Regarding air conditioning and heating, it is crucial to have these in the right location to avoid inefficient use, or infiltration of hot air into cooled space. Measures to increase efficiencies can be simple. For instance, the London Marriott County Hall in the United Kingdom reduced its energy use in rooms by 37%. This was achieved by cleaning filters in the air-conditioning units, as well as the coils. A side-effect was that optimal room temperatures were reached faster. In addition, changes were made to the air conditioning and heating running times in banquet rooms, resulting in significant energy savings. It is also possible to introduce systems to shut down air conditioning automatically, for instance, when balcony doors are opened. Finally, the Mariott's air conditioning system was adjusted according to the season.

Restaurants

Many hotels have restaurants that can make substantial contributions to sustainability. Besides adapting similar measures for mitigation as the hotel, restaurants can, through their choice of foods, heavily influence the carbon-intensity of meals served. Food now accounts for approximately one third of emissions caused by households in industrialized countries, and is thus an important factor in reducing energy use. Generally, locally produced food will have a considerably smaller energy footprint. This is particularly relevant in small tropical islands, where food may often be imported by air. Using local resources, for instance by serving mostly local seafood instead of imported meat dishes, is one such measure. Restaurants can also favour organic or certified raw materials and products, and avoid food that is particularly harmful to the environment, such as shrimps produced in converted mangrove areas. Environmentally oriented restaurants in Europe have also started to serve increasing shares of vegetables, as meat is far more carbon intense.

Water temperature

Guest showers, pools, and especially laundry operations can account for about half of a hotel's energy bill. Most common measures to reduce energy use for water heating include setting water temperatures at no more than 60° C, installing low-flow shower heads and using energy-efficient equipment, for example for laundry. All over the tropics, it is feasible to use solar heating systems, which have been proven to work efficiently and securely.

The Orchid in Mumbai uses economisers in the boiler to recover the heat from the hot exit gas, which is used for preheating the water fed to the boiler. Similarly, the Wellington YHA installed a heat exchanger that recovers heat from shower waste pipes and transfers the waste heat into the incoming cold water, which reduces costs for hot showers by 50%.

Heating costs for swimming pools can also add substantially to a hotel's energy bill. Various technologies are available to reduce these costs, including solar water heaters, heat pumps and pool covers. A heat pump as opposed to traditional heating systems, such as electric boilers or condensing boilers, could save up to 52% of energy use. The investment in a heat pump would be paid back in about 2 years, making heat pumps an interesting alternative both environmentally and financially. [710]

Cooling (food storage)

Energy can be wasted when cooling systems are creating temperatures colder than needed. Refrigerators and freezers operate most efficiently when the refrigerator is set at 3.2° C and the freezer is set between −18° and −15° C. There are a number of zero-cost measures to reduce the need for cooling, including:

- allowing hot food to cool before storing it in refrigerators and freezers;

- not overfilling refrigerators, as best cooling occurs when air can circulate throughout;

- regular checking and cleaning of fans, condensers and compressors;

- ensuring doors fit and close properly, and the seals are in good condition;

- ensuring refrigerator compressor belts maintain proper tension;

- defrosting freezers frequently since frost build-ups reduce efficiency.

Lighting

There are some basic measures to reduce energy needs for lighting. In the temperate and northern zones, the most cost-effective measure is to make best use of daylight (for instance by trimming trees and in the overall siting and design of hotels). Other low-cost measures include energy-saving lighting systems and occupancy sensors installed in common areas and guest rooms. The technology of energy efficient light bulbs has improved so that compact fluorescent lamps and circline fluorescent lamps now closely match the colour of incandescent lighting. An energy-efficient light bulb lasts about ten times longer than conventional lamps and staff spend less time changing bulbs. Many hotels now operate room cards for guest rooms to turn off lights (and other appliances) when leaving the room.

Energy efficiency of tourist attractions

Most of the energy-saving measures outlined for accommodation businesses apply equally for other tourism businesses that operate buildings. Theme parks or large entertainment centres are a good example. Most tourist attractions and activity operators operate at least an office building, in which energy conservation and efficiency measures are relevant.

Some tourist activities require special infrastructure in addition to buildings. Energy demand is often high. A good example is the ski industry, which not only relies on energy for lift operations and trail preparation, but also increasingly for snow-making systems and on-mountain entertainment.

Box 33 Mitigation initiatives in the North American ski industry

As part of the 'Keep Winter Cool' program established by the National Ski Areas Association (NSAA), ski areas in the United States have undertaken a wide range of energy efficiency and renewable energy initiatives to reduce the GHG emissions related to their operations and serve as a model for other tourism sectors.

At the operator level, the Aspen Ski Company (ASC) (Colorado, USA) is an acknowledged international leader in greenhouse gas emission reductions and was the first resort operator to join the Chicago Climate Exchange (in 2001) and thereby legally committing itself to annual accounting of GHG emissions and a 10% emission reduction by 2010 (based on a 1999 baseline year). To accomplish this objective ASC has undertaken multiple initiatives, including: building the largest solar photovoltaic array in the ski industry, constructing an onsite micro-hydroelectric plant (generating 250,000 kWh annually), converting all of its snow-grooming machines to biodiesel, building two of the earliest buildings certified by the US Green Building Council's 'Leadership in Energy and Environmental Design' Program, and most recently purchasing 100% of its electricity use from wind power generators.

More broadly, the NSAA launched its 'Green Power Program' in 2006 to promote investment in renewable power by the ski industry. A total of 58 ski resorts now purchase renewable energy (primarily wind) for all or part of their operational energy use. Impressively, 28 of these resorts purchase 100% of their energy needs from renewable sources (through renewable energy credits where local grid sources are not available). The NSAA estimates that these 28 ski resorts purchased 292 million kWh of green energy in 2006-2007, avoiding over 193,000 tonnes of CO_2 emissions. [711]

Another example is golf tourism. Modern golf courses use energy in a wide range of facilities: in the clubhouse (offices, meeting rooms, bar, restaurant, kitchens, locker rooms, pro shop) and on the golf course (use of green-keeping machinery, pumping irrigation water, operation of maintenance facilities). The world rules and development body and organizer of 'The Open Championship', [712] has developed a four-point plan to energy conservation:

1. **Decide who will be responsible:** note examples of energy wastage, read meters and check fuel bills, encourage others to use energy more efficiently, regularly report findings back to senior management.

2. **Establish the facts:** any signs of exceptional consumption, how costs are changing over the years, seasonal patterns to energy consumption.

3. **Compare your performance:** make some comparisons internally and with other, similar golf clubs, and between years, set priorities and targets for improvement.

4. **Use less energy:** the goal is to eliminate waste, including boiler rooms, offices, function rooms, kitchen, cellar, maintenance facility, and irrigation pump house.

Renewable energy sources

A number of renewable energy sources are relevant for tourism. These are wind, photovoltaic, solar thermal, geothermal, biomass and waste. [713, 714] Several studies have explored the extent to which renewable energy sources can be used for tourism, in particular in island destinations where energy supply based on fossil fuels is expensive and at risk of supply interruptions. These studies come to the conclusion that the use of renewable energy sources is generally economical and technically feasible. [715, 716]

Wind energy is of interest in areas with average wind speeds of more than 5–5.5 metres per second. [717] There are different systems for wind energy, ranging from small scale to medium scale (100–700 kW) and large scale (up to 5 MW output). Tourism businesses require small applications, unless a region invests collectively in larger units. The capital costs of wind power are generally smaller than those of solar power. While windmills produce low-carbon electricity and cause no other air pollution, they are sometimes criticised for other environmental impacts, for example noise or visual impacts. However, in some areas, wind parks have also become tourist attractions. Wind energy has the disadvantage that it needs to be backed up with other energy sources in periods of insufficient wind speeds.

Solar energy can be used in three ways: to heat space, generate hot water, or to produce electricity. Solar thermal systems are probably the most commonly used ones in tourism. Depending on the climate, solar water heaters can meet at least half of the hot water requirements of an accommodation establishment over the year. Additional heating might be required on cloudy days, at times when demand for hot water is high, or in winter. The amortization horizon for solar energy panels depends on the climate and can be between 2 years in tropical destinations and 10 years in higher latitudes.

Another way of using solar energy is photovoltaic; that is solar radiation transformed into electricity by means of a photovoltaic (PV) cell. PV systems are simple to operate and therefore attractive for a range of tourism applications. PVs have low operating maintenance costs and are reliable in terms of energy production. PV cells can be used at most locations, but they must be positioned to capture maximum sunlight. A PV system needs a component for energy storage, usually batteries. [718] A back-up diesel-powered generator can be necessary in some locations; however, it might also be possible to combine PV with, for instance, wind power. PV systems are in the range of 1–50 kW; one-kilowatt rooftop cells can be an interesting option for tourist bungalows, for example to provide electricity for lighting and smaller appliances (e.g., radios). Investment horizons for PV systems without diesel generator may be in the order of less than 5 years. [719] The costs of PV cells are decreasing all the time, making them increasingly competitive with diesel generators. This is of particular relevance in remote areas without connection to electricity grids.

Box 34: Nukubati Island Resort, Fiji [720]

A good example of a business that has placed a lot of effort into the development of green approaches to business is Nukubati Island resort in Fiji. The resort has implemented a series of environmental systems on the island, including:

- Nukubati produces its own electricity with one of the largest solar power plants in the South Pacific islands; from an array of 300 solar panels and four wind generators, Nukubati generate 10 kW electricity output from sun and wind;

- fresh water is collected, rainwater filtered and UV treated;

- hot water is produced from ten solar water heaters;

- sewage is tertiary treated using natural bio-cycle systems with grey water being used for irrigation;

- all organic waste is composted for the gardens and other waste is recycled;

- Nukubati grows its own organic vegetables and fruits, using tropical permaculture techniques.

Figure 12.5 Solar panels on Nukubati Island

Photo credit: Nukubati Island [721]

12.2.2 Integrated Emission Management

Integrated emission management in a tourism establishment goes beyond the use of technology to reduce energy use and includes a wide range of measures:

* the implementation of environmental management systems that include management, technology, and behavioural changes;

* eco-labelling or certification;

* supply chain management and strategic partnerships with other, carbon-efficient operations.

Box 35 Scottish Seabird Centre

The Scottish Seabird Centre is a community inspired project that opened to the public in 2000. [722] It has achieved the 'Gold Level' in the Green Business Tourism Scheme (GBTS). Since opening, the centre has grown to be a world leader in the real-time remote observation of wildlife in its natural habitat without disturbance. The centre was designed and built on strong ecological principles. Materials were locally sourced where possible and environmentally friendly products used in its construction and furbishment.

Examples of specific initiatives include:

* recycling waste (for example bottles, cooking oil, paper);

* food and drink for the café are sourced from local producers and suppliers;

* using solar systems to power the Bass Rock and Isle of May cameras;

* encouraging use of public transport to the centre through the provision of joint travel and admission package with ScotRail.

An Environmental Management System (EMS) is a comprehensive and formal organizational approach designed to achieve environmental care in all aspects of operations. It typically involves the development of an environmental policy for the tourism business, monitoring of impacts (such as emissions), environmental reporting (e.g., in the form of 'triple bottom line' reporting) and certification. Only very few tourism businesses have specific climate change policies (as part of their EMS). The Aspen Skiing Company (see also Box 33) developed a policy in 2001 to (1) acknowledge that climate change is of serious concern to the ski industry and to the environment; and (2) that a proactive approach is the most sensible method of addressing climate change. More importantly, the Aspen Skiing Company established a climate change action plan, committing to the following:

- use of green development principles in new Aspen Skiing Company developments;

- energy efficiency in old buildings through economically viable retrofits;

- continued support of mass transportation and local employee housing;

- annual accounting of greenhouse gas emissions;

- a 10% reduction in greenhouse gas emissions by 2010 based on a 1999 baseline.

As part of wider environmental management, many (typically larger) tourism establishments now use the ISO14001 environmental management standard. The management standard helps to understand, monitor and reduce environmental impacts. Green Globe 21 is an environmental management standard developed specifically for the travel and tourism industry, but it has not managed to reach the market (see Table 12.3 below).

There are also a substantial number of ecolabels, codes of conduct, sustainability reporting schemes, awards, and benchmarking programs in the tourism industry. Font (2002) identified over 100 ecolabels for tourism, hospitality and ecotourism worldwide, while in a more general study, the World Tourism Organization (2002) identified 104 ecolabels, awards and self-commitments. Certifications can aid consumers in sustainable decision-making, and have important roles in marketing. Currently, there are over 60 programs worldwide setting standards and verifying them, with an average of about 50 certified tourism firms per program. [723] A general problem with certifications is that they are based on a wide range of criteria, with only some of these addressing energy use or emissions. Another general issue is the relatively low take-up and recognition of these schemes among the consumers. [724] With regard to climate change mitigation, there is thus considerable potential to improve ecolabels for tourism. As an example, Table 12.3 provides an overview of certifications in Sweden with regard to the area of application, the criteria used and the number of businesses in each programme.

While certifications can contribute to the marketing of destinations and travel products, it is interesting to note that most of the certifications found in Sweden are focusing on quality, rather than environmental issues more generally. Energy use in particular is only part of few certifications, with on-site energy use being the focus of assessments.

Table 12.3 Tourism certifications in Sweden, 2005

Country/ region	Certification	Area of application	Criteria			No. of businesses in the programme
			Quality	Environment	Energy use (at destination)	
Sweden	Bo på Lantgård (Stay on a Farm)	Farm accommodation	x	(x)		428
Sweden	Godkänd Gård för Hästturism (Certified Horse Farm)	Horse farms	x	(x)		40
Southeastern Sweden	Det Naturliga Fisket (Natural Fishing)	Fishing arrangements/ accommodation	x	(x)		35
Sweden	Naturlig Laddning (Natural Charge)	Nature-based activities	x	x		12
Sweden	Naturens bästa (Nature's Best)	Ecotourism operations	x	x	x	220[(a)]

Country/ region	Certification	Area of application	Criteria			No. of businesses in the programme
			Quality	Environment	Energy use (at destination)	
Denmark, Sweden, Greenland, Estonia, France, Lithuania	The Green Key	Accommodation		x	x	254
Sweden, Norway, Finland, Iceland	Svanen (Nordic Swan)	Accommodation		x		111
Europe	EU Flower	Accommodation		x	x	36
Europe	Blue Flag	Beaches/marinas	x	x		3,107
Worldwide	Green Globe 21	Airlines, airports, attractions, car hire, caravan parks, convention centres, cruise boats, exhibition halls, golf courses, hotels, marinas, micro businesses, railways, restaurants, tour operators, cities, destinations, protected areas, resorts		x	x	113

(x): soft criteria (indirectly considered)

(a) number of certified arrangements offered by 70 tour operators

Source: Gössling, S. (2006)

Environmental management, certification and ecolabelling can be a useful basis for managing a businesses' supply chain and developing strategic partnerships.* This means that a tourism business looks beyond the boundaries of its own establishment. While this is often done for economic reasons, environmental benefits can be achieved as well. Such partnerships could, for example, involve cooperation with other, energy efficient businesses. An eco-tourism tour operator will choose to work with – ideally certified – accommodation providers and local attractions. This will enhance the credibility of their own product and also reduce overall carbon emissions. Partnerships are also common between attractions and transport providers. A number of tourist destinations now offer integrated tickets for attractions and public transport systems. For example, the 'Barcelona Card' is a transport and attraction discount card that is issued by the Barcelona Tourism Association. Similarly, the FIFA Soccer World Cup held in Germany in 2006 offered free public transport for ticket-holders on the day of the match. Events held in the Telstra Stadium in Sydney offer similar arrangements.

---

*   See for example Centre for Environmental Leadership and Tour Operators Initiative (2004).

12.2.3 Policies for Tourism Establishments and Destinations

National policies

Tourism establishments are often too small to be specifically considered in energy or climate change policies. Similarly, their emissions are too small to participate effectively in carbon trading. This leaves tourism businesses with few options to participate proactively in government schemes, as other industries might do. Notwithstanding this, tourism stakeholders have the option to be partners in local sustainable development initiatives, such as Agenda 21. The municipality of Calvia in Majorca, for example, has used its Local Agenda 21 to spearhead planning for a more sustainable tourism – focussing on the needs of the local people and future markets. A total of 639 cities are currently part of the ICLEI (Local Governments for Sustainability) network, a worldwide initiative embracing national and regional government organizations with a commitment to sustainable development. [725]

There are a number of policies that seek to improve the energy performance of buildings in the commercial sector that are relevant to tourism. These have been reviewed by the IPCC. [726] Policies typically refer to legislation such as building codes, mandatory energy labelling, and appliance standards. In addition to regulation there are a number of fiscal policies to address energy use and greenhouse gas emissions. One example is the taxation of fuel, as is commonly done in European countries. Governments also provide incentives such as subsidies or grants, or 'green loans' to facilitate technological investments. The Canadian Government supports the design process of commercial buildings through their 'Commercial Building Incentive Program', similar to 'California's Savings By Design' programme and Germany's 'SolarBau'.

It is important that tourism businesses and their associations engage with climate change policies to negotiate agreements that benefit their sector. The 'Climate Change Levy' in the UK, for example, is a levy on some types of energy used by businesses, such as gas and electricity. Many businesses in the food and drink industry are part of 'Climate Change Agreements', which can rebate up to 80% of the levy. From April 2007, the levy will start increasing in line with inflation, providing an added incentive to consider measures to reduce energy use. Voluntary action is an important pathway to reducing emissions from tourism and there are numerous examples, especially from the hotel sector. Certification and eco-labelling are part of voluntary initiatives and have already been discussed above.

Non-commercial accommodation, including, for instance, second homes, poses specific policy problems since it is characterised by lower energy efficiencies than in permanent housing, combined with low occupation rates which renders improvement measures economically less interesting.

Governments can lead by example, too. 'Parks Canada', which welcomes about 16 million visitors each year, for example, have reduced their greenhouse gas emissions substantially as a result of changes in their vehicle fleets, investment into solar pilot projects and retrofitting of historical site buildings. In 2006, they managed to decrease their GHG emissions below their target for 2010.

International policies

The Clean Development Mechanism (CDM) is an international policy instrument developed as part of the Kyoto Protocol. The CDM allows developed countries (Annex I Parties) to invest in GHG emission reduction projects in developing countries (non-Annex I Parties) that benefit from such activities. A CDM project activity needs to be 'additional'; this means that GHG emissions need to be reduced below those that would have occurred in the absence of the CDM project activity. Afforestation and reforestation projects are also eligible under the CDM.

The United Nations Framework Convention on Climate Change (UNFCCC) reports that there are 684 (31 May 2007) registered CDM projects. Most of them are large projects in the area of refrigerant producing factories and biomass energy. There is only one tourism-related project, the ITC Sonar Bangla in Calcutta India. This hotel is the first in the world to obtain Certified Emission Reductions (CERs) under the CDM from its emission reduction initiatives. Carbon dioxide emission reductions have been achieved through energy conservation initiatives such as waste heat recovery, improved pumping systems and better efficiencies in the air conditioning system. This was equivalent to a reduction of the hotel's total annual energy bill by 19%. While this is an impressive example showing the huge potential for tourism operations to get involved in carbon trading, the procedures are however tedious and often go beyond the means of small businesses.

12.3 The Role of Tour Operators and Other Organisations

National tourism industry associations, grouping the medium and small size businesses, can have a role in influencing or applying national policies. In the highly fragmented tourism sector tour operators can play a key role in influencing a range of small tourism facilities and services they own or sub-contract. The Tour Operators' Initiative (supported by UNWTO, UNEP and UNESCO) has developed a series of guidelines for environmental management of tourism establishment, including energy saving measures, and also developed a series of destination partnership initiatives.

Tour operators play a role in climate change mitigation as they bundle products to packages that are purchased by tourists. While one could argue that tourism is largely demand-driven (i.e., tourists determine what is provided through their purchasing behaviour), there is also a dimension of supplier influence, whereby tourists purchase the products they are offered. To some extent tour operators can influence demand for less carbon intensive packages by creating attractive products that meet tourists' needs and desires. Such products could contain rail travel to the destination (instead of short-haul air), cycle options whilst at the destination and the hire of an energy efficient vehicle. Other options for tour operators are to increase length of stay, which would effectively reduce the carbon footprint per tourist day. It has to be noted that tour operators already seek to increase average length of stay, for example through measures such as 'buy 6 nights, stay another night for free'.

There are numerous examples of tour operators that incorporate alternative transport arrangements into their packages. German tour operator Studiosus, for example, offers 'Anreise mit der Bahn' (travel by train). Other organisations are also seeking to provide energy-efficient transport solutions to tourists. The Deutsche Verkehrsclub (VCD), for example, worked with 10 German holiday destinations to provide 'new paths to nature' by developing and marketing car-free packages for visitors. Similar initiatives have been undertaken by the Swiss Alpine Club and the German Forum Anders Reisen.

12.4 Tourist Behaviour

Though it is clear that the industry shapes demand through marketing, tourists still have relative autonomy in the choice of tourist products. It is likely that a greater awareness of the dangers of climate change will affect tourist attitudes (some of these changes can in fact already be seen) and lead to changes in travel behaviour.

Tourists have thus an important role in creating business interest in restructuring towards a sustainable tourism system by choosing destinations at shorter distances from their homes, choosing environmentally friendly means of transport, demanding more environmentally adequate infrastructure, by favouring destinations that seek to be sustainable, by choosing accommodation that is certified, or eating in restaurants providing local and/or organic food. Tourists can also ask to be transported in new, fuel-efficient aircraft, or demand the use of biofuels, both of which can put pressure on companies to improve their work towards sustainable tourism.

"Customers are seeking a quality hotel at a competitive price, while increasingly demanding ethical and environmental business practices which make them feel good about their hotel choice."

Andrew Cosslett, *Chief Executive Officer of Inter-Continental Hotels Group*[727]

12.4.1 Sustainable Demand and Consumer Choices

To reduce their carbon footprint tourists have a number of options. First, they can decide to replace a long-distance holiday with a short-haul one. This has been actively encouraged in some countries. For example, the President of the German Federal Environment Agency urged consumers to do so, on the eve of Berlin's ITB in March 2007: "Anyone who travels to South Asia by plane should be aware that he is producing over six tons of carbon dioxide."

Reducing the demand for aviation-based transport poses a great dilemma for tourism, especially considering equity issues in the context of international development and poverty reduction efforts. Much of the recent growth in tourism can be attributed to the increased accessibility of air travel to a larger part of the population. There is, however, some evidence that a minor share of 'hypermobile' travellers account for the majority of the overall distances travelled. [728] This is both a challenge and an opportunity, as addressing the travel patterns of these hypermobile travellers could lead to substantial reductions in emissions. However, little is currently known about these travellers in terms of their travel motivations and their willingness to reduce travel or to switch to other means of transport.

The second option for tourists is to choose an airline for its performance in fuel efficiency, environmental initiatives and direct routing. The more stops during the journey (i.e., take-offs) the larger the carbon footprint.

Third, tourists can consider how much luggage they want to take on their trip, particularly on long-haul flights. Scandinavian Airlines has just increased passenger baggage allowances to 40 kg, but environmentally responsible travellers should rather attempt to reduce the weight of their baggage. On a flight from Europe to Australia, each kg of additional baggage carried will add an estimated 2 kg of CO_2 emissions. Obviously, this also goes for tax-free purchases in airports or on aircraft. A bottle of wine bought in New Zealand and transported to Europe, for instance, will demand its own weight in fuel use to be carried along.

Fourth, for shorter distances tourists can replace air travel with energy efficient land transport, for example train systems. A trip from southern to northern Sweden (1,000 km), for instance, will result in emissions of less than 10 grams of CO_2 per passenger if made by train, as Swedish Railways use exclusively renewable power generated from wind and water. An aircraft will emit almost 150 kg of CO_2 per passenger on the same journey. [729]

Finally, tourists have the choice to minimise their transport emissions at the destination. Options include the use of public land transport, renting fuel efficiency vehicles, walking and cycling, switching off equipment in hotel rooms and supporting green businesses.

When tourists use their own vehicle to or at the destination, fuel efficiency and emissions are determined to a large extent by driving behaviour. For example, 'aggressive driving' as compared with 'restrained driving' increases specific fuel consumption by about 30%. The use of air-conditioning increases the fuel bill by 10–15%, and an extra load of 100 kg increases fuel consumption by another 7–8%. [730] Changing driving behaviour was found to be among the most promising measures to reduce passenger transportation emissions in Canada. [731]

12.4.2 Carbon Offsetting

The term 'carbon compensation' or 'offsetting' means that an amount of GHG emissions equal to that caused by a certain activity; i.e., a flight, will be reduced elsewhere. Carbon offsetting is growing rapidly, and promoted by many actors, from Al Gore's film "An Inconvenient Truth" to influential guidebooks such as Lonely Planet and Rough Guide. Tourists willing to compensate their travel emissions can calculate these with the help of an online calculator. Tourists can then choose to invest either in energy-efficiency measures (e.g., low-energy light bulbs), energy renewal (e.g., hydro-turbines), or carbon sequestration (usually forestry projects).

There is still a lot of confusion among tourists about what carbon offsetting is, [732] and there is also evidence that particularly hypermobile travellers, who account for the major share of the distances travelled and emissions caused, are not ready to support voluntary carbon offsets. [733, 734] There is also a risk that carbon offsetting, which has been initiated as a voluntary form of carbon reductions, is now becoming the means used by the industry to 'reduce' emissions. This effectively means that producer responsibility is turned into customer responsibility, which may be problematic if no action to reduce fuel use is taken by the airline. As such, carbon offsetting can be seen as a controversial solution to climate protection, because it potentially diverts from the real causes of the problems and therefore bypasses the structural and technological changes that need to be made to achieve long-term GHG reductions. There is also a moral or guilt dimension to carbon offsetting – redemption through payment. Thus, tourists can travel on Air Canada, for example, and pay C\$ 12.80 for the 800 kilograms of CO_2 that they will have released into the atmosphere between Vancouver and Montreal.

The usefulness of forests as sinks in particular is debated for a number of reasons, including the vast areas needed for forestry schemes, the risk of forest fires, pests and climate change as well as social and other factors that may affect the permanency of the forests. Furthermore, space for offsetting competes with space for biofuels, so to some extent, a choice has to be made between these. Concerns also relate to the difficulty of measuring carbon uptake, sinks as being a short-term solution, the insecurity of projects, and the long-term costs of administration/monitoring. Moreover, in tree-planting schemes the initial rates of sequestration are low and, therefore, it can be years before travel emissions are actually offset. Notwithstanding these caveats, the enhancement of carbon sinks through forestry is recognised in the Kyoto Protocol (Article 3) as a mitigation measure.

The second option of offsetting is by investing in measures for energy efficiency elsewhere or in the future (for example in developing countries by using the money to replace a planned coal electricity plant by one driven by gas or including carbon sequestration). This would support the wider goal of tourism as a means to alleviating poverty and can spread the use of renewable technology in these countries. However, substantial criticism has been forwarded against offsetting projects within the CDM, both with regard to their efficiency and sustainable development benefits.

Carbon offsetting is only one of the available mechanisms to mitigate aviation's impacts on climate. An integrated strategy for the mitigation of aviation's impact on climate change should include a number of mechanisms:

- fuel reduction through improved operations and air traffic management;

- demand management;

- research on the use of alternative fuels and engine's efficiency;

- market mechanisms (taxation);

- emission-charges;

- voluntary initiatives.

Another issue regarding carbon offsetting is related to the choice of an offsetting service. Travellers need clear guidelines on how they should choose the best available carbon offsetting service. Although transparency is the main guiding principle for such selection, there is a need for clear criteria and guidelines that will allow the comparison and evaluation of the effectiveness of various carbon offsetting services. These guidelines could be further linked to a set of global principles for sustainable tourism and criteria for sustainable tourism certification programmes.

12.4.3 Long-haul Travel Reductions and Poverty Alleviation

The analysis in Chapter 11 found that a globally averaged tourist journey is estimated to generate 0.25 t of CO_2 emissions. A small share of tourist trips, however, emits much more than this: while the aviation based trips account for 17% of all tourism trips, they cause about 40 % of CO_2 emissions from tourism. Long-haul travel by air between the five UNWTO world tourism regions represents only 2.2% of all tourist trips, international tourist trips (overnight) by coach and rail, which accounts for an estimated 16% of international tourist trips, stands for only 1% of CO_2 emissions by all international tourist trips (transport only). These results show that mitigation initiatives in the tourism sector will possibly focus on the impact of some particular forms of tourism (i.e., particularly those connected with air travel) if substantial reductions in CO_2 emissions are to be achieved. As section 11.1.6 shows that inter-regional (long-haul) trips from high income to developing countries comprise 4.9% of all tourism air trips and 15.6% of all air transport emissions (excluding same-day tourism). Long haul-trips between developing regions comprises only 0.6% of trips and 1.8% of transport emissions (excluding same-day tourism).

Changes in global tourist flows, however, have to be considered in the context of equity and development of more remote or disadvantaged destinations. In recognition of tourism's role in development and in application of the recommendations of the 2002 Johannesburg Summit on Sustainable Development, the UNWTO, for example, launched an initiative called ST–EP (Sustainable Tourism for the Elimination of Poverty) in 2003. The two goals of climate change mitigation and poverty alleviation have to be addressed in a balanced way, ensuring that development objectives are not jeopardised. Long-haul flights cause high emissions, but only a minor share of the toal air travel is directed to poor regions. Considering that tourism contributes significantly to the economy of developing countries, especially LDCs and SIDS, the implementation of mitigation measures in these countries should be supported by international development funds and programmes.

12.5 Tourism Mitigation Scenarios

This Chapter has identified many examples of how to reduce the contribution from tourism to climate change, including reducing energy consumption, increasing energy efficiency, increasing the use of renewable or carbon-neutral energy sources, and sequestering CO_2 emissions. The global tourism CO_2 emissions and radiative forcing model, developed by the experts (see Chapter 11), is used here to explore how the range of mitigation strategies could be used to estimate reductions of the future CO_2 emissions and RF from the tourism sector (see figure 12.6).

Figure 12.6 Overview of scenario development

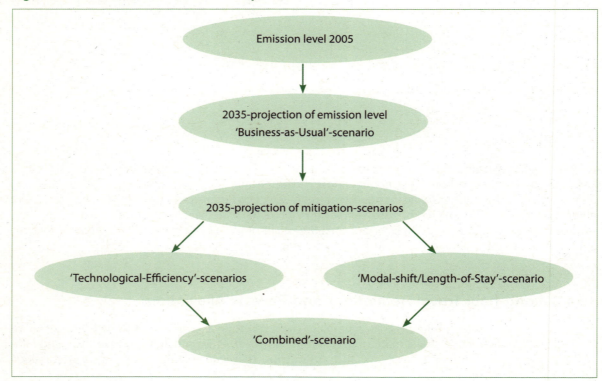

To explore these 'tourism-mitigation-scenarios', the assumptions of the 'business-as-usual' emissions scenario for 2035 that was developed in Chapter 11 are altered to model the potential affect of various mitigation strategies. The purpose is not to provide a political blueprint of measures for a low emission future, but to show the potential responses of the tourism system if certain types of efficiency gains are pursued on a widespread basis and certain types of changes in demand patterns potentially occur. The assumptions of the two mitigation scenarios developed* are outlined below and the resulting GHG emissions are compared with the 'business-as-usual' scenario for 2035.

'Technical-efficiency' scenario

- Reduction in aviation energy consumption per pkm of 50% versus 32% in the 'business-as-usual' scenario;

- additional 2% per year reduction in car transport emissions per pkm over the 'business-as-usual' scenario;

- additional 2% per year reduction in other transport emissions per pkm over the 'business-as-usual' scenario;

- additional 2% per year reduction in accommodation emissions per guest night over the 'business-as-usual' scenario;

- additional 2% per year reduction in activities emissions per trip over the 'business-as-usual' scenario;

'Modal shift/length-of-stay' (LOS) scenario

- No further growth in aviation number of trips and pkm;**

- growth in rail/coach of 2.4% to 5% per year to keep growth in the number of trips constant with the 'business-as-usual' scenario;

- 0.5% per year increase in average LOS instead of a 0.5% reduction per year in the 'business-as-usual' scenario.

The 'technical-efficiency' scenario reduced CO_2 emissions by 38% (Figure 12.7) and RF by 40% versus the 'business-as-usual' scenario in 2035. This scenario did not however achieve absolute reductions in emissions nor in RF versus the 2005 baseline, largely because of the large growth in the number of trips over this timeframe. Emissions of CO_2 were 44% lower in the 'Modal-Shift -Increased LOS Scenario' than the 'business-as-usual' scenario for 2035, but also did not achieve absolute reductions in 2005 baseline emissions (Figure 12.7). However, this scenario does achieve an absolute reduction of RF by 5% with respect to RF in 2005. Notably, when the two scenarios were combined, CO_2 emissions were reduced 68% (equal to 16% below the 2005 baseline – Figure 12.7) and RF reduced by 85%. Several important points emerge from this analysis:

- Increasing LOS is an economically efficient way to save a significant amount of emissions, while retaining the total number of guest nights. Social policies that would contribute to this change in current LOS trends is an important area of further analysis.

---

*   Many other mitigation scenarios with different assumptions are possible; a total 70 were analyzed with the emissions model.

** The number of passenger kilometres is kept constant, using average trip distance as found in the 'business-as-usual' scenario, thus also keeping the number of trips by air transport constant. However, it is possible to keep reach the same emissions reduction with some growth in the number of trips by air transport when the average distance is reduced (i.e. less long-haul and more medium haul)

- Reducing energy use by combinations of modal shift, shift to shorter haul destinations and increased LOS is more effective in reducing CO_2 emissions (–44%) than additional technological energy efficiency improvements alone (–38%).

- Limiting growth of car transport and a modal shift towards rail/coach has a limited impact on CO_2 emissions (–3% if domestic car trips in developed countries is limited to zero growth; –7% if growth in all car trips is limited to zero).

- Aviation efficiency and growth reduction has important impacts on emission reductions (–14% if aviation fuel efficiency is increased to the theoretical limits, and up to –43% if pkm are restricted to current levels). Thus aviation policies are likely to play a crucial role in mitigating tourist emissions.

- 'Aggressive' efficiency measures in accommodations and activities can reduce CO_2 emissions by 14%.

- Only the combination of emission reduction strategies delivered absolute reductions in CO_2 emissions (and RF) in concordance with the goals of the international community for avoiding dangerous climate change and recent discussions of long-term emission reduction targets at the "Vienna Climate Change Talks". In all other mitigation scenarios evaluated, other economic sectors (e.g., agriculture, manufacturing) will have to take a larger share of the mitigation burden as emissions from tourism continued to increase above 2005 baseline levels.

Figure 12.7 Scenarios of CO_2 mitigation potential from global tourism in 2035

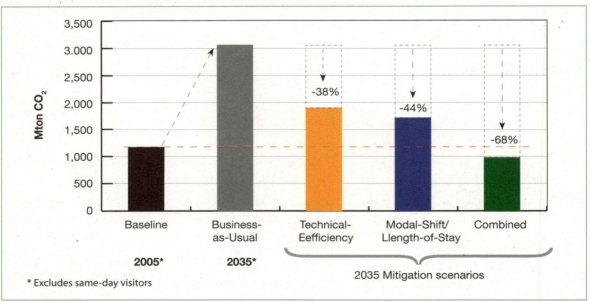

12.6 Conclusion

This Chapter has discussed a wide range of mitigation options for tourism within the aviation and other transport systems, tourism establishments, tour operators and tourists. Mitigation measures range from low-cost initiatives (e.g., using energy-efficient lighting in hotels, monitor energy use) to those that require more effort and investment, for example purchasing more fuel-efficient vehicles, designing a sustainable transport system at a destination, changing transport mode choices or travel patterns. It becomes clear that a combination of measures will be required to reduce the carbon footprint of tourism. This means a wide number of stakeholders need to be involved – airlines, vehicle- and aircraft manufacturers, transport companies, tour operators and travel agents, hotels-resorts, attractions, international organisations, governments at all levels, and tourists themselves – in a suite of activities to reduce emissions, while maintaining the opportunity for tourism development. To achieve this it is important that far more tourism actors become engaged in moving towards mitigate emissions and reduce radiative forcing than is presently the case. So far only relatively few leaders in tourism are actively seeking to reduce their emissions. Voluntary initiatives by a significant percentage of global tourism businesses could have a key role in moving towards sustainability, however, given the uncertainty regarding the effectiveness of voluntary initiatives, a combination of voluntary sector-wide initiatives and consistent government policy and regulatory measures will be needed to generate the far-reaching change required.

In this context it is important to note that there are large differences regarding the effectiveness of various emission reduction initiatives. While there are many options to reduce emissions, the analysis in Chapter 11 and the mitigation scenarios in Section 12.5 suggest that the greatest potential is related to air travel. Reducing growth in the number air transport pkm will achieve more to reduce tourism's contribution to climate change than most other emission reduction measures taken together. As indicated, changes in air travel patterns need to be balanced against other development objectives; however there is considerable potential in many nations for promoting tourism development based on domestic tourism and visitors from neighbouring countries, with relatively low CO_2 emissions per trip.

This Chapter also identified a number of knowledge gaps. Most importantly, there is currently no alternative technology to move to non-fossil-fuel aircraft. Current investments in traditional aircraft mean that the tourism industry will be 'locked into' this technology (and accordingly emissions) for at least a few more decades. In other sectors, such as surface transport and tourism establishments, the non-fossil fuel technology is more advanced and improvements depend more on a successful (and cost-effective) implementation of technologies. This is largely determined by policies (that hinder or encourage such shifts) and by behaviours of the main stakeholders in tourism, including managers who decide to invest in sustainable alternatives and tourists who use these.

Chapter 13

The Way Forward to Adaptation and Mitigation in Tourism

Concern about climate change is increasing worldwide. Compelling evidence suggests that the climate is already changing at an unprecedented rate within human history and the IPCC projects that global mean temperatures will increase between 1.8° C and 4.0° C degrees by the end of the 21st century, compared to the 1980–1999 period, partly depending on the trajectory of GHG emissions in the decades ahead. [735] Even if GHG concentrations were to be stabilised, global warming, sea level rise, and the biogeographical response would continue for centuries. The available evidence suggests that the impacts of global climate change on natural and human systems may be enormous within this century, and that the greater the rate of global warming, the greater the expected impacts. Based on this evidence, the IPCC concluded with very high confidence [736] that climate change would impede the ability of many nations to achieve sustainable development by mid-century and the Stern Review [737] on the Economics of Climate Change concluded that the costs of taking action to reduce GHG emissions now, are much smaller than the costs of economic and social disruption from unmitigated climate change.

As this report has articulated, tourism is not immune to the impacts of climate change as they are becoming evident at destinations as diverse as the European Alps to the Great Barrier Reef. Consequently, UNWTO and a wide range of tourism stakeholders have expressed their shared concern over the potential risks climate change poses for the tourism sector as well as over its non-negligible contribution to climate change through GHG emissions from the transport of tourists, their accommodation and activities. Recognizing that tourism can and must play a significant role in addressing climate change as part of its broader commitment to sustainable development, UNWTO and its partners organised the First International Conference on Climate Change and Tourism in Djerba in 2003. This event was a watershed in terms of raising awareness about the implications of climate change within the international tourism community. As the Davos Conference and this report demonstrates, much has happened since then, with many new climate change initiatives emerging in the tourism sector and substantial progress being made on multiple fronts advance our understanding of the new realities of tourism in an era of global climate change.

13.1 Key Impacts of Climate Change on Tourism

Key impacts of climate change on the tourism sector range from direct impacts on the climate resources of destinations, to indirect environmental impacts (e.g., biodiversity, water resources, landscapes), and to the potential for societal change and political destabilization of some nations. Exploratory studies indicate that a shift of attractive climatic conditions for tourism towards higher latitudes and altitudes is highly probable. As a result, the competitive position of some popular holiday areas are anticipated to decline (e.g., the Mediterranean in summer), whereas other areas (e.g., southern England or southern Canada) are expected to improve. The geographic and seasonal redistribution of climate resources for tourism would have significant impacts at the regional and local scale, producing both 'losers and winners' in terms of visitor flows, but are not anticipated to adversely affect global tourism demand. Conversely, the indirect effects of climate change induced environmental and social change are likely to be largely negative. Impacts such as decreasing natural snow reliability, increasing water shortages, loss of attractive landscapes and biodiversity, and beach erosion will affect many destinations around the world. Like the direct impacts of changing climate conditions, indirect environmental effects are anticipated to have an important impact on tourist demand for specific destinations, but they are not expected to affect overall tourism demand. In contrast, societal changes that may result from climate change, including political and economic instability in some regions, mitigation policies, and changes in consumer patterns and lifestyles, are more likely to adversely affect overall tourism demand as well as demand for particular destinations.

The cumulative effect of direct and indirect impacts of climate change on tourism demand patterns is anticipated to lead to wider impacts on many areas of economic and social policy in destinations, such as employment and labour demand, housing, transport, and social infrastructure. Impacts on the tourism sector would have implications for other economic sectors, such as agriculture supplying tourism demand, handicraft industries and local small business networks that rely on tourism.

13.2 Adaptation to Climate Change

It is unmistakable that all tourism businesses and destinations will need to adapt to climate change in order to minimize the risks and to capitalize upon the opportunities brought about by climate change in an economically, socially and environmentally sustainable manner. The capacity of the tourism sector to adapt to climate change is thought to be relatively high due to its dynamic nature and ability to successfully respond to major challenges in the recent past (e.g., SARS, terrorism attacks in multiple nations, the Asian tsunami, and extreme hurricanes seasons). The most vulnerable destinations (see vulnerability 'hotspots' map in Figure 9.16) will nonetheless require assistance to adapt, particularly in the Least Developed Countries (LDCs) and Small Island Developing States (SIDS), where persistent poverty and environmental needs are anticipated to exacerbate the adverse consequences of climate change, and adaptive capacity is relatively low due to limited financial resources and technical knowledge. Adaptive capacity also varies substantially both within stakeholder groups (e.g., between individual ski area operators) and between stakeholder groups (e.g., between tourists and tourism business operators), depending on financial resources, technical knowledge, capacity to move in most favourable areas or not. Tourists have greater adaptive capacity than owners of a local resort, with the adaptive capacity of tour operators somewhere in the middle of this spectrum. Many adaptation options do not uniquely address the risks of climate change, but represent response to a broader range of climate (e.g., weather extremes, water shortages) and non-climate factors (e.g., general diversification of markets and revenue sources, fuel prices, general commitment to sustainability). The tourism sector must also be cognisant of the implications of climate change adaptation in other economic sectors. As the financial sector incorporates a company's climate change strategy, or lack of one, into its investment criteria, it will influence credit rating and insurance rates.

The causes of climate change are global, however impacts are largely experienced locally and as such these costs cannot just be borne by those affected, especially as those worst affected are likely to be those less able to take action to cope with the changes (e.g., developing countries and local tourism SMMEs). Therefore these costs also need to be addressed by governments and international organisations. The United Nations Secretary-General Ban Ki-moon has called for action by the international community on climate change to be taken in close coordination with action on poverty alleviation and the Millennium Development Goals. The IPCC further contends that there are significant synergies that can be exploited in bringing climate change to the development community and critical development issued to the climate change community, considering especially that until now few discussions about promoting sustainable development have included climate change adaptation. There is an important opportunity for the tourism sector to show leadership in the development of coherent policy agenda that integrates both development and climate change perspectives.

"We cannot achieve a meaningful response to climate change by acting alone. No one can. No single organization. No single sector. Only by working together – as a united travel and tourism force – can we make a difference."

Peter de Jong, *President of the Pacific Asia Travel Association* (2007)

13.3 The Contribution of Tourism to Climate Change

This report represents the first detailed attempt to assess the global share of CO_2 emissions attributable to tourism. The data and research findings assembled in this report indicate that tourism is a non-negligible contributor to climate change and that emissions are expected to grow considerably over the next three decades with a 'business-as-usual' trajectory. International and domestic tourism emissions from three main subsectors (transportation, accommodations, and activities), were estimated to represent between 3.7% and 5.4% of global CO_2 emissions in 2005 (with a best estimate of 4.9%). The contribution of tourism to global warming measured in radiative forcing was estimated to be between 3.7% and 5.4% when cirrus cloud-related effects are excluded (with 4.6% of RF the best estimate).*

Regarding CO_2 emissions by sub-sector, transport generates the largest proportion of emissions (75%). In terms of radiative forcing (contribution to 2005 climate change) the share of transport is larger and ranges from 82% to 90%, with air transport alone accounting for 54% to 75% of the total. Emissions from accommodation and activities were estimated to be lower than transport emissions, but far from negligible.

Variation in emissions from different types of tourist trips is large, with the average trip generating 0.25 tonnes of CO_2. Long-haul and very luxury cruises can however generate up to 9 t CO_2 per trip (i.e., 35 times the emissions caused by an average trip). The majority of tourist trips cause only small amounts of emissions, though. For instance, trips by coach and rail account for 16% of all international tourist trips, but stand only for 1% of CO2 emissions generated by all international tourist trips (transport only). Long-haul travel between the five world regions stands for only 2.2% of all tourist trips, but contributes 16% to global tourist emissions.

The 'business-as-usual' scenario developed for 2035 shows that there will be considerable growth – more than a doubling – in CO_2 emissions and RF in the tourism sector. This strong growth in emission will stand in stark contrast with the objectives of the Kyoto and post-Kyoto Agreements and may thus jeopardize the ability of tourism to contribute fully to United Nation's MDGs. As a consequence, a comprehensive strategy is required to decouple future tourism growth from increased energy consumption, and thus from transport growth.

13.4 Mitigation Potential

Tourism has the responsibility to minimise harmful GHG emissions and there are many technological, behavioural, managerial and policy initiatives that can bring tourism to a more sustainable emissions pathway. For tourism transport, technological improvements are unlikely to be enough to compensate for the rapid growth in demand, in particular for air travel. Large potentials for emission reductions also exist in land transport, accommodation and activities. In particular the energy needed for heating and cooling can be reduced significantly (e.g., through solar heating of water, better insulation, and optimising the use of air-conditioning). The climate change mitigation potential is thought to be relatively high in the tourism sector because efforts to reduce energy consumption and GHG emissions in the sector are still largely in their infancy and thus far have been taken without any vision of a coordinated sector-wide strategic response. [738] The Mitigation Scenarios developed suggest that emissions of the 2035 'business-as-usual' trajectory could be reduced by 38% with the 'technical-efficiency' scenario and 44% with the 'modal-shift' and 'length-of-stay' scenario. Importantly, when these scenarios are combined emissions were able to be reduced to 16% below the 2005 baseline, which is consistent with the desired emissions pathway of the international community, as discussed at the "Vienna Climate Change Talks". ** This study shows that with combinations of strong mitigation effort significant emission reduction is possible by 2035 versus a 'business-as-usual' trajectory, without jeopardizing the growth of

---

*   Because of the large uncertainty related to the radiative forcing effects of cirrus clouds, the radiative forcing for tourism ranges from 3.4% to a possible maximum of 9.0% when the cirrus-related effects are included in the analysis. This range will not be able to be reduced until the scientific understanding of the radiative forcing influence of cirrus clouds improves.

**   The 'Vienna Climate Change Talks 2007' represent the latest international negotiations on GHG emission reductions under the auspices of the United Nations Framework Convention on Climate Change. www.unis.unvienna.org/unis/pressrels/2007/unisinf230.html

world tourism in number of trips or guest nights. Achieving this desirable alternative scenario will not be easy and concerted action by the entire tourism sector must commence in the very near term.

Climate change mitigation policies within tourism will have to find a balance between potentially conflicting objectives. Clearly, decisions on climate change and tourism have implications for local, national and global, as well as inter-generational equity and all these aspects need to be taken into account to arrive at an effective policy mix. For example, the most effective mitigation option for tourism would be to reduce the growth in the demand for flying (e.g., by increasing taxation and/or including the aviation sector in emissions trading schemes). However, such policy options must be weighed carefully against the other socio-economic benefits of tourism, including the needs of developing countries in terms of poverty alleviation and other Millennium Development Goals, and the support of protected areas and biodiversity, especially because long-haul travel from the industrialized countries causes most emissions, while only a minor share of this long-haul travel is directed to poor regions.

> "If we were to turn a switch off tomorrow to the travel industry, far from saving the planet, we would be causing wholesale extinction of species. We would be losing vast areas of wilderness around the planet. [...] there would be no (economic) justification to protect it."
>
> Costas Christ, *Senior Director for Ecotourism, Conservation International* [739]

13.5 Knowledge Gaps and Research Needs

Clearly, this state of knowledge report is not an end product; it is a snapshot of the state of knowledge in a rapidly evolving field of research and policy development. A number of important knowledge gaps have been identified throughout this report. There is a need to improve the knowledge base about the use of weather and climate information in the tourism sector, and specifically ensure the availability of weather data to support the regionally specific decision-making needs of the tourism sector. While our understanding of the impacts of climate change for various destination types has improved, there remain major regional gaps in our knowledge of how climate change will affect the natural and cultural resources critical for tourism in Africa, the Caribbean, South America, the Middle East and large parts of East Asia (see Table 9.8 and Figure 9.16). The lack of common climate change impact indicators in the tourism sector has hindered the comparison and synthesis of existing studies. Many analyses of potential impacts at destinations have focused on a narrow range of impacts (e.g., natural snow cover for skiing), but to understand the implications of climate change for a destination requires the development of an integrated systems approach [740] that holistically considers four-season supply and demand-side impacts and adaptation options. Climate change analogues are an important, but as yet under-utilized, technique to assess the implications of climate change for destinations, when current supply and demand-side adaptations are employed.

Understanding tourist climate preferences, the seasonal triggers for key tourism activities, and their perceptions of the environmental impacts of global climate change at destinations remain important knowledge gaps that need to be addressed to project more accurate potential long-range shifts in tourism demand. In addition, our understanding of the relative importance of climate change vis-à-vis other longer term market trends, as well as the interactions between these trends and climate change remains very limited. To date the limited climate change research on the tourism and recreation sector has examined the implications of a changed climate almost exclusively with the assumption that 'all else will remain equal.' Knowing that 'all will not remain equal' over the next 20 to 80 years in any economic sector, let alone the rapidly evolving tourism sector, future research must also consider how climate change will interact with other major influencing variables in the tourism sector (globalization and economic fluctuations, fuel prices, aging populations in industrialized countries, increasing travel safety and health concerns, increased environmental and cultural awareness, advances in information and transportation technology, environmental limitations – water supply and pollution). The interaction of climate change impacts and other demographic and societal trends shaping tourism development over the coming decades is a fruitful area of further inquiry. This calls for ambitious research on scenario development for the tourism and travel sector.

"Given that climate change is expected to pose an increasing threat to tourism operations in many destinations [...], WMO urges governments and the private sector to increasingly use climate information generated through National Meteorological and Hydrological Services [...], and to take additional steps towards incorporating climate considerations in tourism policies, development and management plans."

Michel Jarraud, *WMO Secretary-General* (2007)

Climate change adaptation is a long-term process that must be anticipated and carefully planned. The information requirements for effective, anticipatory climate change adaptation will be substantial and therefore adaptation is another critical area for future research. Many climate change impact studies for destinations or specific tourism sectors (e.g., ski operations) have not even identified the range of adaptation options available to tourism stakeholders, let alone integrated them into the impact analysis. This can give a very misleading perspective of projected impacts. Much more needs to be done to incorporate adaptation into future impact assessments in the tourism sector given its high adaptive capacity. Climate change is slowly entering into decision-making of a range of tourism stakeholders (e.g., investors, insurance companies, tourism enterprises, governments, and tourists). Studies that have examined the climate change risk appraisal of tourism operators have generally found relatively low levels of concern and little evidence of long-term strategic planning in anticipation of future changes in climate. Consequently, the mainstreaming of climate change into decision-making within the tourism sector would appear several steps away. Climate change adaptation by private and public sector tourism-recreation operators is likely to remain reactive and consist mainly of incremental adjustments of existing climate adaptations. There is some evidence that tourism operators may be overestimating their adaptive capacity (e.g., capacity to make snow under the warmest scenarios), furthering the need for cooperation between the tourism industry and climate change research community to test the ability of current adaptations to cope with projected climate conditions.

In order to refine the baseline calculations of GHG emissions from the tourism sector presented in this report and effectively monitor progress on GHG emission reductions in the future a strategic reassessment of the current system of tourism statistics will be required. Tourism statistics has been successfully evolving to provide more accurate information on tourism's economic impact, through the Tourism Satellite Account system. Specification will be similarly necessary for the collection of appropriate data at the necessary spatial and temporal resolutions, in order to allow a more accurate calculation of tourism-generated emissions. Introducing more accurate information on distance travelled, transport modes and domestic tourism flows, would be a critical first step.

To combat the threat of climate change, more research as well as closer co-ordination between governments, researchers and the private sector is needed to ensure that possible effects are factored into all relevant tourism policies and development and management plans. It is in the best interest of the tourism industry and applicable government agencies (federal, state and local levels) to engage in collaboration when responding to climate change. A joint determination of the potential implications of climate change dispels misinformation and provides the various stakeholders with the best opportunities to minimize the risks and capitalize upon the opportunities likely to be brought about by climate change in an economically and environmentally sustainable manner.

13.6 Time Horizons

Increased understanding is not only needed in relation to the nature and magnitude of climate change impacts, but also to their timing. Figure 13.1 provides a highly generalized timeline, indicating when key types of climate change impacts could shift from being observed and generally minor and limited to a small number of destinations (yellow); to moderate impacts, beyond the possibility of low-effort adaptation, in a substantial number of tourism destinations (orange); to potentially widespread and severe impacts (red). When climate change impacts begin to erode the sustainability of tourism destinations depends of course on the magnitude of climate change realized and specific destination characteristics. For comparison, Figure 13.1 also depicts the working careers of tourism professionals and forward commitment of tourism infrastructure and investment horizons. The unmistakable conclusion is that the significance of climate change to tourism is not in some distant and remote future, and actions should be taken now to prevent negative impacts and to mitigate tourism's contribution to the causes of climate change. Climate change is becoming an important decision-making influence for many already employed in the tourism sector, and the next generation of tourism professionals will need to contend with virtually all of the key impacts identified in this report. Projected impacts are known to be already influencing decision-making within the tourism sector, including tourists, forward looking tourism businesses and investors, and international tourism organizations. The process of adaptation must commence now in particular where critical resources are already affected by climate change (e.g., snow cover, coral reefs) or by multiple stresses (e.g., water, biodiversity), and where long lasting infrastructure investments are made (accommodation and tourism related utilities).

Figure 13.1   Timeline of people, infrastructure and the onset of impacts of climate change in tourism

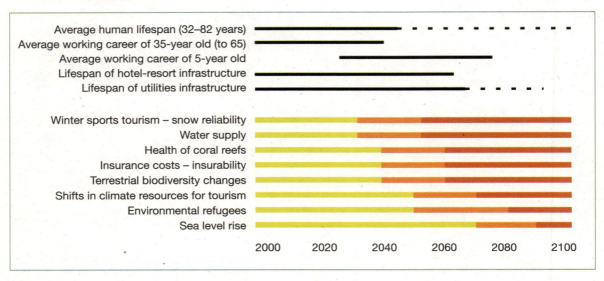

The IPCC has made it clear that global climate change is only just beginning. Its impacts on the tourism sector will steadily intensify, particularly under higher emission scenarios. Climate change would redistribute climate resources for tourism geographically and seasonally and poses a risk to ecosystems around the world. The nature and intensity of climate change impacts will differ for tourism destinations around the world. The most vulnerable regions are in developing countries, which generally also have less adaptive capacity [741], and this will be a particular challenge for their tourist destinations and their host communities. Climate change impacts on the tourism sector could influence other economic sectors, such as agriculture and local business networks supplying tourism. Conversely, climate change impacts on other economic sectors could have significant impacts on tourism, such as insurance coverage. Climate change mitigation also requires the transformation of energy and transportation systems worldwide, with implications for the cost of travel and tourist mobility. Climate change also has the potential to have a serious adverse effect on the global economy and poses a security risk in some regions. Consequently, climate change is anticipated to have profound implications that could fundamentally transform aspects of the global tourism sector.

The future is now – This report makes it clear that the tourism sector has already entered into an era where the observed and potential consequences of global climate change are defining new realities for consumer, business, and government decision-making. While much more work is needed in this rapidly developing area of science and policy, the evidence is clear that the time is now for the tourism community to collectively formulate a strategy to address what must be considered the greatest challenge to the sustainability of tourism in the 21st century.

Methodological Note on UNWTO's Estimates on Worldwide Tourism Volumes

This Annex includes the methodological note on UNWTO's estimates on worldwide tourism volumes and tables of UNWTO approximations of consistent worldwide tourism volumes.

A1.1 Methodological Note on UNWTO's Estimates on Worldwide Tourism Volumes

For almost all countries in the world, tourism represents an important part of the economy. As tourism is a broad and complex concept, which covers a great variety of activities, it is necessary to define it carefully. To understand tourism properly, we should look more closely at what it includes and at the relative weight of the various elements.

Existing tourism data present several constraints for emission inventories. For that reason, UNWTO prepared for the purpose of this report a specific set of tables with approximations of consistent worldwide tourism volumes for the reference year of 2005. These are based on the various indicators available in its database as well as on air transport data from ICAO and IATA. These tables contain a mix of hard data, estimations – missing data is extrapolated or derived from similar countries – and approximations – where only little data is available.

A1.1.1 Definitions

Tourism

According to the System of Tourism Statistics (STS), 'Tourism' is defined as "[…] the activities of persons travelling to and staying in places outside their usual environment for not more than one consecutive year for leisure, business and other purposes not related to the exercise of an activity remunerated from within the place visited".

'Tourism' refers to all activities of visitors, including both 'tourists (overnight visitors)' and 'same-day visitors'.

This concept can be applied to different forms of tourism. Depending upon whether a person is travelling to, from or within a certain country the following forms can be distinguished:

- **Inbound Tourism,** involving the non-residents received by a destination country from the point of view of that destination;

- **Outbound Tourism,** involving residents travelling to another country from the point of view of the country of origin;

- **Domestic tourism,** involving residents of a given country travelling within that country.

Therefore, tourism covers not only international travel (i.e. inbound tourism from the point of view of destinations, or outbound tourism from the point of view of generating markets); it also covers tourism inside one's country of residence (i.e. domestic tourism).

As an economic activity, tourism is defined on the one hand by the demand and consumption of visitors, whether by tourists (i.e. overnight visitors) or by same-day visitors; on the other hand, tourism refers to the goods and services produced to meet that demand. As such it comprises a whole range of different activities, e.g., transport to and at the destination, accommodation, catering, entertainment, shopping, services of travel agencies, outgoing and incoming tour operators, etc.

Users concerned more specifically with the production and analysis of tourism statistics will find additional references in the UNWTO's official documents "*Recommendations on Tourism Statistics*" and "*Tourism Satellite Account (TSA): Recommended Methodological Framework*". These two documents, approved by the United Nations, contain the existing recommendations on tourism statistics. The purpose of the first of these, approved in 1993, was to develop a first set of basic elements of STS, and the second relates to the Tourism Satellite Account (TSA), approved in 2000.

More detailed information on concepts, definitions, classifications, indicators, methods of compiling and units of measure can be obtained also from:

- the Basic References on Tourism Statistics on the UNWTO website under the link <www.unwto.org/statistics/basic_references/index-en.htm> setting out the main components that make up the System of Tourism Statistics (STS);

or from the following UNWTO publications:

- Technical Manual No. 1: Concepts, Definitions, and Classifications for Tourism Statistics (1995);

- Technical Manual No. 2: Collection for Tourism Expenditure Statistics (1995);

- Technical Manual No. 3: Collection of Domestic Tourism Statistics (1995);

- Technical Manual No. 4: Collection and Compilation of Tourism Statistics (1995);

- Data Collection and Analysis for Tourism Management, Marketing and Planning (2000).

A1.1.2 Basic Tourism Facts

International tourism is a major source of income for many destinations. In 2005, the receipts registered for international tourism amounted to over US$ 676 billion. Worldwide this represents around 30% of the total exports of services, a percentage that in Least Developed Countries (LDCs) goes as high as 70%.

Just over half of international tourism is undertaken for the purpose of leisure, recreation and holidays (51%). Business travel accounts for 15% of the total and the remaining 27% is related to other motives, e.g., visiting friends and relatives, religious purposes/pilgrimages, health treatment, while for 7% the purpose of visit is not specified.

Around 45% of international tourists arrive at their destination by means of air transport and another 47% use land (coach, car or rail transport). Sea transport accounts for 7%.

Most international travel takes place to destinations within the same region. Worldwide, four out of five arrivals originate within the region, while the remaining one fifth arrives from other regions of the world. In Europe, the share of intraregional arrivals is as high as 88%, while in Africa and in the Middle East, intraregional arrivals represent less than half of all arrivals (46%).

The industrialised countries of Europe, the Americas and Asia and the Pacific are the main generating markets for tourism. However, in the past decades many emerging economies have started to contribute as well, In 2005, around 60 countries recorded more than US$ 1 billion each year in international tourism expenditure. Of the 152 million interregional arrivals in 2005, most are generated by Europe (69 million), the Americas (39 million) and Asia and the Pacific (33 million).

In addition to international tourism (inbound and outbound), many countries count with a strong domestic tourism market (see A1.1.3.2).

See for more information the *Facts & Figures* section on the UNWTO website at www.unwto.org/facts/ menu.html, as well as the *Tourism Highlights* at www.unwto.org/facts/eng/highlights.htm.

A1.1.3 UNWTO's Estimates on World Tourism Volume

There are various units of measure to quantify the volume of tourism. An overview is set out below:

A1.1.3.1 International tourism

Regarding the international comparability of data, the *Compendium of Tourism Statistics* is the basic reference. The following units of measurement are used:

Unit of measurement			Comment
Visitors	*Arrivals*	• *at frontiers (VF)*	• or at a specific place in case of domestic tourism
Tourists (overnight visitors)	*Arrivals*	• *at frontiers (TF)*	• or at a specific place in case of domestic tourism
		• *at collective tourism establishments (e.g. hotels and other. such as campings. etc.) (TCE)*	• excludes tourism in private accommodation;
		• *at hotels and similar establishments (THS)*	• arrivals are counted in every new accommodation visited
	Nights	• *at collective tourism establishments (e.g., hotels and other) (NCE)*	• excludes tourism in private accommodation;
		• *at hotels and similar establishments (NHS)*	• arrivals are counted in every new accommodation visited

The most common unit of measure used to quantify the volume of International Tourism for statistical purposes is the number of International Tourist Arrivals. For a proper understanding of this unit, two considerations should be taken into account:

• Data refer exclusively to tourists (overnight visitors): 'a visitor who stays at least one night in a collective or private accommodation in the country visited'. Same-day visitors are not included.

• Data refer to the number of arrivals and not to the number of persons. The same person who makes several trips to a given country during a given period will be counted as a new arrival each time, as well as a person who travels through several countries on one trip is counted as a new arrival each time.

Many countries provide both data on overall international visitor numbers as well as on tourists. This has been used to approximate the number of same-day visitors.

A1.1.3.2 Domestic Tourism

International comparable data on domestic tourism is unfortunately still rather scarce. Domestic tourism volumes as presented in the report are approximations by UNWTO based on a combination of data for selected individual countries:

- A limited number of countries provide data on domestic trips, often with varying methodology and coverage.

- Accommodation statistics generally cover the number of nights spent by residents at hotels and similar establishments and / or at all collective tourism establishments.

- Statistics on the demand for domestic air transport and the share of air transport in the overall volume, also allow for an assessment.

Accordingly, domestic tourism demand is approximated to have accounted for about 8 billion trips worldwide in 2005, of which 4 billion are estimated to be from same-day visitors and 4 billion from (overnight) tourists.

Taking into account individual countries with data available on domestic tourism in one way or another – number of trips, number of nights spent or domestic air transport - the breakdown over developing and high-income countries (as classified by the World Bank) is approximated to be roughly half/half. This breakdown is relevant as the emission factors are assumed to differ between developing and high income countries, because of a different modal split (more air and car transport in high-income countries and more bus and train in the case of developing countries), as well as a higher occupation when travelling by car in developing countries.

A1.1.3.3 Transport data

For air transport, data from ICAO is used on overall numbers of passenger kilometres flown, while data from IATA's *World Air Transport Statistics* have been used to subdivide traffic in intraregional and interregional.

When analysing air transport data, it is essential to realise that traffic is based on the country or region of airline registration and that flows reflect both inbound and outbound tourism. When talking for instance about transatlantic traffic from Europe, this refers to both Europeans travelling to the Americas and Americans to Europe as well as to passengers from other regions travelling through Europe to the Americas. Furthermore, passenger numbers cannot be directly compared to international tourist arrivals as reported by destinations, because passengers are counted on each segment of a trip. So a return trip results at least in a passenger count of two and when it is not by a direct flight even in more.

A1.1.4 Sources of Data

Quantitative tourism-related data is based on a selection of data included in the UNWTO database on *World Tourism Statistics.* This database contains a variety of series for over 200 countries and territories covering data for most countries from the 1980's on. The database is maintained by the UNWTO Secretariat and is updated on a continuous base.

Statistical data have been collected by the UNWTO Secretariat from the official institutions of the countries and territories (UNWTO member as well as non-member countries) or from other international bodies. e.g., the Caribbean Tourism Organization (CTO), the International Monetary Fund (IMF), etc.

The data for individual countries are based on full year results, or projections, as communicated to the UNWTO Secretariat by the authorities of the countries and territories or disseminated through news releases, publications or on the Internet. For many countries, figures are still preliminary and frequently subject to revision.

In the world and (sub)regional aggregates, estimates are included for countries and territories with data still missing based upon data available for a part of the year or the general trend for the region. In particular for the Middle East and Africa, the regional and subregional aggregates should be treated with caution as estimations are based on a relatively small number of countries and territories that supplied data for the entire year.

UNWTO tourism statistics generally refer to figures for a country as a whole. In the collection of statistics, however, except for independent states, there are also a number of dependencies or territories of special sovereignty included (for instance Hong Kong, China, or French Polynesia, France). These territories report tourism figures independently and are for the sake of tourism statistics considered as an entity in itself. Because of this, where reference is made to 'countries', the term generally should be taken to mean 'countries and territories'. In a few other cases, dependencies are not separately listed but included in the total for the country they depend upon (for instance Guernsey, Jersey and the Isle of Man in United Kingdom). In general, UNWTO does not collect data on the level of regions, states, provinces or specific destinations within a country. Most countries will have a further regional breakdown available as well as other series not included in the UNWTO database on *World Tourism Statistics*. Please refer to national sources for these data.

The regional country groupings are according to the UNWTO regional commissions. See www.unwto. org/facts/eng/methodological.htm for the countries and territories included in the various regions and subregions.

The World Tourism Organization is aware of the limitations of the available statistical information on tourism. Despite the considerable progress made in recent decades, international tourism statistics are often not uniform, because definitions and methods of data collection tend to differ. Every user of this information should bear in mind that the international comparability of statistical data is still not optimal.

A1.2 Tables of UNWTO Approximations of Consistent Worldwide Tourism Volumes

Table A1.1 International tourist arrivals by generating region and destination region, 2005 (thousand) [a]

From: To:	World	Europe	Asia and the Pacific	Americas	Middle East	Africa	Origin not specified
Word	**802,560**	**453,700**	**153,921**	**135,666**	**22,609**	**21,815**	**14,849**
Europe	**438,723**	**384,271**	**17,480**	**26,393**	**2,198**	**2,761**	**5,618**
Northern Europe	51,040	39,867	3,491	6,328	374	725	255
Western Europe	142,596	121,439	7,509	10,390	654	1,465	1,139
Central/Eastern Europe	87,790	80,836	2,873	1,951	162	87	1,882
Southern/Mediter. Eu.	157,296	142,129	3,607	7,724	1,008	485	2,343
Asia and the Pacific	**155,357**	**19,104**	**121,029**	**10,473**	**965**	**949**	**2,838**
North-East Asia	87,498	7,210	73,447	5,408	161	402	870
South-East Asia	49,312	6,428	37,601	2,890	464	303	1,626
Oceania	10,499	1,968	7,180	1,117	54	86	95
South Asia	8,049	3,498	2,802	1,058	286	158	247
Americas	**133,216**	**23,904**	**9,016**	**96,427**	**218**	**417**	**3,235**
North America	89,891	14,248	8,413	65,028	196	314	1,692
Caribbean	18,800	4,517	77	13,335	2	11	858
Central America	6,288	605	98	5,420	1	3	161
South America	18,237	4,534	427	12,644	19	89	524
Middle East	**38,000**	**10,657**	**5,297**	**1,139**	**17,522**	**1,324**	**2,060**
Africa	**37,264**	**15,763**	**1,099**	**1,234**	**1,706**	**16,364**	**1,099**
North Africa	13,911	10,183	198	204	1,560	1,357	409
Subsaharan Africa	23,353	5,580	901	1,030	146	15,007	690

(a) Including estimates for countries with missing data.

Source: World Tourism Organization

Table A1.2 International tourist trips by generating region and destination region, 2005 (thousand) [a]

From: / To:	World	Europe	Americas	Asia and the Pacific	Middle East	Africa
Word	**746,900**	**432,044**	**125,649**	**145,947**	**22,782**	**20,478**
Europe	**401,297**	**365,528**	**18,550**	**13,181**	**1,811**	**2,227**
Northern Europe	46,321	38,159	4,543	2,699	313	607
Western Europe	125,321	111,288	6,983	5,407	507	1,136
Central/Eastern Europe	82,567	78,673	1,424	2,258	138	74
Southern/Mediter. Eu.	147,088	137,408	5,600	2,817	853	411
Americas	**128,948**	**23,550**	**95,776**	**8,990**	**217**	**414**
North America	88,772	14,237	65,619	8,406	196	314
Caribbean	17,091	4,303	12,702	74	2	10
Central America	5,717	564	5,057	92	1	3
South America	17,369	4,446	12,399	419	19	87
Asia and the Pacific	**144,827**	**16,700**	**9,021**	**117,417**	**862**	**827**
North-East Asia	81,746	6,069	4,552	70,652	136	338
South-East Asia	45,722	5,539	2,491	37,031	400	261
Oceania	9,611	1,655	939	6,900	45	72
South Asia	7,747	3,437	1,039	2,834	281	155
Middle East	**36,709**	**10,732**	**1,147**	**5,334** [b]	**18,163**	**1,333**
Africa	**35,119**	**15,535**	**1,155**	**1,024**	**1,728**	**15,677**
North Africa	13,773	10,387	208	202	1,591	1,384
Subsaharan Africa	21,346	5,147	947	822	137	14,293

(a) Including estimates for countries with missing data.

(b) Some 70% is estimated to originate from South Asia (short- and mid-haul) and some 30% from North-East. South-East Asia and Oceania (long-haul).

Data collected by UNWTO is generally based on arrivals reported by destination countries and not on trips from source markets.   As one trip can produce arrivals in more than one destination. arrivals had to be converted to trips by using assumptions on the average number of arrivals per trip. This conversion factor varied between 1.01 (i.e. from any region to North Africa) and 1.50 (i.e.from Americas to Western Europe) based on the probability of multi destination trips for a certain subregion.

Arrival with origin not specified have been divided over the various regions by ratio.

Color code:

- travel within same region
- short-haul between regions
- long-haul. predominantly from - to
  - high income-developing
  - developing-developing
  - developing-high income
  - high income-high income

Source: World Tourism Organization

Table A1.3 Arrivals by mode of transport, 2005 [a]

	Total	Air	Land	Water	Not specified
	International Tourist Arrivals (million)				
World	**802.6**	**363.7**	**377.2**	**58.1**	**3.5**
Africa	37.3	17.9	16.6	2.6	0.1
Americas	133.2	73.4	52.3	7.4	0.1
Asia and the Pacific	155.4	74.5	62.9	15.3	2.6
Europe	438.7	179.9	227.5	30.6	0.7
Middle East	38.0	18.0	17.8	2.2	0.0
	International Tourist Arrivals (%)				
World	**100**	**45.3**	**47.0**	**7.2**	**0.4**
Africa	100	48.1	44.6	7.1	0.2
Americas	100	55.1	39.3	5.6	0.1
Asia and the Pacific	100	48.0	40.5	9.8	1.7
Europe	100	41.0	51.9	7.0	0.2
Middle East	100	47.5	46.8	5.7	0.0

(a) Including estimates for countries with missing data.

Source: World Tourism Organization

Table A1.4 Arrivals by purpose of visit, 2005 [a]

	Total	Leisure, recreation and holidays	Business and professional	VFR, health, religion, other	Not specified
	International Tourist Arrivals (million)				
World	**802.6**	**404.8**	**122.6**	**218.0**	**57.2**
Africa	37.3	19.9	5.0	10.5	1.9
Americas	133.2	58.6	15.0	31.7	27.9
Asia and the Pacific	155.4	71.1	24.4	33.0	26.8
Europe	438.7	235.3	72.3	130.6	0.6
Middle East	38.0	19.8	5.9	12.2	0.0
	International Tourist Arrivals (%)				
World	**100**	**50.4**	**15.3**	**27.2**	**7.1**
Africa	100	53.5	13.4	28.1	5.0
Americas	100	44.0	11.3	23.8	20.9
Asia and the Pacific	100	45.8	15.7	21.2	17.3
Europe	100	53.6	16.5	29.8	0.1
Middle East	100	52.2	15.6	32.2	0.0

(a) Including estimates for countries with missing data.

Source: World Tourism Organization

Table A1.5 Scheduled services of airlines of ICAO contracting states by ICAO statistical region of airline registration and non-scheduled traffic, 2005

	Passenger transport						Passenger and freight				
	Passengers (PAX)		Revenue Passenger-Km (RPK)		Km per PAX	Load factor	Aircraft departures	Aircraft kms	kms per departure	PAX as part of total(a)	Estimate of PAX per departure
	million	%	billion	%		%	000	million		%	
Total including non-scheduled		3,982									
International non-scheduled traffic(b)		263									
Total scheduled	**2,022**	**100**	**3,720**	**100**	**1,839**	**75**	**24,910**	**30,850**	**1,238**	**71**	**115**
North America	764	37.8	1,335	35.9	1,746	78	10,970	13,170	1,201	71	98
Latin America and Caribbean	108	5.3	159	4.3	1,480	69	1,660	1,630	982	76	85
Europe	542	26.8	1,005	27.0	1,853	76	6,750	7,930	1,175	71	113
Asia and Pacific	501	24.8	967	26.0	1,930	72	4,410	6,340	1,438	64	178
Middle East	68	3.4	169	4.5	2,467	73	560	1,030	1,839	64	191
Africa	38	1.9	85	2.3	2,206	66	560	750	1,339	77	89
International	**704**	**100**	**2,197**	**100**	**3,121**	**75**	**7,070**	**14,810**	**2,095**	**64**	**157**
North America	93	13.3	389	17.7	4,165	79	1,020	2,740	2,686	69	133
Latin America and Caribbean	31	4.4	95	4.3	3,083	71	410	840	2,049	71	107
Europe	361	51.3	866	39.4	2,397	77	4,050	6,360	1,570	69	129
Asia and Pacific	151	21.5	623	28.3	4,115	73	990	3,390	3,424	57	270
Middle East	46	6.5	152	6.9	3,340	73	350	900	2,571	62	211
Africa	22	3.1	72	3.3	3,353	66	250	580	2,320	75	115
Domestic	**1,318**	**100**	**1,522**	**100**	**1,155**	**75**	**17,840**	**16,040**	**899**	**85**	**87**
North America	671	50.9	945	62.1	1,409	77	9,950	10,430	1,048	84	81
Latin America and Caribbean	77	5.8	64	4.2	836	66	1,250	790	632	88	70
Europe	181	13.7	139	9.1	767	69	2,700	1,570	581	93	72
Asia and Pacific	350	26.5	345	22.7	986	71	3,420	2,950	863	86	119
Middle East	23	1.7	16	1.1	719	78	210	130	619	92	117
Africa	17	1.3	13	0.8	746	69	310	170	548	93	59

(a) Where freight and passenger traffic are both measured in tonnekilometres

(b) Covers the non-scheduled traffic of scheduled airlines and non-scheduled operators.

PAX: Passengers carried; Note: this refers to flight segments. i.e. each time a passenger boards an airplane. and not to the number of trips. A return trip involves at least 2 counts. and more if it is through a hub.

RPK: Revenue passenger-kilometres (RPK with one RPK representing one paying passenger transported over one kilometre)

LF: Load factor. The amount of revenue passenger-kilometres divided by the number of passenger kilometres available (ASK)

Source: Compiled by UNWTO from ICAO

Emission Calculations

The purpose of Annex 2 is to give a comprehensive justification of all methods used and assumptions made for the calculation of the emissions.

A2.1 General Method for Emission Inventories

Any detailed calculation of emissions from tourism is dependent on the availability of a comprehensive data set on tourism demand. At the moment, existing data on tourism demand (international and domestic) present several constraints for emission inventories. UNWTO publishes regularly data on international tourism at country level (regional and world data on international visitor arrivals, international tourist arrivals and overnight stays), as well as in an aggregated form, but only limited information is available on domestic tourism. Another problem complicating calculations is that for international tourism, though arrivals are recorded for each transport mode, only for air transport data are available for distances traveled. Comprehensive data on all modes of transport are only available for EU tourism. [742, 743]

For the purpose of this report UNWTO prepared a set of tables with an approximation of consistent worldwide tourism volumes for the baseline year of 2005 containing data on trip numbers (i.e., not arrivals, as one trip may account for various arrivals), domestic and same-day trips, as well as data on average length of stay and air transport distances for major tourism flows based on data from UNWTO, ICAO and IATA (see Annex 1). For car and other transport modes, the total volume of passenger kilometres (pkm) was estimated using typical average distances for the respective transport mode (see Section A2.2.1). Passenger kilometers traveled were then multiplied by emission factors for the respective modes of transport (see Table 11.2 in Chapter 11).

One of the main problems is to calculate emissions from activities undertaken by tourists at the destination. Information in this area is very scattered, and there can be huge differences in the energy-intensity of such activities. However, there is evidence that activities contribute only a minor share to overall emissions from tourism, and the large uncertainty regarding these is likely to only have a marginal impact on overall emissions.

A2.2 Detailed Calculations

A2.2.1 Transport Modal Split, Volumes and Emissions

In order to calculate emissions, tourist transport volumes (measured in number of trips and pkm) needed to be split into shares for air, car and other (coach, rail and water), as these means of transport make substantially different contributions to greenhouse gas emissions, if calculated per pkm (see Table 11.2 in Chapter 11). The goal is, however, to calculate global emissions by multiplying trip numbers by distance (per trip) and to multiply the kilometers traveled by an emission factor for the respective means of transport used. To do this, it needs to be considered that there are large differences between high income and developing countries in terms of transport modes used, the distribution of short- and long-haul trips, and emission factors for transport, accommodation and other activities. The set of tables with approximations of consistent worldwide tourism volumes for the baseline year of 2005 (see Annex

1), initially developed for this report by UNWTO, provided data on the number of trips and distances traveled for air transport and on number of trips for other means of transport (over land and water). Some further development of the data was thus necessary:

- The number of trips over land and water needed to be split into two transport categories, car and other (rail, coach and water, which are rather similar regarding emissions per pkm).

- The distances covered by non-air transport modes needed to be estimated (in pkm).

- The distances covered by air needed to be split up for international intra- and interregional travel, as the length of the flight influences average per pkm emissions.

Table A2.1 provides an overview over the data used as input to the excel model for calculating the final emissions as developed by the experts. This means that the secundary data, those numbers that were directly or indiractly calculated from the primary input data, have been omitted. For example: the numbers of trips for the different source markets are given, but not the total. Full overviews of all coherent results are given in Chapter 11.

Table A2.1 Overview of all input data and the sources used to designate values to them

International tourists		
Input variable	**Value**	**Source**
Number of trips by air transport (trips)	340 million	UNWTO (Annex 1)
Number of trips non-air transport (trips)	410 million	UNWTO (Annex 1)
Number of intra-regional air (trips)	215 million	UNWTO (Annex 1)
Number of inter-regional air (trips)	125 million	UNWTO (Annex 1)
Total number of intra-regional (trips)	615 million	UNWTO (Annex 1)
Total number of inter-regional (trips)	135 million	UNWTO (Annex 1)
Number of intra-regional air (pkm)	833 billion	UNWTO (Annex 1)
Number of inter-regional air (pkm)	1,751 billion	UNWTO (Annex 1)
Share of non-air trips by coach/rail/water	30%	UNWTO *
Average return distance per air trip (km)	7,602	UNWTO (Annex 1)
Average return distance per non-air trip (km)	1,200	MuSTT **
CO_2 emissions coach/rail (kg/pkm)	0.025	MuSTT
CO_2 emissions international air transport (kg/pkm)	0.124	Based on Table A1, Annex 2
CO_2 emissions international (intraregional) air transport (kg/pkm)	0.125	Based on Table A1, Annex 2
CO_2 emissions international (interregional) air transport (kg/pkm)	0.124	Based on Table A1, Annex 2
CO_2 emissions car transport in developed countries (kg/pkm) – average occupancy: 2 persons/car	0.133	MuSTT

* Based on data for 2004 on international modal split for water, road and rail and assuming the amount of coach trips to equal the number of rail trips; see UNWTO (2006), *Tourism Market Trends: World Overview and Tourism Topics.*

** The MuSTT study for EU tourist travel revealed that average return distances for car, coach and rail varied between 1100 and 1240 km. For international travel we estimated this to be 1200 km; data based on Peeters, P. et al. (2004), *European Tourism, Transport and Environment.*

Domestic tourist trips		
Input variable	**Value**	**Source**
Number of trips by air transport (trips)	480 million	UNWTO (Annex 1)
Number of trips non-air transport (trips)	3,520 million	UNWTO (Annex 1)
Share of domestic in high income countries of global domestic trips	50%	Annex 1, 1.1.3.2
Share of non-air trips high income countries	10%	Gössling [744]
Share of non-air trips developing countries by coach/rail/water	70%	Gössling [745]
Average return distance per air trip (km)	2,791	UNWTO (Annex 1)
Average return distance in high income countries per non-air trip (km)	1,100	MuSTT *
Average return distance in developing countries per non-air trip (km)	900	MuSTT **
CO_2 emissions air transport (kg/pkm)	0.138	Based on Table A1, Annex 2
CO_2 emissions car transport in high income countries (kg/pkm) – average car occupancy: 2 persons/car	0.133	MuSTT
CO_2 emissions car transport in developing countries (kg/pkm) – average car occupancy: 3 persons/car	0.089	MuSTT
CO_2 emissions coach/rail (kg/pkm)	0.025	MuSTT

* The MuSTT study for EU tourist travel revealed that average return distances for car, coach and rail varied between 1100 and 1240 km. For domestic tourism in developed countries this was is estimated this to be 1100 km; data based on Peeters, P. et al. (2004), European Tourism, Transport and Environment.

** For domestic travel in developing countries we assume then infrastructure quality allows a lower travel speed and thus, due to the travel time budget, we estimated this to be 900 km; data based on Peeters, P. et al. (2004), *European Tourism, Transport and Environment;* travel time budget on Schafer, A. and Victor, D. G. (2000), The Future Mobility of the World Population.

Same-day trips		
Input variable	**Value**	**Source**
International air transport (trips)	10 million	UNWTO (Annex 1)
International non-air transport (trips)	990 million	UNWTO (Annex 1)
Domestic air (trips)	40 million	UNWTO (Annex 1)
Domestic non-air trips	3,960 million	UNWTO (Annex 1)
Share of same-day domestic air pkm in developed countries	79%	UNWTO (Annex 1)
Share of non-air trips developed countries by coach/rail/water	10%	Gössling [746]
Share of non-air trips developing countries by coach/rail/water	70%	Gössling [747]
CO_2 emissions international and domestic air transport (kg/pkm)	0.177	Based on Table A1, Annex 2
CO_2 emissions car transport in high income countries (kg/pkm) – average car occupancy: 2 persons/car)	0.133	Based on Table A1, Annex 2
CO_2 emissions car transport in developing countries (kg/pkm) – average car occupancy: 3 persons/car)	0.089	Based on Table A1, Annex 2
CO_2 emissions coach/rail (kg/pkm)	0.025	Based on Table A1, Annex 2

Information as provided in Table A2.1 covers most of the data needs. For unknown data, some assumptions are made by the experts (see Table A2.2).

Table A2.2 Assumptions for data by transport mode, trip number and distance based on expert estimates

Assumptions	
Indicator	Value
Average car seat occupancy international tourism trips (persons/car)	2
Average car seat occupancy domestic tourism trips in high income countries (persons/car)	2
Average car seat occupancy in domestic tourism trips in developing countries (persons/car)	3
International non-air share of trips by car for same-day trips	80%
Share of same-day in high income countries of global domestic trips	70%
Average international return distance per non-air trip (km)	250
Average domestic return distance in high income countries per non-air trip (km)	250
Average return distance in developing countries per non-air trip (km)	200

A2.2.2 Tourism's Share in Aviation

To calculate the tourism-related share of aviation, specific corrections needed to be made regarding CO_2 emissions and RF as existing CO_2 emission inventories for aviation include all commercial aviation (i.e., freight transport and passenger transport). [748, 749, 750] As only the share of tourism is to be included in calculations, emissions caused by transport of freight needed to be subtracted from total emissions. A conversion rate of 160 kg/pax was used to compare passenger and full freight versions of the same aircraft. [751, 752] Interpolation of data for 1997 and 2010 shows that 19.5% of all aviation transport volume (revenue ton kilometers) would have been freight [753] (see also Annex 1). Consequently, 80.5% of all aviation emissions can be attributed to passenger trips. As the commercial aircraft fleet carries freight and passengers more or less evenly, this share is assumed to reflect fuel consumption and emissions. It should be taken into account that a small percentage of passenger traffic is not tourism, as passengers might use the plane to commute or travel for a period longer than a year. Even though, the 80.5% estimate is a conservative one, as international tourism itself entails some movement of freight by air to cater for the consumption of tourists.

Passenger transport by air almost fully corresponds to overnight trips; same-day trips are estimated to represent only some 1% of trips. As distance travelled on same-day trips can be expected substantially lower than the overall average, the share in overall distance travelled and in emissions will be even lower than 1%.

The emission factors for air transport are based on the figures and a method recently published by Peeters et al.[754] This reference gives a distance correction factor (see Table A1) and furthermore a wind correction factor (all emission factors are normally based on ISA (ICAO International Standard Atmosphere) and no wind condition. Due to wind, more energy is lost at the head-wind sections than gained at the tail-wind ones, a world average of 1.05 can be used. [755] The basic optimum emission factor for 3500 can be set at 0.111 kg/pkm (ISA, no wind). [756] Using this value, we may fit for the different average distances for the purpose of this report (see Table A2.3).

Table A2.3 Distance factor and final operational emission factor for the different air transport markets

Market	Average one-way (km)	Distance factor (–)	Emission factor (ISA, plus wind) (kg/pkm)
Same day	600	1.50	0.177
Domestic	1396	1.17	0.138
Intra-regional	1938	1.06	0.125
Inter-regional	7006	1.05	0.124
International	3801	n/a	0.124

However, there is another effect we should reckon with: the relation between distance flown and emission factor is not linear. That means that if for a market the average distance is used, the deviation of the emission factor, at for example 30% lower than the average, is larger than the deviation of the emission factor at 30% above the average distance. Therefore, the operational average emission factor will be a bit higher. Furthermore, we know the overall emissions (515 Mt) and distance by air (3,984 billion pkm), and thus the average emission factor (0.129 kg/pkm). As the initial emission factors – found with the data given above – was a bit too low, we calculated a correction factor that thus also accounts for the nonlinearity and for the impact that part of the flights consist of more legs with shorter average distances, and thus generally higher emission factors. This factor was found to be 1.013. Table A2.3 and Figure A2.1 give the final results.

Figure A2.1 Emission factors as function of average one-way distance

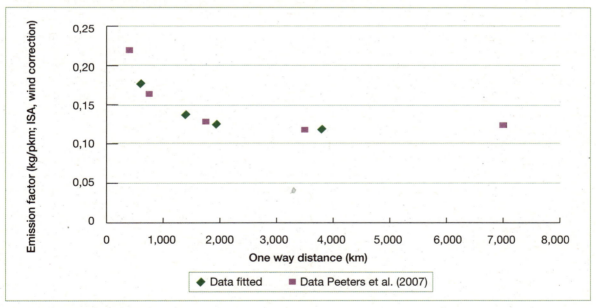

Source: Peeters, P. et al. (2007a)

Current radiative forcing data are based on all aviation emissions, including military emissions, which thus need to be deducted from the total. Linearly interpolated from Penner et al. (1999: table 9.4) [757], the share of military fuel consumption was 12.2% in 2005. However, for non-CO_2 RF only part of the impact of high altitude cruise flight is relevant because military flights usually take place at low altitudes. As the RFI is 1.9 [758] for all aviation, the military correction factor will be $((1.0 - 0.122) + 0.9)/1.9 = 0.93$. The share of tourism aviation of all aviation CO_2 emissions would consequently be 73%.

A2.2.3 Accommodation

Energy use in hotels varies considerably, both with respect to the sources of energy used and the amount of energy consumed. A more recent review found values for hotel accommodations of between 51 MJ/guest night (Majorca) and 256 MJ/guest night (Zanzibar). [759] Hilton hotels were found to consume an average of 322 MJ/guest night, while Scandic hotels used an average of 172 MJ/guest night. Hotels investigated in the Seychelles showed energy uses of 36–108 MJ per bed night, excluding the use of fossil fuels for cooking, etc. [760] Hotels with self-supporting power generation may use more energy per bed night. A survey in Zanzibar, Tanzania found that energy consumption was 221 MJ per guest night for established smaller hotels and up to 916 MJ per guest night for newly opened resort hotels with still low occupancy rates. [761] The estimated average for well-established hotels was 256 MJ per guest night. These values exclude primary energy sources such as gas for cooking.

Hotels use generally more energy per visitor than other types of accommodation, as they have energy intense facilities, such as bars, restaurants, pools, and more spacious rooms. [762] Pensions may have a comparably low number of beds and occupancy rates are assumed to be somewhat lower than those of hotels. Even though a rather high energy-consumption values in bed & breakfast facilities in New Zealand of 110 MJ per guest night was reported, [763] a lower average of 50 MJ is assumed here for all accommodation establishments in this category. Campsites were assumed to have the lowest energy use of all categories, with 25 MJ per guest night, while holiday villages were calculated at 90 MJ per guest night. No data is available for self-catering facilities and vacation homes. These were assumed to consume 120 MJ and 100 MJ per bed night. For the worldwide mix of tourism accommodations in 2001, a value of 98 MJ/guest night was established. [764] Hotels tend to become more and more luxurious, resorts seem to use large amounts of energy, specifically in the booming market for long haul destinations in developing countries. It is thus assumed that this average value has increased to 120 MJ/guest night, or 19.0 kg CO_2/guest night for all tourists from developed countries, as well as for international tourists and domestic tourists in developed countries using commercial accommodation. *

For domestic tourists in developing countries, it seems reasonable to use a lower value for commercial accommodation. The average developed country amount of CO_2 emissions per capita is 13.1 tonnes/year (or 36 kg CO_2/day). [765] If half of this is attributable to housing, this corresponds to 18 kg CO_2/day, a value near the 19.0 kg/guest night used for domestic tourism in developed countries. For VFR tourists in developing countries, this value cannot be used, though, as the average energy consumption, of people living in developing countries corresponds to 2.2 tonnes of CO_2 per year on average. [766] This corresponds to 6 kg per head per night. However, this includes emissions from other economic sectors, such as agriculture, transport, or industry. Household emissions will be less than half of this, and most VFR tourism will thus lead to concomitantly low emission levels. However, a share of non-VFR domestic tourism will use high standard accommodation, and thus contribute to the same emission levels as international tourists (19.0 kg/guest night), significantly increasing the overall domestic developing countries average. An average of 4 kg CO_2/guest night for domestic tourists in developing countries is thus assumed for calculations.

---

*   Note that some hotels running generators may cause substantially higher emissions, with known values of up to 125 kg CO2 per bed night (excluding imports of food by air; Gössling, unpublished data).

List of Abbreviations

AR4	IPCC Fourth Assessment Report
ASK	Available Seat Kilometre
CDD	Cooling Degree Day
CDM	Clean Development Mechanism
CERs	Certified Emission Reductions
CO_2	Carbon-Dioxide
eCLAT	Experts on Climate Change and Tourism
EC	European Commission
EMS	Environmental Management System
EU	European Union
GCM	Global Climate Models
GDP	Gross Domestic Product
GEF	Global Environment Facility
GHG	Greenhouse Gases
HDD	Heating Degree Day
IATA	International Air Transport Association
ICAO	International Civil Aviation Organization
ICLEI	Local Governments for Sustainability
IHEI	International Hotels Environment Initiative
IPCC	Intergovernmental Panel on Climate Change
LDC	Least Developed Countries
LOS	Length of Stay
MDG	United Nations Millennium Development Goals
MJ	Mega Joule
Mt	Megatonne = 10^6 kg
NGO	Non-governmental Organization
NOAA	US National Oceanic and Atmospheric Administration
Pkm	Passenger kilometre
PV	Photovoltaic
RCM	Regional Climate Models
RCOF	Regional Climate Outlook Forum

RF	Radiative Forcing
RFI	Radiative Forcing Index
SBB	Swiss Federal Railways
SIDS	Small Island Developing States
SMMEs	Small, Micro and Mediumsized Enterprises
SRES	Special Report on Emissions Scenarios
ST–EP	Sustainable Tourism – Eliminating Poverty
TAR	IPCC Third Assessment Report
UNCCD	United Nations Convention to Combat Desertification
UNDP	United Nations Development Programme
UNEP	United Nations Environment Programme
UNESCO	United Nations Educational, Scientific and Cultural Organization
UNFCCC	United Nations Framework Convention on Climate Change
UNWTO	World Tourism Organization
VFR	Visits to Friends and Relatives
WG 1,2,3	IPCC Working Groups
WMO	World Meteorological Organization

List of Boxes

List of Figures

List of Tables

List of References

Executive Summary

[1] IPCC (2007a), 'Summary for Policymakers', in S. Solomon et al. (eds.), *Climate Change 2007: The Physical Science Basis – Contribution of Working Group I to the Fourth Assessment Report of the Intergovernmental Panel on Climate Change,* University Press Cambridge, Cambridge and New York.

[2] Ibid.

[3] Ibid.

[4] IPCC(2007b), 'Summary for Policymakers', in M. L. Parry et al. (eds.), *Climate Change 2007: Impacts, Adaptation and Vulnerability – Contribution of Working Group II to the Fourth Assessment Report of the Intergovernmental Panel on Climate Change,* University Press Cambridge, Cambridge and New York.

[5] IPCC (2007a), *The Physical Science Basis – Summary for Policymakers.*

[6] Ibid.

[7] IPCC (2007b), *Impacts, Adaptation and Vulnerability – Summary for Policymakers.*

[8] Ibid.

[9] IPCC (2007c), *Climate Change 2007: Mitigation. Contribution of Working Group III to the Fourth Assessment Report of the Intergovernmental Panel on Climate Change* [B. Metz et al. (eds.)], University Press Cambridge, Cambridge and New York.

[10] Stern, N. (2006), *The Economics of Climate Change: The Stern Review,* Cambridge University Press, Cambridge.

[11] Yohe, G.W. et al. (2007), 'Perspectives on Climate Change and Sustainability', in M. L. Parry et al. (eds.), *Climate Change 2007: Impacts, Adaptation and Vulnerability. Contribution of Working Group II to the Fourth Assessment Report of the IPCC* Cambridge University Press, Cambridge and New York, pp. 811–841.

[12] Stern, N. (2006), *The Stern Review.*

[13] UNWTO (2003), *Climate Change and Tourism: Proceedings of the First International Conference on Climate Change and Tourism, Djerba, Tunisia, 9–11 April 2003,* UNWTO, Madrid, (Online), available: http://www.unwto.org/sustainable/climate/brochure.htm (17-12-2007).

[14] Gössling, S. and Hall, C. M. (2006a), 'An Introduction to Tourism and Global Environmental Change', in S. Gössling and C.M. Hall (eds.), *Tourism and Global Environmental Change,* Routledge, London, pp.1–34.

[15] Scott, D. (2006a), 'Climate Change and Sustainable Tourism in the 21st Century', in J. Cukier (ed.), *Tourism Research: Policy, Planning, and Prospects,* Department of Geography Publication Series, University of Waterloo, Waterloo, Ontario, pp.175–248.

[16] Becken, S. and Hay, J. (2007), *Tourism and Climate Change – Risks and Opportunities,* Channel View Publications, Cleveland.

[17] Peeters, P. (2007), *Tourism and Climate Change Mitigation – Methods, Greenhouse Gas Reductions and Policies,* NHTV Academics Studies No. 6, NHTV, Breda University, Breda.

[18] Frangialli, F. (2007), *Tourism Development and Climate Change: Understanding, Anticipating, Adapting, Participating in the Common Effort,* (Background Paper), UNWTO, Madrid.

19   Wilbanks, T. J. et al. (2007), 'Industry, Settlement and Society', in M. L. Parry et al. (eds.), *Climate Change 2007: Impacts, Adaptation and Vulnerability. Contribution of Working Group II to the Fourth Assessment Report of the IPCC,* Cambridge University Press, Cambridge and New York, pp. 357–390.

20   Peeters, P. (2007), *Tourism and Climate Change Mitigation – Methods, Greenhouse Gas Reductions and Policies.*

21   Gössling, S. (2002), 'Global Environmental Consequences of Tourism', *Global Environmental Change,* Part A, 12 (4), pp. 283–302.

22   IPCC (2007b), *Impacts, Adaptation and Vulnerability –Summary for Policymakers.*

23   United Nations (2007a), 'Climate Change and Development Must be Tackled Together – Ban Ki-moon', *UN News Centre,* 9 May 2007, (Online), available:
http://www.un.org/apps/news/story.asp?NewsID=22498&Cr=commission&Cr1=sustainable (17-12-2007).

24   UNWTO (2003), *Proceedings of the First International Conference on Climate Change and Tourism.*

25   Scott, D. et al. (2005a), *Climate, Tourism and Recreation: A Bibliography* – 1936 to 2005, University of Waterloo, Waterloo, Ontario.

26   Amelung, B. et al. (2008 – in press), 'The Place of Tourism in the IPCC Fourth Assessment Report: A Review', *Tourism Review International.*

27   IPCC (2007b), Impacts, Adaptation and Vulnerability – *Summary for Policymakers.*

28   UNWTO (2003), *Proceedings of the First International Conference on Climate Change and Tourism.*

29   Gössling, S. and Hall, C. M. (2006a), *An Introduction to Tourism and Global Environmental Change.*

30   Scott, D. (2006a), *Climate Change and Sustainable Tourism in the 21st Century.*

31   Becken, S. and Hay, J. (2007), Tourism and Climate Change – *Risks and Opportunities.*

32   Scott, D. et al. (2004), 'Climate Change and the Distribution of Climatic Resources for Tourism in North America', *Climate Research,* 27 (2), pp. 105–117.

33   Amelung, B. and Viner, D. (2006), 'Mediterranean Tourism: Exploring the Future with the Tourism Climatic Index', *Journal of Sustainable Tourism,* 14 (4), pp. 349–366.

34   Amelung, B. et al. (2007), 'Implications of Global Climate Change for Tourism Flows and Seasonality', *Journal of Travel Research,* 45 (3), pp. 285–296.

35   Scott, D. (2006b), 'Global Environmental Change and Mountain Tourism', in S. Gössling and C. M. Hall (eds), *Tourism and Global Environmental Change,* Routledge, London, pp. 54–75.

36   Abegg, B. et al. (2007), 'Climate Change Impacts and Adaptation in Winter Tourism', in S. Agrawala (Ed.), *Climate Change in the European Alps: Adapting Winter Tourism and Natural Hazards Management,* Organization for Economic Co-operation and Development, Paris, pp. 25–60.

37   Scott, D. et al. (2007a), 'Climate Change and Québec's Ski Industry', *Global Environmental Change,* 17 (2), pp. 181–190.

38   IPCC (2007a), The Physical Science Basis – *Summary for Policymakers.*

39   IPCC (2007b), Impacts, Adaptation and Vulnerability – *Summary for Policymakers.*

40   UNWTO (2003), *Proceedings of the First International Conference on Climate Change and Tourism.*

41   Gössling, S. and Hall, C. M. (2006a), *An Introduction to Tourism and Global Environmental Change.*

42   Scott, D. (2006a), *Climate Change and Sustainable Tourism in the 21st Century.*

43   Becken, S. and Hay, J. (2007), *Tourism and Climate Change – Risks and Opportunities.*

44   UNESCO-WHC (2007), *Case Studies on Climate Change and World Heritage,* UNESCO-WHC, Paris. (Online), available: http://whc.unesco.org/documents/publi_climatechange.pdf (07-01-2008).

45   Amelung, B. et al. (2008 – in press), *The Place of Tourism in the IPCC Fourth Assessment Report: A Review.*

46   Bartlett, L. (2007), 'Australia Fears Jet Flight Guilt Could Hit Tourism', *Agence France-Presse,* 18 April 2007, (Online), available:
     http://www.spacemart.com/reports/Australia_Fears_Jet_Flight_Guilt_Could_Hit_Tourism_999.html (17-12-2007).

47   Boyd, A. (2007), 'Carbon Tax Threatens to Ground Asia Tourism', *Asian Times Online,* (Online), available:
     http://www.atimes.com/atimes/Asian_Economy/ID19Dk01.html (17-12-2007).

48   Caribbean Hotel Association and Caribbean Tourism Organization (2007), CHA-CTO *Position Paper of Global Climate Change and the Caribbean Tourism Industry,* (Online), available:
     http://www.caribbeanhotels.org/ClimateChangePosition0307.pdf (17-12-2007).

49   IPCC (2007b). *Impacts, Adaptation and Vulnerability –Summary for Policymakers.*

50   Stern, N. (2006), *The Stern Review.*

51   Barnett, J. (2001), *Security and Climate Change,* Tyndall Centre Working Paper No. 7, (Online), available:
     http://www.tyndall.ac.uk/publications/working_papers/wp7.pdf (17-12-2007).

52   German Advisory Council on Global Change (2007), *World in Transition: Climate Change as a Security Risk,* German Advisory Council on Global Change, Berlin, (Online), available: http://www.wbgu.de/wbgu_jg2007_engl.pdf (17-12-2007).

53   Ibid.

54   Ibid.

55   German Advisory Council on Global Change (2007), *World in Transition: Climate Change as a Security Risk.*

56   Liotta, P. H. and Shearer, A. W. (2005), *The Use of Scenarios in Assessing Climate Change, Human Security, and Potential Outcomes, P*ell Center for International Relations and Public Policy, Rhode Island, (Online), available: http://www.gechs.org/downloads/holmen/Liotta_Shearer.pdf (17-12-2007).

57   Feakin, T. (2005), *Climate Change and the Threat to Global Security,* Royal United Services Institute for Defence and Security Studies, London, (Online), available:
     http://www.rusi.org/downloads/assets/HSM_05_p12-13_Climate.pdf (17-12-2007).

58   Barnett, J. (2001), *Security and Climate Change.*

59   German Advisory Council on Global Change (2007), *World in Transition: Climate Change as a Security Risk.*

60   Feakin, T. (2005), *Climate Change and the Threat to Global Security.*

61   Hall, C. M. et al (2004), 'Security and Tourism: Towards a New Understanding?', *Journal of Travel and Tourism Marketing,* 15, (2/3), 1–18.

62   Sonmez, S. (1998), 'Tourism, Terrorism, and Political Instability', *Annals of Tourism Research,* 25, (2), pp. 416–456.

63   UNWTO (2003), *Proceedings of the First International Conference on Climate Change and Tourism.*

64   Frangialli, F. (2007), Tourism Development and Climate Change: *Understanding, Anticipating, Adapting, Participating in the Common Effort.*

65   Becken, S. (2004a), Climate Change and Tourism in Fiji: Vulnerability, *Adaptation and Mitigation, (Final Report),* University of the South Pacific, Suva.

66   Mitchell, T. and Tanner, T. (2006), *Adapting to Climate Change: Challenges and Opportunities for the Development Community,* Tearfund Report, Institute of Development Studies, Brighton, (Online), available: http://www.tearfund.org/webdocs/website/Campaigning/policy%20and%20research/Adapting%20to%20 climate%20change%20discussion%20paper.pdf (17-12-2007).

67   Simpson, M. C. (2008 – in press), 'Global Climate Change and the Implications for Tourism Resilience in Small Island Developing States (SIDS)', in *Building Tourism Resilience in SIDS: Maximising Economic Benefits and Sustaining Tourism Development,* SIDS Tourism Organization, Bahamas.

68   Stern, N. (2006), *The Stern Review.*

69   IPCC (2007b). *Impacts, Adaptation and Vulnerability –Summary for Policymakers.*

70   Gössling, S. and Hall, C. M. (2006a), *An Introduction to Tourism and Global Environmental Change.*

71   Scott, D. (2006a), *Climate Change and Sustainable Tourism in the 21st Century.*

72   Becken, S. and Hay, J. (2007), *Tourism and Climate Change – Risks and Opportunities.*

73   Wall, G. (1992), 'Tourism Alternatives in an Era of Global Climate Change', in V. Smith and W. Eadington (eds.), *Tourism Alternatives,* University of Pennsylvania, Philadelphia, pp. 194–236.

74   Elsasser, H. and Bürki, R. (2002), 'Climate Change as a Threat to Tourism in the Alps', *Climate Research,* 20, pp. 253–257.

75   Scott, D. et al. (2008a – in press), 'Climate Change Adaptation in the Recreation and Tourism Sector', in K. Ebi and P. Hoeppe (eds.), *Biometeorology For Adaptation,* Springer, New York.

76   Becken, S. (2004a), *Climate Change and Tourism in Fiji: Vulnerability, Adaptation and Mitigation.*

77   Simpson, M. C. (2008 – in press), *Global Climate Change and the Implications for Tourism Resilience in Small Island Developing States (SIDS).*

78   Elsasser, H. and Bürki, R. (2002), *Climate Change as a Threat to Tourism in the Alps.*

79   Scott, D. et al. (2002), *The Vulnerability of Winter Recreation to Climate Change in Ontario's Lakelands Tourism Region,* Department of Geography Publication Series Occasional Paper 18, University of Waterloo, Waterloo, Ontario.

80   Raksakulthai, V. (2003), *Climate Change Impacts and Adaptation for Tourism in Phuket, Thailand,* Asian Disaster Preparedness Centre, Pathumani.

81   Scott, D. et al. (2005b), Climate Change: *A Long-term Strategic Issue for the National Capital Commission (Tourism and Recreation Business Lines) – Executive Summary,* Report prepared for the National Capital Commission, University of Waterloo, Waterloo, Ontario.

82   Sievanen, T. et al. (2005), *Nature-based Tourism, Outdoor Recreation and Adaptation to Climate Change,* FINADAPT Working Paper 11, Finnish Environment Institute, Helsinki.

83   Wolfsegger, C. et al. (2008 – in press), 'Climate Change Risk Appraisal in the Austrian Ski Industry', *Tourism Review International.*

84   Hamilton, J. M. et al. (2005a), 'Effects of Climate Change on International Tourism', *Climate Research,* 29, pp. 245–254.

85   Berrittella, M. et al. (2006), 'A General Equilibrium Analysis of Climate Change Impacts on Tourism', *Tourism Management,* 27, pp. 913–924.

86   Gössling, S. and Hall, C. M. (2006a), *An Introduction to Tourism and Global Environmental Change.*

87   Scott, D. (2006a), *Climate Change and Sustainable Tourism in the 21st Century.*

88   Stern, N. (2006), *The Stern Review.*

89   Berrittella, M. et al. (2006), *A General Equilibrium Analysis of Climate Change Impacts on Tourism.*

90   UK Department for Transport (2007a), *Attitudes towards transport,* (Online), available: http://www.dft.gov.uk/pgr/statistics/datatablespublications/trsnstatsatt (17-12-2007).

91   Conference Board of Canada (2007), 'Travellers Keen on Going Green', *Tourism Intelligence Bulletin,* 39, May 2007, (Online), available: http://www.corporate.canada.travel/docs/research_and_statistics/trends_and_outlook/tib/2007/TIB_May_2007_EN.pdf (17-12-2007).

92   Njegovan, N. (2006), 'Elasticities of Demand for Leisure Air Travel: A System Modeling Approach', *Journal of Air Transport Management,* 12, pp. 33–39.

93   Gillen, A. (2004), *Air Travel Demand Elasticities: Concepts, Issues and Measurements,* Ottawa: Department of Finance Canada, Ottawa, (Online), available: http://www.fin.gc.ca/consultresp/Airtravel/airtravStdy_e.html (17-12-2007).

94   Conference Board of Canada (2007), *Travellers Keen on Going Green.*

95   UK Department for Transport (2007b), *Public attitudes towards climate change and the impact of transport,* (Online), available: http://www.dft.gov.uk/pgr/statistics/datatablespublications/trsnstatsatt/publicexperiencesofandattitu1824?page=0null (17-12-2007).

96   Scott, D. (2006a), *Climate Change and Sustainable Tourism in the 21st Century.*

97   IPCC (2007a), *The Physical Science Basis – Summary for Policymakers.*

98   ICAO (2007), *Environmental Unit,* (Online), available: http://www.icao.int/env/ (17-12-2007).

99   Peeters, P. and Middel, J. (2006), 'Historical and Future Development of Air Transport Fuel Efficiency', *Transport and Climate Change (TAC) Conference,* 25–29 June 2006, Oxford, (Online), available: http://www.pa.op.dlr.de/tac/proceedings/15-71.pdf (17-12-2007).

100 Uemura, Y. et al. (2003), 'Potential of renewable energy sources and its applications in Yakushima Island', *Renewable Energy,* 29, pp. 581–591.

101 Cavallaro, F. and Ciraolo, L. (2005), 'A Multicriteria Approach to Evaluate Wind Energy Plants on an Italian Island', *Energy Policy,* 33, pp. 235–244.

102 Bergsma G. et al. (2007), *Biofuels and their global influence on land availability for agriculture and nature: A first evaluation and a proposal for further fact finding,* CE, Delft, (Online), available: http://www.ce.nl/eng/index.html (17-12-2007).

103 Becken, S. (2004b), 'How Tourists and Tourism Experts Perceive Climate Change and Forest Carbon Sinks', *Journal of Sustainable Tourism,* 12 (4), pp. 332–345.

104 Becken, S. (2007), 'Climate Change Policies for International Air Travel – A Tourist Perspective', *Journal of Sustainable Tourism',* 15 (4), pp. 351–368.

105 Gössling, S. et al. (2008 – submitted), 'Swedish Air Travellers and Voluntary Carbon Offsets: Towards the Co-Creation of Environmental value?', *Current Issues in Tourism.*

106 IPCC (2007b), *Impacts, Adaptation and Vulnerability –Summary for Policymakers.*

107 Frangialli, F. (2007), *Tourism Development and Climate Change: Understanding, Anticipating, Adapting, Participating in the Common Effort.*

108 Stern, N. (2006), *The Economics of Climate Change: The Stern Review,* University Press Cambridge, Cambridge.

Introduction

109 IPCC (2007a), *The Physical Science Basis – Summary for Policymakers.*

110 Ibid.

111 Ibid.

112 IPCC (2007b), *Impacts, Adaptation and Vulnerability – Summary for Policymakers.*

113 Ibid.

114 IPCC (2007c), *Mitigation.*

115 Stern, N. (2006), *The Stern Review.*

116 UN Global Compact, (Online), available: http://www.unglobalcompact.org (13-12-2007).

[117] Stern, N. (2006), *The Stern Review.*

[118] Yohe, G.W. et al. (2007), *Perspectives on Climate Change and Sustainability.*

[119] United Nations (2007b), *UN Millennium Development Goals,* (Online), available: http://www.un.org/millenniumgoals/ (13-12-2007).

[120] UNWTO (2003), *Proceedings of the First International Conference on Climate Change and Tourism.*

[121] Gössling, S. and Hall, C. M. (2006a), *An Introduction to Tourism and Global Environmental change.*

[122] Scott, D. (2006a), *Climate Change and Sustainable Tourism in the 21st Century.*

[123] Becken, S. and Hay, J. (2007), *Tourism and Climate Change – Risks and Opportunities.*

[124] Peeters, P. (2007), *Tourism and Climate Change Mitigation – Methods, Greenhouse Gas Reductions and Policies.*

[125] Frangialli, F. (2007), *Tourism Development and Climate Change: Understanding, Anticipating, Adapting, Participating in the Common Effort.*

[126] Wilbanks, T. J. et al. (2007), *Industry, Settlement and Society.*

[127] Gössling, S. (2002), *Global Environmental Consequences of Tourism.*

[128] Peeters, P. (2007), *Tourism and Climate Change Mitigation.*

[129] Frangialli, F. (2007), *Tourism Development and Climate Change: Understanding, Anticipating, Adapting, Participating in the Common Effort.*

[130] United Nations (2007a), Climate Change and Development Must Be Tackled Together.

[131] IPCC (2007b), *Impacts, Adaptation and Vulnerability – Summary for Policymakers.*

[132] UNWTO (2003), *Proceedings of the First International Conference on Climate Change and Tourism.*

[133] WMO (2005a), *The Abridged Final Report with Resolutions and Recommendations of the Fourteenth Session of the Commission for Climatology, Beijing, China, 3–10 November 2005,* WMO-No, 996.

[134] Scott, D. et al. (2005a), *Climate, Tourism and Recreation: A Bibliography –1936 to 2005.*

[135] Amelung, B. et al. (2008 – in press), *The Place of Tourism in the IPCC Fourth Assessment Report: A Review.*

[136] Hall, C.M. (2008 – submitted), 'Tourism and Climate Change: Knowledge Gaps and Issues', *Tourism Recreation Research.*

Advances in Climate Change Science and Implications for the Tourism Sector

[137] WMO (1988), *Technical Regulations,* Vol. I, WMO Publication No. 49, WMO, Geneva.

[138] IPCC (2007c), *Glossary of Terms,* (Online), available: http://www.ipcc.ch/pdf/glossary/tar-ipcc-terms-en.pdf (13-12-2007).

[139] Scott, D. et al. (2005c), 'The Evolution of the Climate Change Issue in the Tourism Sector', in M. Hall and G. Higham (eds.), *Tourism Recreation and Climate Change,* Channelview Press, London, pp. 44–60.

[140] Paul, A. (1972), 'Weather and the Daily Use of Outdoor Recreation Areas in Canada', in J. Taylor (ed.) *Weather Forecasting for Agriculture and Industry,* David and Charles Newton Abbott, pp. 132–146.

[141] Crowe, R. B. et al. (1973), *The Tourist and Outdoor Recreation Climate of Ontario – Volume 1: Objectives and Definitions of Season,* Report Number REC-1-73, Atmospheric Environment Service, Environment Canada, Toronto.

[142] Besancenot, J. P. et al. (1978), 'Les Conditions Climatiques du Tourisme', Littoral, Norois, 99, pp. 357–382.

143 Yapp, G. and McDonald, N. (1978), 'A Recreation Climate Model', *Journal of Environmental Management*, 7, pp. 235–252.

144 Mieczkowski, Z. (1985), 'The Tourism Climatic Index: A Method of Evaluating World Climates for Tourism', *Le géographe canadien*, XXIX (3), pp. 220–233.

145 Besancenot, J-P. (1989), *Climat et Tourisme*, Masson, Paris.

146 Harlfinger, O. (1991), 'Holiday Biometeorology: A Study of Palma de Majorca, Spain', *Geojournal*, 25, pp. 377–381.

147 de Freitas, C. R. et al. (2004), 'A New Generation Climate Index for Tourism and Recreation', in A. Matzarakis et al. (eds.), *Advances in Tourism Climatology*, Berichte des Meteorologischen Institutes der Universität Freiburg, Freiburg, pp.19–27.

148 Gómez Martín, B. (2004), 'An Evaluation of the Tourist Potential of the Climate in Catalonia (Spain): A Regional Study', *Geografiska Annaler*, 86, pp. 249–264.

149 Gómez Martín, B. (2006), 'Climate Potential and Tourist Demand in Catalonia (Spain) during the summer season', *Climate Research*, 32, pp. 75–87.

150 Besancenot, J-P. (1989), *Climat et Tourisme*.

151 Scott, D. et al. (2008b – in press), 'Climate Preferences for Diverse Tourism Environments: Evidence from Canada, New Zealand and Sweden', *Climate Research*.

152 Hu, Y, and Ritchie, J. (1993), 'Measuring Destination Attractiveness: A Contextual Approach', *Journal of Travel Research*, 32 (20), pp. 25–34.

153 Williams, P. et al. (1997), 'The Influence of Weather Context on Winter Resort Evaluations by Visitors', *Journal of Travel Research*, Fall, pp. 29–36.

154 Lohmann, M. and Kaim, E. (1999), 'Weather and Holiday Preference – Image, Attitude and Experience', *Revue de Tourisme*, 2, pp. 54–64.

155 Kozak, M. (2002), 'Comparative Analysis of Tourist Motivations by Nationality and Destinations', *Tourism Management, 23*, pp. 221–232

156 Hamilton, J. M. and Lau, M. (2005), 'The Role of Climate Information in Tourist Destination Choice Decision-making', in S. Gössling and C.M. Hall (eds.), *Tourism and global environmental change*, Routledge, London, pp. 229–250.

157 Gössling, S. and Hall, C. M. (2006b), 'Uncertainties in Predicting Tourist Travel Flows Based on Models: Editorial Essay', *Climatic Change*, 79 (3–4), pp. 163–173.

158 Agnew, M. and Palutikof, J. (2006), 'Impacts of Short-term Climate Variability in the UK on Demand for Domestic and International Tourism', *Climate Research*, *31*, pp. 109–120.

159 Altalo, M. and Hale, M. (2002), *Requirements of the US Recreation and Tourism Industry for Climate, Weather, and Ocean Information*, National Oceanic and Atmospheric Administrations, Washington.

160 ANENA (2002), 'Prévenir le risque d'avalanche grace à la météo', *Espaces, 190*, pp. 29–31.

161 UNWTO-WMO (1998), *Handbook on Natural Disaster Reduction in Tourism Areas*.

162 Altalo, M. and Hale, M. (2002), *Requirements of the US Recreation and Tourism Industry for Climate, Weather, and Ocean Information*.

163 WMO (2005b), 'Special Issue on Climate and Tourism', *World Climate News, 27th edition*, (Online), available: http://www.wmo.int/pages/publications/world_climate_news/documents/wcn27.pdf (17-12-2007).

164 WMO (2007), *Expert Team on Climate and Tourism*, (Online), available: http://www.wmo.ch/pages/prog/wcp/ccl/opags/opag4/et4.3/et4.3_members_tors.htm (17-12-2007).

165 IPCC (2007a), *The Physical Science Basis – Summary for Policymakers*.

166 Stern, N. (2006), *The Stern Review*.

[167] Hallegatte, S. et al. (2007), 'Using Climate Analogues for Assessing Climate Change Economic Impacts'. *Climatic Change*, 82 (1–2), pp. 47–60.

[168] IPCC (2007a), *The Physical Science Basis – Summary for Policymakers*.

[169] Scott, D. et al. (2007b), 'Using an Analogue Approach to Examine Climate Change Vulnerability of the New England (USA) Ski Tourism Industry', *Proceedings of the 3rd International Conference on Climate, Tourism and Recreation*, International Society of Biometeorology, Commission on Climate Tourism and Recreation, Alexandropolis, 19–22 September 2007.

[170] Alvord, C. et al. (2007), 'Climate and Tourism on the Colorado Plateau: A Workshop Summary'. *Bulletin of the American Meteorological Society*, (Online), http://wwa.colorado.edu/products/forecasts_and_outlooks/intermountain_west_climate_summary/articles/WWA_Jun_2007_focus.pdf (14-04-2008).

[171] Wilby, R. et al. (2004), *Guidelines for Use of Climate Scenarios Developed from Statistical Downscaling Methods*, IPCC, Task Group on Data and Scenarios Support for Impacts and Climate Analysis, Geneva.

[172] Ibid.

[173] IPCC (2007a), *The Physical Science Basis – Summary for Policymakers*.

[174] IPCC (2007b), *Impacts, Adaptation and Vulnerability – Summary for Policymakers*.

[175] Ibid.

[176] Id. at page 10.

[177] IPCC (2007a), *The Physical Science Basis – Summary for Policymakers*.

[178] IPCC (2007d), *Guidance Notes for Lead Authors of the IPCC Fourth Assessment Report on Addressing Uncertainties*, (Online), available:
http://www.ipcc.ch/pdf/supporting-material/uncertainty-guidance-note.pdf (17-12-2007).

[179] Ibid.

[180] Ibid.

[181] Raupach, M. R. et al. (2007), 'Global and Regional Drivers of Accelerating CO_2 Emissions', *Proceedings of the National Academy of Sciences,* (early edition), (Online), available: http://www.pnas.org/cgi/reprint/0700609104v1.pdf (14-12-2007).

[182] Pittock, A. B. (2006), 'Are Scientists Underestimating Climate Change?', *Eos, 87* (34), pp. 340–341.

[183] IPCC (2007a), *The Physical Science Basis – Summary for Policymakers*.

[184] Ibid.

[185] Ibid.

[186] Ibid.

[187] Ibid.

[188] Ibid.

[189] Ibid.

[190] Altalo, M. and Hale, M. (2002), *Requirements of the US Recreation and Tourism Industry for Climate, Weather, and Ocean Information*.

[191] WMO (2005b), *Special Issue on Climate and Tourism*.

[192] IPCC (2007a), *The Physical Science Basis – Summary for Policymakers*.

Impacts and Adaptation for Tourism Destinations

[193] UNWTO (2003), *Proceedings of the First International Conference on Climate Change and Tourism.*

[194] Scott, D. (2006a), *Climate Change and Sustainable Tourism in the 21st Century.*

[195] Gössling, S. and Hall, C. M. (2006a), *An Introduction to Tourism and Global Environmental change.*

[196] Becken, S. and Hay, J. (2007), *Tourism and Climate Change – Risks and Opportunities.*

[197] IPCC (2007b), *Impacts, Adaptation and Vulnerability – Summary for Policymakers.*

[198] IPCC (2007a), *The Physical Science Basis – Technical Summary.*

[199] IPCC (2007b), *Impacts, Adaptation and Vulnerability – Summary for Policymakers.*

[200] Scott, D. et al. (2004), *Climate Change and the Distribution of Climatic Resources for Tourism in North America.*

[201] Amelung, B. and Viner, D. (2006), 'Mediterranean Tourism: Exploring the Future with the Tourism Climatic Index.

[202] Hamilton, J. M. et al. (2005a), *Effects of Climate Change on International Tourism.*

[203] Pateman, E. (2001), 'Rising Energy Costs Cause Concern in the Lodging Industry', *Hotel Online Special Report*, March 2001, (Online), available: http://www.hotel-online.com/News/PR2001_1st/Mar01_Pateman_Energy.html (17-12-2007).

[204] Bohdanowicz, P. (2002), 'Thermal Comfort and Energy Savings in the Hotel Industry', *Proceedings of the 16th Congress of the International Society of Biometeorology, 27 Oct.–1 Nov., Kansas City, Missouri*, American Meteorological Society, Boston, pp. 396–400.

[205] IPCC (2007a), *The Physical Science Basis – Technical Summary.*

[206] UNESCO (2006), 'Water and Tourism', *UNESCO Water Portal Weekly Update,* No. 155, (Online), available: http://www.unesco.org/water/news/newsletter/155.shtml (17-12-2007).

[207] Ibid.

[208] WWF (2003), *Development in the Drought: The Incompatibility of the Ebro Water Transfer with Sustainable Development in the Southeast Region of Spain,* (Online), available: http://assets.panda.org/downloads/developmentinthedrought_5104.pdf (17-12-2007).

[209] Price, M. (1999), *Global Change in the Mountains,* Parthenon, New York.

[210] Lollino, G. and Audisio, C. (2006), 'UNESCO World Heritage Sites in Italy Affected by Geological Problems, Specifically Landslide and Flood Hazard', *Landslides, 3* (4), pp. 311–321.

[211] UNESCO-WHC (2007), *Case Studies on Climate Change and World Heritage.*

[212] Ibid.

[213] Perry, C. P. (2003), 'Reef Development at Inhaca Island, Mozambique: Coral Communities and Impacts of the 1999/2000 Southern African Floods', *Ambio, 32* (2), pp. 134–139.

[214] IPCC (2007b), *Impacts, Adaptation and Vulnerability – Summary for Policymakers.*

[215] IPCC (2002), *IPCC Technical Paper V: Climate Change and Biodiversity*, IPCC, Geneva.

[216] UNEP (2002a), *How Tourism Can Contribute to Environmental Conservation,* (Online), available: http://www.uneptie.org/pc/tourism/sust-tourism%5Cenv-conservation.htm (13-12-2007).

[217] Green, R. E. (2003), *Global Climate Change and Biodiversity*, University of East Anglia, Norwich, Online), available: http://www.jncc.gov.uk/pdf/MJHGlobalclimatechange_14.08.03.pdf (13-12-2007).

[218] IPCC (2007b), *Impacts, Adaptation and Vulnerability – Summary for Policymakers.*

219 IPCC (2002), *Climate Change and Biodiversity.*

220 Hall, M. and Farge, D. (2003), 'Modeled Climate-induced Glacier Change in Glacier National Park: 1850–2100', *BioScience, 53* (2), pp. 131–140.

221 Scott, D. and Jones, B. (2006b), *Climate Change and Nature-Based Tourism – Executive Summary*, Report prepared for the Government of Canada Climate Change Action Fund, University of Waterloo, Waterloo, Ontario.

222 UNESCO-WHC (2007), *Case Studies on Climate Change and World Heritage.*

223 UNWTO (2003), *Proceedings of the First International Conference on Climate Change and Tourism.*

224 Gössling, S. and Hall, C. M. (2006a), *An Introduction to Tourism and Global Environmental change.*

225 UNESCO-WHC (2007), *Case Studies on Climate Change and World Heritage.*

226 OECD (2006), *Climate Change and Winter Tourism. Report on Adaptation,* (Online), available: http://www.oecd.org/dataoecd/58/4/37776193.pdf (14-12-2007).

227 UNESCO-WHC (2007), *Case Studies on Climate Change and World Heritage.*

228 IPCC (2007b), *Impacts, Adaptation and Vulnerability – Summary for Policymakers.*

229 Brooks, N. et al. (2005), 'The Determinants of Vulnerability and Adaptive Capacity at the National Level and the Implications for Adaptation', *Global Environmental Change, 15*, pp. 51–163.

230 Alberini, A. et al. (2005), *Using Expert Judgment to Assess Adaptive Capacity to Climate Change: Evidence from a Conjoint Choice Survey*, Fondazione Eni Enrico Mattei, Milano, (Online), available: http://papers.ssrn.com/sol3/papers.cfm?abstract_id=812972 (14-12-2007).

231 Campbell-Lendrum, D. et al. (2005), *The Global Burden of Disease Due to Climate Change: Quantifying the Benefits of Stabilization for Human Health,* (Online), available: http://www.stabilisation2005.com/39_Sari_Kovats.pdf (14-12-2007).

232 Ngugi, V. W. et al. (2003), *Application of Climate Information and Predictions in Mitigating the Impacts of Drought on Tourism in the Gha (Great Horn of Africa) Region*, UNWTO, Madrid.

233 Martens, P. et al. (1999), 'Climate Change and Future Populations at Risk of Malaria', *Global Environmental Change,* 9(1), pp. 89–107.

234 IPCC (2007b), *Impacts, Adaptation and Vulnerability – Summary for Policymakers.*

235 Ibid.

236 Jones, G. et al. (2005), 'Climate Change and Global Wine Quality', *Climatic Change, 73* (3), pp. 319–343.

237 Webb, L. et al. (2006), *Wine Industry 'Winners and Losers' from Climate Change (in Australia)*, Commonwealth Scientific and Industrial Research Organisation, Dickson.

238 Jones, G. et al. (2005), *Climate Change and Global Wine Quality.*

239 IPCC (2007b), *Impacts, Adaptation and Vulnerability – Summary for Policymakers.*

240 Barnett, J. (2001), *Security and Climate Change.*

241 Stern, N. (2006), *The Stern Review.*

242 German Advisory Council on Global Change (2007), *World in Transition: Climate Change as a Security Risk.*

243 Godard, O. (2007), *Climat et générations futures – Un examen crititque du débat académicque suscité par le Rapport Stern*, Report number DDX-07-12, École Polytechnique, Paris.

244 Stern, N. (2006), *The Stern Review.*

245 IPCC (2007b), *Impacts, Adaptation and Vulnerability – Summary for Policymakers.*

246 Munasinghe, M. and Swart, R. (2000), 'Climate Change and Its Linkages with Development, Equity, and Sustainability', *Proceedings of the IPCC Expert Meeting, Columbo, Sri Lanka, 27–29 April 1999*, LIFE, Columbo, RIVM, Bilthoven, and World Bank, Washington, DC.

247 Paavola, J. and Adger, W. N. (2002), *Justice and Adaptation to Climate Change*, Tyndall Centre for Climate Change Research Working Paper 23, (Online), available: http://www.tyndall.ac.uk/publications/working_papers/wp23.pdf (17-12-2007).

248 Muller, B. (2002), *Equity in Climate Change: The Great Divide*, Oxford Institute for Energy Studies, Oxford University, Oxford.

249 Stern, N. (2006), *The Stern Review*.

250 German Advisory Council on Global Change (2007), *World in Transition: Climate Change as a Security Risk*.

251 Liotta, P. H. and Shearer, A. W. (2005), *The Use of Scenarios in Assessing Climate Change, Human Security, and Potential Outcomes*.

252 The CAN Corporation (2007), *National Security and the Threat of Climate Change*, http://securityandclimate.cna.org/report/National%20Security%20and%20the%20Threat%20of%20Climate%20Change.pdf (17-12-2007).

253 Campbell, K.M. et al. (2007), *The Age of Consequences: The Foreign Policy and National Security Implications of Global Climate Change*, (Online), available: http://www.cnas.org/attachments/contentmanagers/1278/CSIS-CNAS_AgeofConsequences_October07.pdf (17-12-2007).

254 Barnett, J. (2001), *Security and Climate Change*.

255 Feakin, T. (2005), *Climate Change and the Threat to Global Security*.

256 German Advisory Council on Global Change (2007), *World in Transition: Climate Change as a Security Risk*.

257 Xiong, W. et al. (2007), 'Climate Change and Critical Thresholds in China's Food Security', *Climactic Change*, *81* (2), pp. 205–221.

258 The CAN Corporation (2007), *National Security and the Threat of Climate Change*.

259 Frangialli, F. (2007), *Tourism Development and Climate Change: Understanding, Anticipating, Adapting, Participating in the Common Effort*.

260 Becken, S. (2004a), *Climate Change and Tourism in Fiji: Vulnerability, Adaptation and Mitigation*.

261 Mitchell, T. and Tanner, T. (2006), *Adapting to Climate Change: Challenges and Opportunities for the Development Community*.

262 Simpson, M. C. and Ladle, R. (2006), 'Selecting and Evaluating Destinations for the Sustainable Tourism Zone of the Caribbean (STZC)', Keynote Presentation at the *7th Meeting of the Experts in Sustainable Tourism Indicators Association of Caribbean States (ACS) Technical Seminar*, Bayahibe.

263 Simpson, M. C. (2008 – in press), *Global Climate Change and the Implications for Tourism Resilience in Small Island Developing States (SIDS)*.

264 Simpson, M. C. (2003), 'Tourism, Livelihoods, Biodiversity, Conservation and the Climate Change Factor in Developing Countries', *NATO Advanced Research Seminar on Climate Change and Tourism: Assessment and Coping Strategies*, November 2003, Warsaw.

265 IPCC (2007b), *Impacts, Adaptation and Vulnerability – Summary for Policymakers*.

266 Hulme, M. (ed.) (1996), *Climate Change in Southern Africa: An Exploration of Some Potential Impacts andImplications in the SADC Region*, Climatic Research Unit, University of East Anglia, Norwich.

267 Ngugi, V. W. et al. (2003), *Climate Information and Predictions in Mitigating the Impacts of Drought on Tourism*.

268 Simpson, M. C. (2003), *Tourism, Livelihoods, Biodiversity, Conservation and the Climate Change Factor in Developing Countries*.

269   Price, M. (1999), *Global Change in the Mountains*.

270   Beniston, M. (2003), 'Climatic Change in Mountain Regions: A Review of Possible Impacts', *Climatic Change, 59* (1–2), pp. 5–31.

271   Scott, D. (2006b), *Global Environmental Change and Mountain Tourism*.

272   Erickson, J. (2005), 'Changes in the Air, Part 3: Bleak Forecast for the Ski Industry', *Rocky Mountain News,* 19 March 2005, (Online), available at: http://www.rockymountainnews.com/news/2005/mar/19/part-3-bleak-forecast-for-ski-industry/ (17-12-2007).

273   Scott, D. (2006b), *Global Environmental Change and Mountain Tourism*.

274   Abegg, B. et al. (2007), *Climate Change Impacts and Adaptation in Winter Tourism*.

275   König, U. and Abegg, B. (1997), 'Impacts of Climate Change on Tourism in the Swiss Alps', *Journal of Sustainable Tourism, 5* (1), pp. 46–58.

276   Breiling, M. and Charamza, P. (1999), 'The Impact of Global Warming on Winter Tourism and Skiing: A Regionalized Model for Austrian Snow Conditions', *Regional Environmental Change*, 1 (1), pp. 4–14.

277   Elsasser, H. and Messerli, P. (2001), 'The Vulnerability of the Snow Industry in the Swiss Alps', *Mountain Research and Development*, 21 (4), pp. 335–339.

278   Elsasser, H. and Bürki, R. (2002), *Climate Change as a Threat to Tourism in the Alps*.

279   Abegg, B. et al. (2007), *Climate Change Impacts and Adaptation in Winter Tourism*.

280   Wolfsegger, C. et al. (2008 – in press), *Climate Change Risk Appraisal in the Austrian Ski Industry*.

281   Abegg et al. (2007), *Climate Change Impacts and Adaptation in Winter Tourism*.

282   Agrawala, S. (ed.) (2007), *Climate Change in the European Alps: Adapting Winter Tourism and Natural Hazards Management*, OECD, Paris.

283   Nogués-Bravo, D. and Araújo, M.B. (2006), 'Species Richness, Area and Climate Correlates', *Global Ecology and Biogeography,* 15, pp. 452–460.

284   UNEP (2007b), *Europe Set for Warmer Northern Winters, Hotter Southern Summers and Worsening Droughts and Floods,* Press release 10 April 2007, (Online), available: http://www.unep.org/Documents.Multilingual/Default.asp?DocumentID=504&ArticleID=5560&l=en (17-12-2007).

285   Luterbacher, J. et al. (2007), 'Exceptional European Warmth of Autumn 2006 and Winter 2007: Historical Context, the Underlying Dynamics and its Phonological Impacts', *Geophysical Research Letters*, 34, pp. 1–6.

286   Harrison, S. et al. (1999), 'The Potential Effects of Climate Change on the Scottish Tourist Industry, *Tourism Management, 20*, pp. 203–211.

287   Ibid.

288   Scott, D. et al. (2003), 'Climate Change and the Skiing Industry in Southern Ontario (Canada): Exploring the Importance of Snowmaking as a Technical Adaptation', *Climate Research, 23*, pp. 171–181.

289   Scott, D. et al. (2007a), *Climate Change and Québec's Ski Industry*.

290   Scott, D. et al. (2003), *Climate Change and the Skiing Industry in Southern Ontario*.

291   Scott, D. et al. (2007a), *Climate Change and Québec's Ski Industry*.

292   Scott, D. et al. (2008c – in press), 'Climate Change Vulnerability of the Northeast US Winter Tourism Sector', *Mitigation and Adaptation Strategies to Global Change*.

293   International Snowmobile Manufacturers Association (2006), *International Snowmobile Industry Facts and Figures,* (Online), available: http://www.snowmobile.org/pr_snowfacts.asp (17-12-2007).

294 McBoyle, G. et al. (2007), 'Climate Change and the Future of Snowmobiling in Non-Mountainous Regions of Canada'. *Managing Leisure*, Volume 12, Number 4, pp 237-250.

295 Scott, D. et al. (2008c – in press), *Climate Change Vulnerability of the Northeast US Winter Tourism Sector*.

296 Hayhoe, K. et al. (2004), 'Emission Pathways, Climate Change, and Impacts on California', *Proceedings of the National Academy of Sciences, 101* (34), pp. 12422-12427.

297 Aspen Global Change Institute (2006), *Climate change and Aspen: An assessment of Impacts and Potential Responses*, Aspen Global Change Institute, Aspen, (Online), available: http://www.agci.org/pdf/Canary/ACIA_Report.pdf (17-12-2007).

298 Reuer, M. (2006), 'Regional Challenges of Future Climate Change: Endless Summer or Business-As-Usual?', *The 2006 Colorado College State of the Rockies Report Card* (pp. 85–103). Colorado Springs: Colorado College.

299 König, U. (1998), *Tourism in a Warmer World: Implications of Climate Change due to Enhanced Greenhouse Effect for the Ski Industry in the Australian Alps*, Wirtschaftsgeographie und Raumplanung, Volume 28, University of Zurich, Zurich.

300 Hennessy, K. et al. (2003), *The Impact of Climate change on Snow Conditions in Mainland Australia*, CSIRO Atmospheric Research, Aspendale.

301 Scott, D. et al. (2007a), *Climate Change and Québec's Ski Industry*.

302 McBoyle, G. and Wall, G. (1992), 'Great Lakes Skiing and Climate Change', in A. Gill and R. Hartmann (eds.), *Mountain Resort Development*, Policy and Research, Simon Fraser University Burnaby, BC, pp. 70–81.

303 Bürki, R. et al. (2003a), 'Climate Change and Winter Sports: Environmental and Economic Threats', Paper presented at the *5th World Conference on Sport and Environment*, Turin, 2–3 December 2003.

304 Elsasser, H. and Bürki, R. (2002), *Climate Change as a Threat to Tourism in the Alps*.

305 Bürki, R. et al. (2003b), 'Climate Change – Impacts on the Tourism Industry in Mountain Areas', *1st International Conference on Climate Change and Tourism, Djerba, April 2003*.

306 Scott, D. et al. (2007a), *Climate Change and Québec's Ski Industry*.

307 Scott, D. et al. (2008c – in press), *Climate Change Vulnerability of the Northeast US Winter Tourism Sector*.

308 Greenwood, G. (2005), 'What are the Important Global Change Themes and Issues in Mountain Biosphere Reserves?', in *Global Change Impacts in Mountain Biosphere Reserves*, UNESCO, Paris, pp. 179–194.

309 Cullen R. et al. (2001), *Tourism, Water and Waste in Westland: Implications of Increasing Demand on Infrastructure*, Report No. 27/2001, Tourism Recreation Research and Education Centre, Lincoln University, Canterbury.

310 Scott, D. and Jones, B. (2006a), *Climate Change and Seasonality in Canadian Outdoor Recreation and Tourism – Executive Summary*, Report prepared for the Government of Canada Climate Change Action Fund, University of Waterloo, Waterloo, Ontario.

311 Martin, C. and Chehebarf, C. (2001), 'The National Parks of Argentinian Patagonia – Management Policies for Conservation, Public Use, Rural Settlements and Indigenous Communities', *Journal of The Royal Society of New Zealand, 5* (4), pp. 845–864.

312 Dyurgerov, M. (2003), 'Mountain and Subpolar Glaciers Show an Increase in Sensitivity to Climate Warming and Intensification of the Water Cycle', *Journal of Hydrology, 282*, pp. 164–176.

313 Haeberli, W. and Beniston, M. (1998), 'Climate Change and its Impacts on Glaciers and Permafrost in the Alps', *Ambio, 27*, pp. 258–265.

314 Luckman, B. and Kavanagh, T. (2000), 'Impact of Climate Fluctuations on Mountain Environments in the Canadian Rockies', *Ambio, 29*, pp. 371–380.

315 Hall, M. and Farge, D. (2003), *Modeled Climate-induced Glacier Change in Glacier National Park*.

316   Global Warming Art (2007), *Muir and Riggs Glaciers,* (Online), available: http://www.globalwarmingart.com/wiki/Image: Muir_Glacier_jpg (17-12-2007).

317   Saunders, S. and Easley, T. (2006), *Losing Ground: Western National Parks Endangered by Climate Disruption,* The Rocky Mountain Climate Organization, Louisville, CO and Natural Resources Defense Council, New York.

318   Walther, G. R. et al. (2005), 'Climate Change and High Mountain Vegetation Shifts', in G. Broll and B. Keplin (eds.), *Mountain Ecosystems,* Springer Publishing, New York, pp. 77–96.

319   UNESCO (2005), *Global Change Impacts in Mountain Biosphere Reserves,* UNESCO, Paris.

320   UNESCO (2002), *Mountain Summit Opens In Kyrgyzstan,* Press Release No.2002-84, (Online), available: http://www.unesco.org/bpi/eng/unescopress/2002/02-88e.shtml (17-12-2007).

321   Scott, D. and Jones, B. (2006a), *Climate Change and Seasonality in Canadian Outdoor Recreation and Tourism.*

322   Elsasser, H. and Bürki, R. (2002), *Climate Change as a Threat to Tourism in the Alps.*

323   Scott, D. et al. (2004), *Climate Change and the Distribution of Climatic Resources for Tourism in North America.*

324   Amelung, B. et al. (2007), *Implications of Global Climate Change for Tourism Flows and Seasonality.*

325   IPCC (2007b), *Impacts, Adaptation and Vulnerability – Summary for Policymakers.*

326   Shea, E. L. et al. (2001), *Preparing for a Changing Climate: The Potential Consequences of Climate Variability and Change – Pacific Islands,* US Global Research Program, East-West Center, Honalulu, Hawaii.

327   Hay, J. et al. (2003), *Climate Variability and Change and Sea level Rise in the Pacific Islands Region: A Resource Book for Policy and Decision Makers, Educators and other Stakeholders.* South Pacific Regional Environment Programme, Japan Ministry of the Environment, Tokyo.

328   Simpson, M. C. (2008 – in press), *Global Climate Change and the Implications for Tourism Resilience in SIDS.*

329   IPCC (2007b), *Impacts, Adaptation and Vulnerability – Summary for Policymakers.*

330   Shea, E. L. et al. (2001), *Preparing for a Changing Climate: The Potential Consequences of Climate Variability and Change – Pacific Islands.*

331   Hay, J. et al. (2003), *Climate Variability and Change and Sea level Rise in the Pacific Islands Region.*

332   Simpson, M. C. (2008 – in press), *Global Climate Change and the Implications for Tourism Resilience in SIDS.*

333   Berz, B. (2005), 'Windstorm and Storm Surges in Europe: Loss Trends and Possible Counter-actions from the Viewpoint of an International Reinsurer', *Philosophical Transactions: Mathematical, Physical and Engineering Sciences, 363* (1831), pp. 1431–1440.

334   Leckebusch, G. C. and Ulbrich, U. (2004), 'On the Relationship between Cyclones and Extreme Windstorm Events over Europe under Climate Change', *Global and Planetry Science, 44,* pp. 181–193.

335   Bell, G. and Chelliah, M. (2006), 'Leading Tropical Modes Associated with Interannual and Multidecadal Fluctuations in North Atlantic Hurricane Activity', *Journal of Climate,* 19, pp. 590–612.

336   Halverson, J. B. (2006), 'A Climate Conundrum', *Weatherwise,* 59 (2), pp. 108–23.

337   Webster, P. J. et al. (2005), 'Changes in Tropical Cyclone Number, Duration, and Intensity in a Warming Environment', Science, 16 (309), No. 5742, pp. 1844–1846, (Online), available: http://www.sciencemag.org/cgi/content/full/309/5742/1844 (13-12-2007).

338   Holland, G. and Webster, P. J. (2007), 'Heightened Tropical Cyclone Activity in the North Atlantic: Natural Variability or Climate Trend?', *Philansophical Transactions of the Royal Society,* (Online), available: http://publishing.royalsociety.org/media/philtrans_a/Holland%20and%20Webster%201.pdf (13-12-2007)

339 Santer, B. D. et al. (2006), 'Forced and Unforced Ocean Temperature Changes in Atlantic and Pacific Tropical Cyclone Genesis Regions', *Proceedings of the National Academy of Sciences*, USA 103, 13, pp. 905–910, and (Online), at: http://www.pnas.org/cgi/reprint/0602861103v1 (13-12-2007).

340 Holland, G. and Webster, P. J. (2007), *Heightened Tropical Cyclone Activity in the North Atlantic: Natural Variability or Climate Trend?*.

341 Ibid.

342 IPCC (2007b), *Impacts, Adaptation and Vulnerability – Summary for Policymakers*.

343 Webster, P. J. et al. (2005), *Changes in Tropical Cyclone Number, Duration, and Intensity in a Warming Environment*.

344 IPCC (2007a), *The Physical Science Basis – Technical Summary*.

345 Webster, P. J. et al. (2005), *Changes in Tropical Cyclone Number, Duration, and Intensity in a Warming Environment*.

346 Emanuel, K. (2005) 'Increasing destructiveness of tropical cyclones over the past 30 years', *Nature*, 436, pp. 686–688.

347 Bell, G. D. et al. (2006a), 'The Tropics: The Atlantic Basic: State of the Climate in 2005', in K. A. Shein (ed.) (2005), *Bull. Amer. Meteor. Soc.*, 87, pp. 33–37.

348 Bell, G. D. et al. (2006b), 'The Record Breaking 2005 Atlantic Hurricane Season: State of the Climate in 2005', in K. A. Shein (Ed), *Bull. Amer. Meteor. Soc.*, 87, pp. 44–45.

349 Pachauri, R. K, Jallow, B. (2007), *Presentation of the WG I Report at the GMEF and UNEP GC-24 Nairobi, 6 February 2007*, (Online), available: http://www.ipcc.ch/pdf/presentations/wg1-report-2007-02.pdf (13-12-2007).

350 Saunders, M. A. and Lea, A. S. (2006), 'Hurricanes and Global Warming'. Presentation at *Oxford University Centre for the Environment*, May 2006.

351 Lea, A. S. and Saunders, M. A. (2006), 'How Well Forecast Were the 2004 and 2005 Atlantic and US Hurricane Seasons?', *Weather*, 61, no. 9, pp. 245–249.

352 DFID (2004), *Adaptation to Climate Change: Making Development Disaster-proof*, Department for International Development, London, (Online), available: http://www.dfid.gov.uk/pubs/files/climatechange/6disasterproof.pdf (13-12-2007).

353 Erickson, N. et al. (1997), *Socio-economic Implications of Climate Change for Bangladesh*, Briefing Document 4, (Online), available: http://www.waikato.ac.nz/igci/downloads/BriefingDoc4.pdf (13-12-2007).

354 United States Environmental Protection Agency (1999), 'Global Climate Change: What Does it Mean for South Florida and the Florida Keys', *Report on the Environmental Protection Agency Public Consultations in coastal cities*, May 24–28. Washington, DC: Environmental Protection Agency.

355 Deravi, M. and. Smith, P. (2005), *Economic impact Alabama travel industry 2004*, Bureau of Tourism and Travel, Montgomery, AL.

356 Bhatnagar, P. (2005), 'Uncertainty and Fear to Rebuild: Mississippi Officials Say Casino Companies are Hesitant to Rebuild, State could Lose Billions', *CNN*, 6 September 2005, (Online), available: http://money.cnn.com/2005/09/05/news/economy/katrina_business/ (13-12-2007)

357 Ruosteenoja, K. et al. (2003), *Future Climate in World Regions: An Intercomparison of Model-based Projections for the New IPCC Emissions Scenarios*, The Finnish Environment 644, Finnish Environment Institute, Helsinki, (Online), available: http://www.environment.fi/download.asp?contentid=25835&lan=en (20-12-2007).

358 IPCC (2007a), *The Physical Science Basis – Technical Summary*.

359 Pelling, M. and Uitto, J. (2001), 'Small Island Developing States: Natural Disaster Vulnerability and Global Change', *Global Environmental Change Part B: Environmental hazards*, 3 (2), pp. 49–62.

360 Ibid.

361 UK Department for Environment, Food and Rural Affairs (DEFRA) (2005), *Climate Change Impacts on Sea Level in India,* Department for Environment, Food and Rural Affairs, London, (Online), available: http://www.defra.gov.uk/environment/climatechange/internat/devcountry/pdf/india-climate-4-sealevel.pdf (13-12-2007).

362 EUROSION (2004), *Coastal Erosion – Evaluation of the Need for Action,* (Online), available: http://www.eurosion.org/reports-online/part1.pdf (13-12-2007).

363 National Drought Mitigation Center (1998), *Reported Effects of the 1997–98 El Niño,* National Drought Mitigation Center, Lincoln, Nebraska, 11p.

364 Glantz, M. (2000), *Reducing the Impact of Environmental Emergencies through Early Warning and Preparedness: The Case of the 1997–98 El Niño.* UNEP, NCAR, UNU, and WMO.

365 UNESCO-WHC (2007), *Case Studies on Climate Change and World Heritage.*

366 Hoegh-Guldberg, H. and Hoegh-Guldberg, O. (2004), *The Implications of Climate Change for Australia's Great Barrier Reef,* WWF Australia, Sydney.

367 Lesser, M. (2007), Coral Reef Bleaching and Global Climate Change: Can Corals Survive the Next Century?', *Proceedings of the National Academy of Sciences,* 104 (13), pp. 5259–5260.

368 Gössling, S. et al. (2007), 'Diving and Global Environmental Change: A Mauritius Case Study', in B. Garrod and S. Gössling (eds.), *New Frontiers in Marine Tourism: Diving Experiences, Management and Sustainability,* Elsevier, Amsterdam.

369 Hall, C. M. (2006), 'Tourism, Biodiversity and Global Environmental Change', in S. Gössling and C.M. Hall (eds.), *Tourism and Global Environmental Change,* Routledge, London, pp. 211–226.

370 Johnston, M. (2006), 'Impact of Global Environmental Change on Tourism in the Polar Regions, in S. Gössling and C.M. Hall (eds.), *Tourism and Global Environmental Change,* Routledge, London, pp. 37–53.

371 Chaplin III, F. S. et al. (2000), 'Consequences of Changing Biodiversity', *Nature, 405,* pp. 234–242.

372 Myers, N. et al. (2000), 'Biodiversity Hotspots for Conservation Priorities', *Nature, 403,* pp. 853–858.

373 IPCC (2001), *Climate Change 2001: Impacts, Adaptation and Vulnerability – Contribution of Working Group II to the Third Assessment Report of the IPCC,* [J. J McCarthy et al. (eds.)], Cambridge University Press, Cambridge and New York.

374 IPCC (2002), *Climate Change and Biodiversity (Technical Paper V),* IPCC. Geneva.

375 Green, R. E. (2003), *Global Climate Change and Biodiversity.*

376 Thomas, C. D. et al. (2004), 'Extinction Risk from Climate Change', *Nature* 427, pp. 145–148.

377 Pounds, J. A. et al. (2006), 'Widespread Amphibian Extinctions from Epidemic Disease Driven by Global Warming' *Nature, 439,* pp. 161–166.

378 Hall, C. M. (2006), *Tourism, Biodiversity and Global Environmental Change.*

379 Beniston, M. (2003), *Climatic Change in Mountain Regions: A Review of Possible Impacts.*

380 Baker, J. D. et al. (2006), 'Potential Effects of Sea level Rise on the Terrestrial Habitats of Endangered and Endemic Megafauna in the Northwestern Hawaiian Islands', *Endangered Species Research, 2,* pp. 21–30.

381 Janzen, F. J. (1994), 'Climate Change and Temperature-Dependent Sex Determination in Reptiles', *Proceedings of the National Academy of Sciences, 91,* pp. 7487–7490.

382 Carthy, R. R. et al. (2003), 'Incubation Environment of Loggerhead Turtle Nests: Effects on Hatching Success and Hatchling Characteristics', in A.B. Bolten and B.E. Witherington (eds.), *Loggerhead Sea Turtles,* Smithsonian Institution, Washington DC, pp. 144–153.

383 UNESCO-WHC (2007), *Case Studies on Climate Change and World Heritage.*

384 Ibid.

385 Gössling, S. and Hickler, T. (2006), 'Tourism and Forest Ecosystems', in S. Gössling and C.M. Hall (eds.), *Tourism and Global Environmental Change*, Routledge, London, pp. 95–106.

386 Price, J. and Glick, P. (2002), *The Birdwatcher's Guide to Global Warming*, National Wildlife Federation and The Plains, Virgina, and American Bird Conservancy, Virginia.

387 Lemoine, N. and Bohning-Gaese, K. (2003), 'Potential Impact of Global Climate Change on Species Richness of Long-distance Migrants', *Conservation Biology*, *17*, 2, pp. 577–586.

388 Scott, D. et al. (2005b), *Climate Change: A Long-term Strategic Issue for the National Capital Commission.*

389 Parry, R. (2005), 'Cherry Trees Programmed to Blossom for Tourists', *The Times Online*, 9 June 2005, (Online), available: http://www.timesonline.co.uk/tol/news/world/article1080206.ece (13-12-2007).

390 Richardson, D.M. et al. (2000), 'Invasive Alien Species and Global Change: A South African Perspective', in H.A. Mooney and R.J. Hobbs (eds.), *Invasive Species in a Changing World*, Island Press, Washington DC, pp. 303–350.

391 Rutherford, M.C. et al. (1999), 'Climate Change in Conservation Areas of South Africa and its Potential Impact on Floristic Composition: A First Assessment', *Diversity and Distributions*, 5 (6), pp. 253–262.

392 UNESCO-WHC (2007), *Case Studies on Climate Change and World Heritage.*

393 Hall, C. M. (2006), *Tourism, Biodiversity and Global Environmental Change.*

394 Christ, C. et al. (2003), *Tourism and Biodiversity: Mapping Tourism's Global Footprint.* UNEP/Conservation International, (Online), available: http://www.unep.org/PDF/Tourism_and_biodiversity_report.pdf (13-12-2007).

395 Eagles, P. (2001), *International Trends in Park Tourism*, Task Force on Tourism and Protected Areas, World Commission on Protected Areas, World Conservation Union (IUCN), Gland.

396 UNEP (2002a), *How Tourism Can Contribute to Environmental Conservation.*

397 Lollino, G. and Audisio, C. (2006), *World Heritage Sites in Italy Affected by Geological Problems, Specifically Landslide and Flood Hazard.*

398 UNESCO-WHC (2007), *Case Studies on Climate Change and World Heritage.*

399 Ibid.

400 Koohafkan, P. (2006), 'Conservation and Adaptive Management of Globally Important Agricultural Heritage Systems (GIAHS)', *International Conference on Endogenous Development and Bio-Cultural Diversity*, 3–5 October, 2006, Geneva, Switzerland, (Online), available: http://www.bioculturaldiversity.net/Downloads/Papers%20participants/Koohafkan.pdf (13-12-2007)

401 Ford, J. and Smit, B. (2004), 'Human Implications of Climate Change in the Canadian Arctic: A case study of Arctic Bay, Nunavut', *Proceedings of the Third Northern Research Forum: The Resilient North – Human Responses to Global Change*, 15–18 September 2006, Yellowknife, Canada, (Online), available: http://www.nrf.is/Publications/The%20Resilient%20North/Plenary%204/3rd%20NRF_Plenary%204_Ford%20and%20Smit_YR_paper.pdf (13-12-2007)

402 IUCN (2006a), *Coral Reef Resilience and Resistance to Bleaching*, IUCN Global Marine Programme, (Online), available: http://www.iucn.org/dbtw-wpd/edocs/2006-042.pdf (13-12-2007)

403 IUCN (2006b), *Managing Mangroves for Resilience to Climate Change*, IUCN Global Marine Programme, (Online), available: http://www.iucn.org/dbtw-wpd/edocs/2006-041.pdf (13-12-2007)

404 UNESCO-WHC (2007), *Case Studies on Climate Change and World Heritage.*

405 Ibid.

406 Ibid.

407 Thompson, L. et al. (2002), 'Kilimanjaro Ice Core Records: Evidence of Holocene Climate Change in Tropical Africa', *Science* 298, pp. 589–593.

408 UNESCO-WHC (2007), *Case Studies on Climate Change and World Heritage.*

409 London Climate Change Partnership (2002), *Climate Change Impacts in a London Evaluation Study, Final Report,* (Online), available: http://www.london.gov.uk/gla/publications/environment/londons_warming_tech_rpt_all.pdf (13-12-2007).

410 Lowe, J. (2003), *The Effects of Climate Change on Storm Surges Around the UK, in The Big Flood: An International Scientific Meeting on North Sea Storm Surges.*

411 Lowe, J. A. and Gregory, J. M. (2005), 'The Effects of Climate Change on Storm Surges Around the UK', *Philosophical Transacation Royal Society*, (A) 363 (1831), pp. 1313–1328.

412 IPCC (2007b), *Impacts, Adaptation and Vulnerability – Summary for Policymakers.*

413 Adger, W. N. et al. (2005), 'Adapting to Climate Change: Perspectives Across Scales', *Global Environmental Change*, 15, pp. 75–76.

414 Scott, D. et al. (2008a – in press), *Climate Change Adaptation in the Recreation and Tourism Sector.*

415 Adger, W. et al. (2007), 'Assessment of Adaptation Practices, Options, Constraints and Capacity', in IPCC (ed.), *Climate Change 2007: Climate Change Impacts, Adaptation and Vulnerability,* Cambridge University Press, Cambridge.

416 Wall, G. (1992), *Tourism Alternatives in an Era of Global Climate Change.*

417 Maddison, D. (2001), 'In Search of Warmer Climates? The Impact of Climate Change on Flows of British Tourists', *Climatic Change, 49* (1/2), pp. 193–208.

418 Elsasser, H. and Bürki, R. (2002), *Climate Change as a Threat to Tourism in the Alps.*

419 Scott, D. (2006a), *Climate Change and Sustainable Tourism in the 21st Century.*

420 Gössling, S. and Hall, C. M. (2006a), *An Introduction to Tourism and Global Environmental change.*

421 Becken, S. and Hay, J. (2007), *Tourism and Climate Change – Risks and Opportunities.*

422 Ibid.

423 Awareness and Preparedness for Emergencies at the Local Level (APELL) (2001), *Explaining APELL,* (Online), available: http://www.uneptie.org/pc/apell/publications/pdf_files/explaining_apell.pdf (13-12-2007).

424 Kovats, R. S. and Ebi , K. (2006), 'Heatwaves and Public Health in Europe', *The European Journal of Public Health, 16* (6), pp. 592–599.

425 Patz, J. A. et al. (2005), 'Impact of Regional Climate Change on Human Health', *Nature, 438* (17), pp. 310–317.

426 Hawker, M. (2007), 'Climate Change and the Global Insurance Industry', *The Geneva Papers, 32*, pp. 22–28.

427 UNEP (2007a), 'Insuring for Sustainability: Why and How the Leaders are Doing it', UNEP Financial Initiative, UNE, Geneva

428 Hawker, M. (2007), *Climate Change and the Global Insurance Industry.*

429 Becken, S. (2005), 'Harmonizing climate change adaptation and mitigation: The case of tourist resorts in Fiji', *Global Environmental Change – Part A, 15* (4), pp. 381–393.

430 Association of British Insurers (2004), *A Changing Climate for Insurance: A Summary Report for Chief Executives and Policymakers,* (Online), available: http://www.abi.org.uk/Display/File/Child/552/A_Changing_Climate_for_Insurance_2004.pdf (13-12-2007).

431 Mills, E. et al. (2005), *Availability and Affordability of Insurance under Climate Change: A Growing Challenge for the US,* Ceres, (Online), available: http://www.ceres.org/pub/docs/Ceres_insure_climatechange_120105.pdf (13-12-2007).

432 O'Brien, R. (2007), 'Guardian Insurance', *2nd UK-Caribbean Business Forum on Climate Change*, Trinidad and Tobago, 8 June 2007.

433 Becken, S. (2004a), *Climate Change and Tourism in Fiji: Vulnerability, Adaptation and Mitigation.*

434 Becken, S. (2005), *Harmonizing climate change adaptation and mitigation: The case of tourist resorts in Fiji.*

435 IUCN (2004) *Securing Protected Areas in the Face of Global Change: Issues and Strategies,* (Online), available: http://www.iucn.org/themes/wcpa/pubs/pdfs/securingpas.pdf (13-12-2007).

436 UNESCO-WHC (2007), *Case Studies on Climate Change and World Heritage.*

437 Hawker, M. (2007), *Climate Change and the Global Insurance Industry.*

438 Gill, J. and Watkinson A. (2004), *Linking Sea Level Rise, Coastal Biodiversity and Economic Activity in Caribbean Island States: Towards the Development of a Coastal Island Simulator*, Tyndall Centre for Climate Change Research, Technical Report 9, (Online), available: http://www.tyndall.ac.uk/research/theme4/final_reports/it1_38.pdf (13-12-2007).

439 Tompkins, E. and Adger, N. (2003), *Building Resilience to Climate Change through Adaptive Management of Natural Resources*, Tyndall Centre for Climate Change Research, Working Paper 27, (Online), available: http://www.tyndall.ac.uk/publications/working_papers/wp27.pdf (13-12-2007).

440 Gill, J. and Watkinson A. (2004), *Linking Sea Level Rise, Coastal Biodiversity and Economic Activity in Caribbean Island States.*

441 Ecologic (2007), *Time to Adapt – Climate Change and The European Water Dimension,* Key Messages, Converence, *12–14 February 2007, Berlin Germany,* (Online), available: http://www.climate-water-adaptation-berlin2007.org/documents/key_ messages.pdf (13-12-2007).

442 EEA (2007), *Climate Change and Water Adaptation Issues*, EEA Technical report No 2/2007, EEA, Copenhagen, (Online), available: http://reports.eea.europa.eu/technical_report_2007_2 (13-12-2007).

443 Zhou, Y. and Tol, R. S. J. (2005), 'Evaluating the Costs of Desalination and Water Transport', *Water Resources Research, 41*, (3), W03003.

444 Raksakulthai, V. (2003), *Climate Change Impacts and Adaptation for Tourism in Phuket.*

445 Wheeler, D. (1995), 'Majorca's Water Shortages Arouse Spanish Passions', *Geography, 80*, pp. 283–286.

446 Becken, S. (2005), *Harmonizing Climate Change Adaptation and Mitigation: The Case of Tourist Resorts in Fiji.*

447 Simmons, P. (2005), 'Swiss Plan to Wrap Up their Glaciers', *The Times*, 30 March 2005.

448 Abegg et al. (2007), *Climate Change Impacts and Adaptation in Winter Tourism.*

449 Fukushima, T. et al. (2003), 'Influences of Air Temperature Change on Leisure Industries: Case Study on Ski Activities', *Mitigation and Adaptation Strategies for Climate Change, 7*, pp. 173–189.

450 Abegg et al. (2007), *Climate Change Impacts and Adaptation in Winter Tourism.*

451 Scott, D. et al. (2003), *Climate Change and the Skiing Industry in Southern Ontario.*

452 Scott, D. et al. (2007a), *Climate Change and Québec's Ski Industry.*

453 Wolfsegger, C. et al. (2008 – in press), *Climate Change Risk Appraisal in the Austrian Ski Industry.*

454 Bicknell, S. and McManus, P. (2006), 'The Canary in the Coalmine: Australian Ski Resorts and their Response to Climate Change', *Geographical Research, 44* (4), pp. 386–400.

455 Wolfsegger, C. et al. (2008 – in press), *Climate Change Risk Appraisal in the Austrian Ski Industry.*

456 Boinet, T. (2007), 'Snowless in a Warming World, Ski Resort in French Alps bids adieu', *Associated Press*, 19 July 2007, (Online), available: http://www.iht.com/articles/2007/07/19/travel/0720francewarm.php (13-12-2007).

457   Knauer, S. (2007), 'Endangered Ski Slopes in the Bavarian Alps: Snow Cannons Against the Apocalypse', *Spiegel Online*, 3 January 2007, (Online), available: http://www.spiegel.de/international/spiegel/0,1518,457498,00.html (13-12-2007).

458   IPCC (2007b), *Impacts, Adaptation and Vulnerability – Summary for Policymakers*.

459   Olefs, M. et al. (2007), 'The Role of Artificial Increase of Accumulation within Glacier Skiing Resorts: A Feasibility Study', *Geophysical Research Abstracts*, 9, 06576, (Online), available: http://www.cosis.net/abstracts/EGU2007/06576/EGU2007-J-06576.pdf (13-12-2007).

460   Simmons, P. (2005), *Swiss Plan to Wrap Up their Glaciers*.

461   Efron, S. (2005), 'The Race to Protect Year-round Skiing: Plan to Preserve Horstman Glacier Could be a Model for Other Resorts', *Globe and Mail*, 9 July 2007, (Online), available: http://www.theglobeandmail.com/servlet/ArticleNews/TPStory/LAC/20050709/BCGLACIER09 (13-12-2007).

462   Jahn, G. (2005), 'Glacial Cover-Up Won't Stop Global Warming, But It Keeps Skiers Happy', *Environmental News Network*, (Online), available: http://www.enn.com/top_stories/article/2060 (13-12-2007).

463   König, U., and Abegg, B. (1997), 'Impacts of Climate Change on Tourism in the Swiss Alps', *Journal of Sustainable Tourism*, 5 (1), pp. 46–58.

464   Elsasser, H. and Bürki, R. (2002), *Climate Change as a Threat to Tourism in the Alps*.

465   Breiling, M. and Charamza, P. (1999), *The Impact of Global Warming on Winter Tourism and Skiing*.

466   Tommasini, D. (2003), *Personal Communication*, North Atlantic Regional Studies (NORS), University of Roskilde, Roskilde.

467   Wipe, S. et al. (2005), 'Effects of Ski Piste Preparation on Alpine Vegetation', *Journal of Applied Ecology*, 42, pp. 306–316.

468   Rixen, C. et al. (2003), 'Does Artificial Snow Production Affect Soli and Vegetation of Ski Pistes? – A review', *Perspectives in Plant Ecology, Evolution and Systematics*, 5 (4), pp. 219–230.

469   Scott, D. and McBoyle, G. (2006), 'Climate Change Adaptation in the Ski Industry', *Mitigation and Adaptation Strategies to Global Change*, [Electronic], SpringerLink.

470   Union of Concerned Scientists (2007), *Northeast Climate Impact Assessment*, (Online), available: http://www.northeastclimateimpacts.org (13-12-2007).

471   The Economist (1998), 'Winter Wonderlands', *The Economist*, 31 January 1998.

472   Cockerell, N. (1994), 'Market Segments: The International Ski Market in Europe', *EIU Travel Tourism Analyst*, 3, pp. 34–55.

473   Wickers, D. (1994), 'Snow Alternative', *Sunday Times* 27 November 1994.

374   Frangialli, F. and Passaquin, F. (2003), 'Sustainable Tourism and Climate Change: An Example in the French Alps – The Case of Morzine-Avoriaz, France', *Proceedings of the First International Conference on Climate Change and Tourism, Djerba, Tunisia, 9–11 April*. Madrid, Spain: UNWTO, (Online), available: http://www.unwto.org/sustainable/climate/pres/Passaquin.pdf (13-12-2007).

475   Thorne, P. (2006), *World Snowdomes*, Snow Hunter Ltd, Kiltarlity Inverness.

476   Becken, S. and Hay, J. (2007), *Tourism and Climate Change – Risks and Opportunities*.

477   Simpson, M. C. (2008 – in press), *Global Climate Change and the Implications for Tourism Resilience in SIDS*.

478   UN General Assembly (1994), *Report of the Global Conference on the Sustainable Development of Small Island Developing States*: UN General Assembly, New York, (Online), available: http://www.un.org/documents/ga/conf167/aconf167-9.htm (13-12-2007).

479   Barnes, B. (2002), 'The Heat Wave Vacation', *The Wall Street Journal*, 2 August 2002, W1.

480 Sandals Resorts (2006), 'Blue Chip Hurricane Guarantee', *Beaches*, (Online), available: http://www.beaches. com/general/hurricane.cfm 13-12-2007.

481 Johnson, A. (2005), 'Early Start to Hhurricane Season Forces Travelers, Resorts to Adjust', *The Wall Street Journal*, 21 July 2005, D5.

482 Becken, S. (2004a), *Climate Change and Tourism in Fiji: Vulnerability, Adaptation and Mitigation.*

483 Becken, S. and Hay, J. (2007), *Tourism and Climate Change – Risks and Opportunities.*

484 Agrawala, S. et al. (2003), *Development and Climate Change in Nepal: Focus on Water Resources and Hydropower.* OECD, (Online), available: http://www.oecd.org/dataoecd/6/51/19742202.pdf (13-12-2007).

485 UNEP (2002b), *Inventory of Glaciers, Glacier Lakes, Glacier Lake Outburst Floods Monitoring and Early Warning Systems in the Hindu Kush-Himalayan Region, Nepal and Bhutan*, International Centre for Integrated Mountain Development, UNEP, (Online), available: http://www.rrcap.unep.org/glofnepal/start. htm (14-12-2007).

486 IUCN (2003), *Evaluation of the Cape Floral Region for the World Heritage Committee*, World Heritage Nomitation – IUCN Technical Evaluation, (Online), available: http://whc.unesco.org/archive/advisory_body_ evaluation/1007rev.pdf (14-12-2007).

487 Bomhard, B. and Midgley, G. (2005), *Securing Protected Areas in the Face of Global Change: Lessons Learned from the South African Cape Floristic Region.* IUCN, Bangkok, and SANBI, Capetown.

488 UNESCO-WHC (2007), *Case Studies on Climate Change and World Heritage.*

489 Iyer, P. (2007), '20 Places to See Before *They* Die', *Condé Nast Traveler*, May 2007, (Online), available, http:// www.concierge.com/cntraveler/articles/detail?articleId=10772 (14-12-2007).

490 Klein, R. J. T. et al. (2005), 'Integrating Mitigation and Adaptation into Climate and Development Policy: Three Research Questions', *Environmental Science and Policy*, 8, pp. 579–588. and (Online), available: http:// www.tyndall.ac.uk/publications/working_papers/wp40.pdf (13-12-2007).

491 Paavola, J. and Adger, W.N. (2002), *Justice and Adaptation to Climate Change.*

492 Becken, S. and Hay, J. (2007), *Tourism and Climate Change – Risks and Opportunities.*

493 Asian Development Bank (2005), *Climate Proofing: A Risk-based Approach to Adaptation,* (Online), available: http://www.adb.org/Documents/Reports/Climate-Proofing/climate-proofing.pdf (14-12-2007).

494 Stern, N. (2006), *The Stern Review.*

495 Elsasser, H. and Bürki, R. (2002), *Climate Change as a Threat to Tourism in the Alps.*

496 Scott, D. et al (2002), *The Vulnerability of Winter Recreation to Climate Change in Ontario's Lakelands Tourism Region.*

497 Raksakulthai, V. (2003), *Climate Change Impacts and Adaptation for Tourism in Phuket.*

498 Becken, S. (2004a), *Climate Change and Tourism in Fiji: Vulnerability, Adaptation and Mitigation.*

499 Scott, D. and Jones, B. (2005), *Climate Change and Banff: Implications for Tourism and Recreation – Executive Summary,* Report prepared for the Government of Canada Climate Change Action Fund and Town of Banff, Alberta, University of Waterloo, Waterloo, Ontario.

500 Scott, D. et al. (2005c), *Climate Change: A Long-term Strategic Issue for the National Capital Commission.*

501 Sievanen, T. et al. (2005), *Nature-based Tourism, Outdoor Recreation and Adaptation to Climate Change.*

502 Wolfsegger, C. et al. (2008 – in press), *Climate Change Risk Appraisal in the Austrian Ski Industry.*

503 Simpson, M. C. (2008 – in press), *Global Climate Change and the Implications for Tourism Resilience in SIDS.*

504 SWCCIP, Devon County Council and South East Climate Change Partnership (2007), *Climate Change and Tourism in the South of England,* (Online), available: http://www.oursouthwest.com/climate/archive/tourism- leaflet-2007.pdf (17-12-2007).

505   Elsasser, H. and Bürki, R. (2002), *Climate Change as a Threat to Tourism in the Alps.*

506   Scott, D. et al (2002), *The Vulnerability of Winter Recreation to Climate Change in Ontario's Lakelands Tourism Region.*

507   Raksakulthai, V. (2003), *Climate Change Impacts and Adaptation for Tourism in Phuket.*

508   Becken, S. (2004a), *Climate Change and Tourism in Fiji: Vulnerability, Adaptation and Mitigation.*

509   Scott, D. and Jones, B. (2005), *Climate Change and Banff.*

510   Scott, D. et al. (2005c), *Climate Change: A Long-term Strategic Issue for the National Capital Commission.*

511   Sievanen, T. et al. (2005), *Nature-based Tourism, Outdoor Recreation and Adaptation to Climate Change.*

512   Wolfsegger, C. et al. (2008 – in press), *Climate Change Risk Appraisal in the Austrian Ski Industry.*

513   Simpson, M. C. (2008 – in press), *Global Climate Change and the Implications for Tourism Resilience in SIDS.*

514   Stern, N. (2006), *The Stern Review.*

515   Paavola, J. and Adger, W. N. (2002), *Justice and Adaptation to Climate Change.*

Implications of Climate Change for Tourism Demand Patterns

516   Higham, J. and Hinch, T. (2002), 'Tourism, Sport and Seasons: The Challenges and Potential of Overcoming Seasonality in the Sport and Tourism Sectors', *Tourism Management, 23* (2), pp. 175–185.

517   Jang, S. C. (2004), 'Mitigating Tourism Seasonality: A Quantitative Approach', *Annals of Tourism Research, 31* (4), pp. 819–836.

518   Mintel International Group (1991), 'Special Report – Holidays', *Leisure Intelligence*, Mintel International Group, London.

519   Ontario Ministry of Tourism and Recreation (2002), *If the Future Were Now: Impacts of Aging in the Canadian Market on Tourism in Ontario*, Ontario Ministry of Tourism and Recreation, Toronto.

520   Kozak, M. (2002), *Comparative Analysis of Tourist Motivations by Nationality and Destinations.*

521   Gössling, S. and Hall, C. M. (2006b), *Uncertainties in Predicting Tourist Travel Flows Based on Models.*

522   Lohmann, M. and Kaim, E. (1999), *Weather and Holiday Preference.*

523   Hamilton, J. M. and Lau, M. (2005), *The Role of Climate Information in Tourist Destination Choice Decision-making.*

524   Butler, R. (2001), 'Seasonality in tourism: Issues and implications', in T. Baum and S. Lundtorp (eds.), *Seasonality in Tourism* (pp. 5–22), Pergamon, London.

525   Hu, Y. and Ritchie, J. (1993), *Measuring Destination Attractiveness.*

526   Bigano, A. et al. (2006), 'The Impact of Climate on Holiday Destination Choice', *Climatic Change, 76* (3–4), pp. 389–406.

527   Aguilo, E. et al. (2005), 'The Persistence of the Sun and Sand Tourism Model', *Tourism Management, 26*, pp. 219–231.

528   Giles, A. and Perry, A. (1998), 'The Use of a Temporal Analogue to Investigate the Possible Impact of Projected Global Warming on the UK Tourist Industry', *Tourism Management, 19*, 1, pp. 75–80.

529   Jorgensen, F. and Solvoll, G. (1996), 'Demand Models for Inclusive Tour Charter: The Norwegian Case', *Tourism Management, 17*, pp. 17–24.

530   Agnew, M. and Palutikof, J. (2006), *Impacts of Short-term Climate Variability in the UK on Demand for Domestic and International Tourism.*

531 Wilton, D. and Wirjanto, T. (1998), *An Analysis of the Seasonal Variation in the National Tourism Indicators*, Canadian Tourism Commission, Ottawa.

532 Williams, P. et al. (1997), *Influence of Weather Context on Winter Resort Evaluations by Visitors*.

533 Hamilton, J. M. et al. (2005b), 'Climate Change and International Tourism: A Simulation Study', *Global Environmental Change*, *15*, pp. 253–266.

534 Berrittella, M. et al. (2006), *A General Equilibrium Analysis of Climate Change Impacts on Tourism*.

535 Gössling, S. and Hall, C. M. (2006b), *Uncertainties in Predicting Tourist Travel Flows Based on Models*.

536 Berrittella, M. et al. (2006), *A General Equilibrium Analysis of Climate Change Impacts on Tourism*.

537 AKI (2005), *Global Warming Threatens Mediterranean Tourism*, 2 July 2007, AKI, Rome.

538 Reuters (2005), *Global Warming to Wreck Med Paradise*, 2 July 2007 Reuter, London.

539 Freesun News (2005), 'The Mediterranean: Too Hot to Holiday?', *Freesun News* (Belgium), 18 November 2005.

540 Guardian (2006), 'Climate Change could Bring Tourists to UK – Report', *The Guardian*, 28 July 2006, (Online), available: http://www.guardian.co.uk/travel/2006/jul/28/travelnews.uknews.climatechange (14-12-2007).

541 Randerson, J. (2006), 'Med to Lose Pull as Earth Heats Up', *The Guardian*, 9 August 2006, (Online), available: http://www.guardian.co.uk/science/2006/aug/09/travelnews.environment (14-12-2007).

542 Easier Travel (2006), 'Climate Change to Drive Radical Changes in Global Tourism', *easier TRAVEL*, (Online), available: www.easier.com/view/News/Travel/arctiklce-66761.html (14-12-2007).

543 BBC News (2006), 'Package Holiday Will be History', *BBC News*, August 26 2006, http://news.bbc.co.uk/2/hi/science/nature/5288092.stm (14-12-2007).

544 Guardian (2006), *Climate Change could Bring Tourists to UK*.

545 Easier Travel (2006), *Climate Change to Drive Radical Changes in Global Tourism*.

546 BBC News (2006), *Package Holiday Will be History*.

547 Halifax Travel Insurance (2006), *Holiday 2030*, (Online), available: http://www.hbosplc.com/media/pressreleases/articles/halifax/2007-02-14-WINTERHOLI.asp?section=halifax (14-12-2007).

548 Scott, D. et al. (2008d – accepted), 'Climate Preferences for Tourism: Evidence from Canada, New Zealand and Sweden', *Climate Research*.

549 Kjellström, E. et al. (2006), *Modelling Daily Temperature Extremes: Recent Climate and Future Changes over Europe*, (Online), available: http://prudence.dmi.dk/public/publications/PSICC/Kjellstrom-et-al.pdf (14-12-2007).

550 Lagadec, P. (2004), 'Understanding the French 2003 Heat Wave Experience: Beyond the Heat, a Multi-Layered Challenge', *Journal of Contingencies and Crisis Management*, 12 (4), 160-169.

551 Létard, V. et al. (2004), *Rapport d'Information Fait au Nom de la Mission: La France et les Français Face à la Canicule: les Leçons d'une Crise*, Report No. 195 (2003-2004) to the Parlament, Government of France.

552 Ibid.

553 Amelung, B. et al. (2007), *Implications of Global Climate Change for Tourism Flows and Seasonality*.

554 Scott, D. et al. (2007c), 'Implications of Climate and Environmental Change for Nature-based Tourism in the Canadian Rocky Mountains: A Case Study of Waterton Lakes National Park', *Tourism Management*, *28* (2), pp. 570–579.

555 Wood, J. et al. (2004), *Long-Term World Oil Supply Scenarios*, United States Energy Information Administration, (Online), available: http://www.eia.doe.gov/pub/oil_gas/petroleum/feature_articles/2004/worldoilsupply/oilsupply04.html (14-12-2007).

556 Jones, B. and Scott, D. (2006), 'Climate Change, Seasonality and Visitation to Canada's National Parks', *Journal of Parks and Recreation Administration*, 24 (2), pp. 42–62.

557 Professional Golfers Association of America (2007), *PGA CEOs Detail Golf's Economic Impact at Global Economic Summit*, (Online), available: http://www.pga.com/news/show/2007/news/summittranscript012507. html (14-12-2007).

558 Research and Markets (2004), *Opportunities in the Global Golf Club Market 2004–2010*, (Online), available: http://www.researchandmarkets.com/reportinfo.asp?report_id=227053 (14-12-2007).

559 Scott, D. and Jones, B. (2006a), *Climate Change and Seasonality in Canadian Outdoor Recreation and Tourism.*

560 Scott, D. et al. (2007c), *Implications of Climate and Environmental Change for Nature-based Tourism in the Canadian Rocky Mountains.*

561 Royal and Ancient Golf Club of St. Andrews (2000), *On Course for Change – Tackling the Challenges Facing Golf in the First Decades of the New Millennium*, Fife, The Royal and Ancient Golf Club of St. Andrews, St. Andrews.

562 Golf Environment Europe (2007), *Golf and Environment*, (Online), available: http://www.golfenvironmenteurope. org/golfandenvironment02.html (14-12-2007).

563 Royal and Ancient Golf Club of St. Andrews (2000), *On Course for Change – Tackling the Challenges Facing Golf in the First Decades of the New Millennium.*

564 The R&A (2004), *Climate Change,* (Online), available: https://www.bestcourseforgolf.org/content/environment/ key_environment/climate_change/en (14-12-2007).

565 Royal and Ancient Golf Club of St. Andrews (2000), *On Course for Change – Tackling the Challenges Facing Golf in the First Decades of the New Millennium.*

566 Beard, J. B. (1982), *Turf Management for Golf Courses*, Macmillan Publishing Company, New York.

567 König, U. (1998), *Tourism in a Warmer World: Implications of Climate Change due to Enhanced Greenhouse Effect for the Ski Industry in the Australian Alps.*

568 Burki, R. (2000), *Klimaaenderung und Tourismus im Alpenraum – Anpassungsprozesse von Touristen und Tourismusverantwortlichen in der Region Ob- und Nidwalden* (Thesis), Department of Geography, University of Zurich, Zurich.

569 König, U. (1998), *Tourism in a Warmer World: Implications of Climate Change due to Enhanced Greenhouse Effect for the Ski Industry in the Australian Alps.*

570 Burki, R. (2000), *Klimaaenderung und Tourismus im Alpenraum.*

571 Fukuskima, T. et al. (2003), 'Influences of Air Temperature Change on Leisure Industries: Case Study on Ski Activities', *Mitigation and Adaptation Strategies for Climate Change*, 7, pp. 173-189.

572 Scott, D. (2006b), *Global Environmental Change and Mountain Tourism.*

573 Gössling, S. and Hall, C. M. (2006b), *Uncertainties in Predicting Tourist Travel Flows Based on Models.*

574 Scott, D. (2006a), *Climate Change and Sustainable Tourism in the 21st Century.*

575 IPCC (2007b), *Impacts, Adaptation and Vulnerability – Summary for Policymakers.*

576 Cesar, H. (2000), *Impacts of the 1998 Coral Bleaching Event on Tourism in El Nido, Phillippines*, Prepared for Coastal Resources Center Coral Bleaching Initiative, University of Rhode Island, Narragansett.

577 Gössling, S. et al. (2007), *Diving and Global Environmental Change: A Mauritius Case Study.*

578 Uyarra, M. et al. (2005), 'Island-Specific Preferences of Tourists for Environmental Features: Implications of Climate Change for Tourism-Dependent States', *Environmental Conservation*, 32 (1), pp. 11–19.

579 Amelung, B. and Viner, D. (2006), *Mediterranean Tourism: Exploring the Future with the Tourism Climatic Index.*

580 Braun, O. et al. (1999), 'Potential Impact of Climate Change Effects on Preference for Tourism Destinations: A Psychological Pilot Study', *Climate Research, 11*, pp. 247–254.

581 Great Barrier Reef Marine Park Authority (GBRMPA) (2007a), *Coral Bleaching on the Great Barrier Reef,* GBRMPA, Australian Government, (Online), available: http://www.gbrmpa.gov.au/corp_site/key_issues/climate_change/climate_change_and_the_great_barrier_reef/coral_bleaching_on_the_great_barrier_reef (14-12-2007).

582 Ibid.

583 Prideaux, B. (2006), 'The Use of Scenarios to Project the Imapct of Global Warming on Future Visitation to the Great Barrier Reef', *Tourism After Oil: ATLAS Asia Pacific 2006 Conference,* 2–5 December 2006, Dunedin.

584 Great Barrier Reef Marine Park Authority (GBRMPA) (2007b), *Great Barrier Reef Coral Bleaching Response Plan: Summer 2006–2007,* GBRMPA, Australian Government, (Online), available: http://www.gbrmpa.gov.au/__data/assets/pdf_file/0020/13169/Coral_Bleaching_Response_Plan_2006-07_Final.pdf (14-12-2007).

585 Wall, G. (1992), *Tourism Alternatives in an Era of Global Climate Change.*

586 Elsasser, H. and Bürki, R. (2002), *Climate Change as a Threat to Tourism in the Alps.*

587 UNWTO (2003), *Proceedings of the First International Conference on Climate Change and Tourism.*

588 Richardson, R. and Loomis, J. (2004), 'Adaptive Recreation Planning and Climate Change: A Contingent Visitation Approach', *Ecological Economics, 50,* pp. 83–99, and (Online), available: http://www.nrel.colostate.edu/projects/star/papers/Richardson&Loomis-2004.pdf (14-12-2007).

589 Scott, D. et al. (2007c), *Implications of Climate and Environmental Change for Nature-based Tourism in the Canadian Rocky Mountains.*

590 Scott, D. and Jones, B. (2006a), *Climate Change and Seasonality in Canadian Outdoor Recreation and Tourism.*

591 Egan, T. (2005), 'The Race to Alaska Before It Melts', *The New York Times,* 25 June 2005, (Online), available: http://www.nytimes.com/2005/06/26/travel/26alaska.html?ex=1277438400anden=e88a719ca3494a76and ei=5090andpartner=rssuserlandandemc=rss (14-12-2007).

592 Agnew, M. D. and Viner, D. (2001), 'Potential Impacts of Climate Change on International Tourism', *International Journal of Tourism and Hospitality Research,* 3(1), pp. 37–60.

593 Bürki, R. et al. (2003a), *Climate Change and Winter Sports.*

594 Saunders, S. and Easley, T. (2006), *Western National Parks Endangered by Climate Disruption.*

595 Scott, D. et al. (2008e – in press), 'Exploring Potential Visitor Response to Climate-induced Environmental Changes in Canada's Rocky Mountain National Parks', *Tourism Review International.*

596 Pack, T. (2004), 'Florida Tourism Problem: Survey Shows 1 in 4 Less Likely to Visit Florida Next Year', *Tribute Business News,* (Online), available: http://www.hotel-online.com/News/PR2004_4th/Oct04_FloridaNextYear.html (14-12-2007).

597 Butler, A. (2002), 'Tourism Burned: Visits to Parks Down Drastically, Even Away from Flames', *Rocky Mountain News,* July 15 2002.

598 IPCC (2007b), *Impacts, Adaptation and Vulnerability – Summary for Policymakers.*

599 Duval, D. T. (2006), 'Coasian Economics and the Management of International Aviation Emissions, International', *Journal of Innovation and Sustainable Development,* 1(3), pp. 201–213, and (Online), available: http://www.inderscience.com/filter.php?aid=12422 (14-12-2007).

600 Ibid.

601 Gillen, A. (2004), *Air Travel Demand Elasticities: Concepts, Issues and Measurements.*

602 Brons, M. et al. (2002), 'Price Elasticities of Demand for Passenger Air Travel: A Meta-analysis', *Journal of Air Transport Management,* 8(3), pp. 165–175.

603 UK Department for Transport (2007a), *Attitudes Towards Transport*.

604 Conference Board of Canada (2007), *Travellers Keen on Going Green*.

605 UK Department for Transport (2007b), *Public Attitudes Towards Climate Change and the Impact of Transport*.

606 Travel Insurance Web (2007), *TIW Customers Willing to Pay Green Flight Tax*. http://news.bigg.net/n37667-TIW_Customers_Willing_to_Pay_Green_Flight_Tax.html (14-12-2007)

607 UK Department for Transport (2007b), *Public Attitudes Towards Climate Change and the Impact of Transport*.

608 Ibid.

609 Ibid.

610 Conference Board of Canada (2007), *Travellers Keen on Going Green*.

611 Adventure Travel Trade Association (2007), 'TripAdvisor Travelers Keen on Going Green', *ATTA Member Inkaterra Draws TripAdvisor Notice*, (Online), available: http://www.adventuretravel.biz/release041707_tripadvisor.asp (14-12-2007).

612 Bartlett, L. (2007), *Australia Fears Jet Flight Guilt Could Hit Tourism*.

613 Boyd, A. (2007), *Carbon Tax Threatens to Ground Asia Tourism*.

614 Caribbean Hotel Association and Caribbean Tourism Organization (2007), *CHA-CTO Position Paper of Global Climate Change and the Caribbean Tourism Industry*.

615 Ibid.

616 Ceron, J. P. and Dubois, G. (2006), *Demain le voyage. La mobilité de tourisme et de loisirs des français face au développement durable : scénarios à 2050*: Ministère des transports, de l'équipement, du tourisme et de la mer, Paris.

617 Stern, N. (2006), *The Stern Review*.

618 Amelung, B. et al. (2002), 'Tourism in Motion: Is The Sky The Limit?', in P. Martens and J. Rotmans (eds.), *Transitions in a Globalising World*, Swets and Zeitlinger Publishers, Linne, pp. 85–110.

619 UNWTO (2003), *Proceedings of the First International Conference on Climate Change and Tourism*.

620 Stern, N. (2006), *The Stern Review*.

621 Hall, C. M. et al. (2004), *Security and Tourism: Towards a New Understanding?*.

622 Sonmez, S. (1998), *Tourism, Terrorism, and Political Instability*.

623 German Advisory Council on Global Change (2007), *World in Transition: Climate Change as a Security Risk*.

624 Stern, N. (2006), *The Stern Review*.

Emissions from Tourism: Status and Trends

625 World Tourism Organization (2007d), *Basic References on Tourism Statistics*, (Online), available: http://www.world-tourism.org/statistics/basic_references/index-en.htm (01.04.2008).

626 Forster, P. M. et al. (2006), 'It is Premature to Include Non-CO_2 Effects of Aviation in Emission Trading Schemes', *Atmospheric Environment*, 40 (6), pp. 1117–1121.

627 Peeters, P. et al. (2007a), 'Air Transport Greenhouse Gas Emissions', in P. Peeters (ed.), *Tourism and Climate Change Mitigation – Methods, Greenhouse Gas Reductions and Policies* (pp. 29–50), NHTV Academics Studies, No. 6, NHTV, Breda University, Breda.

628 Stern, N. (2006), *The Stern Review*.

629 IPCC (2007a), *The Physical Science Basis – Summary for Policymakers*.

630 Shine, K. P. et al. (2005), 'Scientific Issues in the Design of Metrics for Inclusion of Oxides of Nitrogen in Global Climate Agreements', *Proceedings of the National Academy of Sciences, 102* (44), pp. 15768–15773.

631 Prather, M. and Sausen, R. (1999), 'Potential Climate Change from Aviation', in J. E. Penner et al. (eds.), *Aviation and the Global Atmosphere: A Special Report of IPCC Working Groups I and III*, Cambridge University Press, Cambridge, pp. 185–215.

632 Sausen, R. et al. (2005), 'Aviation Radiative Forcing in 2000: An Update on IPCC (1999)', *Meteorologische Zeitschrift*, 14 (4), pp. 555–561.

633 Becken, S. (2002), *Energy use in the New Zealand tourism sector* (Thesis), Lincoln University, Canterbury.

634 Dubois, G. and Ceron, J.-P. (2006), 'Tourism/Leisure Greenhouse Gas Emissions Forecasts for 2050: Factors for Change in France', *Journal of Sustainable Tourism, 14* (2), pp. 172–191.

635 Gössling, S. (2002), *Global Environmental Consequences of Tourism.*

636 Peeters, P. et al. (2007b), 'Major Environmental Impacts of European Tourist Transport', *Journal of Transport Geography, 15*, pp. 83–93.

637 Ibid.

638 Ibid.

639 Ibid.

640 Peeters, P. et al. (2004), *European Tourism, Transport and Environment, (Final Version)*, NHTV CSTT, Breda.

641 Kim, B. Y. et al. (2006 and 2005), *System for Assessing Aviation's Global Emissions (SAGE), Version 1.5, Global Aviation Emissions Inventories for 2000 through 2004,* Federal Aviation Administration, Washington DC, (Online), available: http://www.faa.gov/about/office_org/headquarters_offices/aep/models/sage/media/FAA-EE-2005-02__SAGE-Inventory_Report-Text.pdf (14-12-2007).

642 Sausen, R. et al. (2005), *Aviation Radiative Forcing in 2000: An Update on IPCC (1999).*

643 Peeters, P. et al. (2007a), 'Air Transport Greenhouse Gas Emissions', in P. Peeters (ed.), *Tourism and Climate Change Mitigation – Methods, Greenhouse Gas Reductions and Policies* (pp. 29–50), NHTV Academics Studies, No. 6, NHTV, Breda University, Breda.

644 IPCC (2007a), *The Physical Science Basis – Summary for Policymakers.*

645 Becken, S. and Hay, J. E. (2007), *Tourism and Climate Change: Risks and Opportunities.* Channel View Publications.

646 Peeters, P. et al. (2007b), *Major Environmental Impacts of European Tourist Transport.*

647 Gössling, S. (2002), Global environmental consequences of tourism. *Global environmental change part A, 12* (4), 283-302.

648 Becken, S. (2002), *Energy use in the New Zealand tourism sector. Doctoral thesis* Lincoln University New Zealand.

649 Gössling, S. (2002), Global environmental consequences of tourism. *Global environmental change part A, 12* (4), 283-302.

650 UNWTO (2006), *Tourism Market Trends: World Overview and Tourism Topics,* (2005 Edition), UNWTO, Madrid, p. 36.

651 Sausen, R. et al. (2005), *Aviation Radiative Forcing in 2000: An Update on IPCC (1999).*

652 IPCC (2007a), *The Physical Science Basis – Summary for Policymakers.*

653 Lamers, M. and Amelung, B. (2007), 'The Environmental Impacts of Tourism to Antarctica: A Global Perspective', in P. Peeters (ed.), *Tourism and Climate Change Mitigation: Methods, Greenhouse Gas Reductions and Policies*, Breda: NHTV, Breda, pp. 51–62.

[654] Gössling, S. et al. (2005), 'The Eco-efficiency of Tourism', *Ecological Economics,* 54(4), pp. 417–434.

[655] Gössling, S. et al. (2007), *Diving and Global Environmental Change: A Mauritius Case Study.*

[656] Calculated with the 'Emissions calculator' from www.atmosfair.de.

[657] Byrnes, T. A. and Warnken, J. (2006), 'Greenhouse Gas Emissions from Marine Tours: A Case Study of Australian Tour Boat Operators', *Journal of Sustainable Tourism,* 14(3), pp. 255–270.

[658] UNWTO (2000), *Tourism Vision 2020, Volume 7: Global Forecasts and Profiles of Market Segments,* UNWTO, Madrid.

[659] National Bureau of Statistics of China (2007), *China Statistical Yearbook – 2006,* (Online), available: http://www.stats.gov.cn/tjsj/ndsj/2006/indexee.htm (17-12-2007).

[660] Federation of Hotel and Restaurant Association (2006), *Department of Tourism Matters, India,* (Online), available: http://www.fhrai.com/Mag-News/newsletDOT.asp (14-12-2007; not working).

[661] UNWTO (2000), *Tourism Vision 2020.*

[662] Peeters, P. et al. (2007b), *Major Environmental Impacts of European Tourist Transport.*

[663] Peeters, P. M. and Middel, J. (2007), 'Historical and Future Development of Air Transport Fuel Efficiency', in: Sausen, R., Blum, A., Lee, D. S. and Brüning, C. (Eds.) *Proceedings of an International Conference on Transport, Atmosphere and Climate (TAC); Oxford, United Kingdom, 26th to 29th June 2006,* 42-47. Oberpfaffenhoven: DLR Institut für Physic der Atmosphäre.

[664] Boeing (2006), *Current Market Outlook 2006,* Boeing Commercial Airplanes, Marketing, Seattle, (Online), available: http://www.boeing.com/commercial/cmo/pdf/CMO_06.pdf (14-12-2007).

[665] Peeters, P. et al. (2004), *European Tourism, Transport and Environment.*

[666] Jones, C. D. et al. (2006), 'Impact of Climate-carbon Cycle Feedbacks on Emissions Scenarios to Achieve Stabilisation', in J. Schellnhuber et al. (eds.), *Avoiding Dangerous Climate Change,* Cambridge University Press, Cambridge, pp. 323–331.

Mitigation Policies and Measures

[667] Becken, S. and Hay, J. (2007), *Tourism and Climate Change – Risks and Opportunities.*

[668] Hanlon, P. (2007), *Global Airlines: Competition in a Transnational Industry,* (third edition), Butterworth-Heinemann, Oxford.

[669] Penner, J. et al. (1999), *Aviation and the Global Atmosphere: A Special Report of IPCC Working Groups I and III,* Published for the IPCC, Cambridge University Press, Cambridge.

[670] Peeters, P. and Middel, J. (2006), *Historical and Future Development of Air Transport Fuel Efficiency.*

[671] Dalhuijsen, J. L. and Slingerland, R. (2004), 'Preliminary Wing Optimization for very large Transport Aircraft with Wingspan Constraints', *42nd AIAA Aerospace Sciences Meeting and Exhibit,* 5–8 January 2004, AIAA, Reno.

[672] Penner, J. et al. (1999), *Aviation and the Global Atmosphere.*

[673] Dings, J. et al. (2000), *ESCAPE: Economic Screening of Aircraft Preventing Emissions,* (main report), Centrum voor Energiebesparing en Schone Technologie, Delft.

[674] Green, J. E. (2003), 'Civil Aviation and the Environmental Challenge', *The Aeronautical Journal, 107,* pp. 281–299.

[675] European Commission (2007), *GALILEO European Satellite Navigation System,* http://ec.europa.eu/dgs/energy_transport/galileo/index_en.htm (14-12-2007).

[676] French Environment and Energy Agency (ADEME) (2006), *Bilan carbone. Calcul des facteurs d'émissions et sources bibliographiques utilisées,* (version 4.0), ADEME, MIES, Paris.

677 Air France and KLM (2007), *Air France KLM Corporate social responsibility report 2006–07*, Air France, KLM, Paris, (Online), avalaible: http://www.klm.com/travel/corporate_en/images/CSR%20report%202006-07_tcm172-83337.pdf (14-12-2007).

678 SAS Group (2002), *The SAS Group Environmental Report 2001*, SAS Group, Stockholm, (Online), available: http://www.corporateregister.com/search/report.cgi?num=7097-ERzVbHgl4X2 (14-12-2007).

679 JAL (2007), *CSR Report 2006*, Japan Airlines, Tokyo, (Online), available: http://www.jal.com/en/corporate/csr2006/index2.html (14-12-2007).

680 Van den Brink, R. M. and Van Wee, B. (2001), 'Why has Car-fleet Specific Fuel Consumption not Shown any Decrease since 1990?, Quantitative Analysis of Dutch Passenger Car-fleet Specific Fuel Consumption', *Transportation Research Part D, 6*, pp. 75–93.

681 Baas, P. et al. (2005), *Light Vehicle Fleet – Energy Use*, Prepared for the Energy Efficiency and Conservation Authority, *Auckland,* (Online), available: http://www.eeca.govt.nz/eeca-library/transport/report/light-vehicle-fleet-energy-use-report-05.pdf (14-12-2007).

682 UNEP (2000), '*Natural Selection: Evolving Choices for Renewable Energy Technology and Policy'*, DTIE, Paris, (Online), available: http://www.unep.fr/energy/publications/files/naturalselection.htm (14-12-2007).

683 MSNBC (2007), 'Toyota Worldwide Hybrid Sales Top 1 Million', *MSNBC,* 7 June 2007, (Online), available: http://www.msnbc.msn.com/id/19088667/ (14-12-2007).

684 Transportation Association of Canada (1999), 'Transportation and Climate Change: Options for Action', Options Paper of the *Transportation Climate Change Table*, November 1999, (Online), available: http://www.tc.gc.ca/programs/environment/climatechange/subgroups1/Options_Paper/English/Trans_Final_OR-en.pdf (14-12-2007).

685 Bergsma, G. et al. (2007), *Biofuels and their Global Influence on Land Availability for Agriculture and Nature.*

686 SBB (2007), *SBB Environmental Topics – Energy,* (Online), available: http://mct.sbb.ch/mct/konzern_engagement/konzern_umwelt/konzern_energie.htm (14-12-2007).

687 Jorgensen, M. W. and Sorenson, S. C. (1997), 'Estimating Emissions from Railway Traffic', *Report for the Project MEET: Methodologies for Estimating Air Pollutant Emissions from Transport,* Department of Energy Engineering, Technical University of Denmark, Lyngby, (Online), available: http://www.inrets.fr/infos/cost319/MEETDeliverable17.PDF (14-12-2007).

688 UIC (2007), *Energy Efficiency Technologies for Railways – Database,* International Union of Railways, Paris, (Online), available: http://www.railway-energy.org/tfee/index.php?ID=200 (14-12-2007).

689 Becken, S. and Hay, J. (2007), *Tourism and Climate Change – Risks and Opportunities.*

690 Smith, S. et al. (2006), *Air and Rail Competition and Complementarity,* (Final Report), SDG Project, Number P206600, Steer Davies Gleave, London, (Online), available: http://ec.europa.eu/transport/rail/studies/doc/2006_08_study_air_rail_competition_en.pdf (14-12-2007).

691 Peeters, P. et al. (2004), *European tourism, transport and environment.*

692 Babikian, R. et al. (2002), 'The Historical Fuel Efficiency Characteristics of Regional Aircraft from Technological, Operational, and Cost Perspectives', *Journal of Air Transport Management,* 8(6), pp. 389–400.

693 Lumsdon, L. et al. (2006), 'Transport for Tourism: Can Public Transport Encourage a Modal Shift in the Day Visitor Market?', *Journal of Sustainable Tourism,* 14 (2), pp. 139–156.

694 Wheeler, S. (1998), *Planning Sustainable and Livable Cities*, Routledge, New York.

695 Wonderful Copenhagen (2007), Free City Bikes, (Online), available: http://www.visitcopenhagen.com/composite-378.htm (10-12-2007)

696 Network for Soft Mobility in European Tourism (2007), *NETS Hompage,* (Online), available: http://www.soft-mobility.com/english/index.htm (10-12-2007)

697 Ayuntamiento de Málaga (2007), *Ayuntamiento de Málaga Homepage,* (Online), available: www.ayto-malaga.es (10-12-2007)

698   Sustrans (2007), *Sustrans Homepage,* (Online), available: http://www.sustrans.org.uk (10-12-2007)

699   Becken, S. (2008 – accepted), 'Indicators for Managing Tourism in the Face of Peak Oil', *Tourism Management*.

700   Gössling, S. et al. (2005), *The Eco-efficiency of Tourism.*

701   Becken, S. (2002b), 'Analysing International Tourist Flows to Estimate Energy Use Associated with Air Travel', *Journal of Sustainable Tourism*, 10 (2), pp. 114–131.

702   German Advisory Council on Global Change (2002), *Charging the Use of Global Commons,* WBGU, Berlin, (Online), available: http://www.wbgu.de/wbgu_sn2002_engl.pdf (14-12-2007).

703   Becken, S. and Hay, J. (2007), *Tourism and Climate Change – Risks and Opportunities*

704   Njegovan, N. (2006), *Elasticities of Demand for Leisure Air Travel: A System Modelling Approach.*

705   Gillen, A. (2004), *Air Travel Demand Elasticities.*

706   IPCC (2007), *Climate Change 2007: Mitigation of climate change. IPCC Fourth Assessment Report, Working Group III. Summary for policy makers.* Geneva: International Panel on Climate Change.

707   Ibid.

708   Hasek, Glenn (2006), 'Accor NA's Energy Star: Dan Gilligan', *Green Lodging News*, (Online), available: http://www.greenlodgingnews.com/Content.aspx?id=715 (14-12-2007).

709   Bohdanowicz P. and Martinac I. (2007), 'Determinants and Benchmarking of Resource Consumption in Hotels – Case Study of Hilton International and Scandic in Europe', *Energy and Buildings*, 39, pp. 82–95.

710   Chan, W. W. and Lam, J. C. (2003), 'Energy-saving Supporting Tourism: A Case Study of Hotel Swimming Pool Heat Pump', *Journal of Sustainable Tourism*, 11 (1), pp. 74–83.

711   National Ski Areas Association (2007), *Green Power Program Fact Sheet,* (Online), available: http://www.nsaa.org/nsaa/press/0607/green-power-fact-sheet.asp (14-12-2007).

712   The R&A (2004), *Climate change.*

713   UNEP (2003), *Switched on: Renewable Energy Opportunities for the Tourism Industry*, UNEP, Paris, (Online), available:
http://www.iclei-europe.org/fileadmin/user_upload/tourism/Switched_on_2003_1-5.pdf (14-12-2007).

714   Twinshare (2005), *Twinshare: Tourism Accommodation and the Environment.* http://twinshare.crctourism.com.au/aboutTwinshare.asp (14-12-2007).

715   Uemura, Y. et al. (2003), *Potential of Renewable Energy Sources and its Applications in Yakushima Island.*

716   Cavallaro, F. and Ciraolo, L. (2005), *A Multicriteria Approach to Evaluate Wind Energy Plants on an Italian Island.*

717   Ibid.

718   UNEP (2003), *Switched on: Renewable Energy Opportunities for the Tourism Industry.*

719   Twinshare (2005), *Twinshare: Tourism Accommodation and the Environment.*

720   South Pacific Tourism (no date), *A Green Business Benchmark*, (Online), available: http://nztri.aut.ac.nz/pacifictoolkit/pages/viewsuccess.php?successstory=16 (14-12-2007).

721   Nukubati Islands (2007), *Environment and Ecology,* (Online), available:
http://www.nukubati.com/environment.asp (14-12-2007).

722   Visit Scotland (2004), *Greening Scottish Tourism: Ten Best Practice Case Studies,* (Online), available: http://www.greentourism.org.uk/greening-scotland-booklet.pdf (14-12-2007).

723   Skinner, E. et al. (2004), 'Does Stewardship Travel Well? Benchmarking, Accreditation and Certification', *Corporate Social Responsibility and Environmental Management*, 11, pp. 121–132.

724 Reiser, A. and Simmons, D.G. (2005), 'A Quasi-Experimental Method for Testing the Effectiveness of Ecolabel Promotion', *Journal of Sustainable Tourism*, 13 (6), pp. 590–616.

725 ICLEI (2007), *About ICLEI – Local Governments for Sustainability*, (Online), available: http://www.iclei.org/index.php?id=global-about-iclei (10-12-2007).

726 IPCC (2007), *Mitigation – Summary for Policymakers*.

727 International Business Leader Forum (2007), *Going Green: Minimum Standards Towards a Sustainable Hotel*, (Online), available: http://www.iblf.org/media_room/general.jsp?id=123932 (10-12-2007).

728 Gössling, S. et al. (2006), 'Tourist Perceptions of Climate Change: A Study of International Tourists in Zanzibar', *Current Issues in Tourism*, 9 (4–5), pp. 419–435.

729 Swedish Railways (2007), *SJ Environmental Calculation*, (Online), available: http://www.sj.se/sj/jsp/polopoly.jsp?d=6783andl=en (14-12-2007).

730 Van den Brink, R. M. and Van Wee, B. (2001), *Quantitative Analysis of Dutch Passenger Car-fleet Specific Fuel Consumption*.

731 Transportation Association of Canada (1999), *Transportation and Climate Change: Options for Action*.

732 Becken, S. (2004b), *How Tourists and Tourism Experts Perceive Climate Change and Forest Carbon Sinks*.

733 Becken, S. (2007), *Climate Change Policies for International Air Travel – A Tourist Perspective*.

734 Gössling, S. et al. (2008 – submitted), *Swedish Air Travellers and Voluntary Carbon Offsets: Towards the Co-Creation of Environmental value?*.

The Way Forward to Adaptation and Mitigation in Tourism

735 IPCC (2007a), *The Physical Science Basis – Summary for Policymakers*.

736 Yohe, G. W. et al. (2007), *Perspectives on Climate Change and Sustainability*.

737 Stern, N. (2006), *The Stern Review*.

738 Frangialli, F. (2007), *Tourism Development and Climate Change: Understanding, Anticipating, Adapting, Participating in the Common Effort*.

739 Browne, D. (2007), 'Global Warming Emerges as Key Issue for Industry Leaders', *eTurboNews, Travel Industry Review*, (Online), available: http://www.travelindustryreview.com/news/5410 (14-12-2007).

740 Gössling, S. and Scott, D. (2008 – in press), 'Editorial – Special Issue on Climate Change and Tourism: Exploring Destination Vulnerability', *Tourism Review International*.

741 IPCC (2007b), *Impacts, Adaptation and Vulnerability – Summary for Policymakers*.

Annex

742 Peeters, P. et al. (2007b), *Major Environmental Impacts of European Tourist Transport*.

743 Peeters, P. et al. (2004), *European Tourism, Transport and Environment*.

744 Gössling, S. (2002), *Global Environmental Consequences of Tourism*.

745 Ibid.

746 Ibid.

747 Ibid.

[748] Eyers, C. J. et al. (2004), *AERO2K Global Aviation Emissions Inventories for 2002 and 2025*, QinetiQ Ltd., Farnborough, (Online), available: http://www.aero-net.org/pdf-docs/AERO2K_Global_Aviation_Emissions_Inventories_for_2002_and_2025.pdf (14-12-2007).

[749] Kim, B. Y. et al. (2005 and 2006), *System for assessing Aviation's Global Emissions (SAGE), Version 1.5, Global Aviation Emissions Inventories for 2000 through 2004.* FAA-EE-2005-02 Washington DC: Federal Aviation Administration.

[750] Kim, B. Y. et al. (2007), 'System for Assessing Aviation's Global Emissions (SAGE), Part 1: Model Description and Inventory Results', *Transportation Research*, D 12, pp. 325–346.

[751] Wit, R. C. N. et al. (2002), *Economic Incentives to Mitigate Greenhouse Gas Emissions from Air Transport in Europe*, 02.4733.10, CE, Delft, (Online), available: http://www.rapportsysteem.nl/artikel/index.php?id=121&action=read (14-12-2007).

[752] Peeters, P. et al. (2005), *Fuel Efficiency of Commercial Aircraft: An Overview of Historical and Future Trends*, Peeters Advies/National Aerospace Laboratory, Amsterdam.

[753] Pulles, J. W. et al. (2002), *AERO Main Report: Aviation Emissions and Evaluation of Reduction Options*, Dutch Ministry of Transport, Public Works and Water Management, Den Haag.

[754] Peeters, P. et al. (2007a), *Air Transport Greenhouse Gas Emissions*.

[755] Daggett, D. L. et al. (1999), *An Evaluation of Aircraft Emissions Inventory Methodology by Comparisons with Reported Airline Data*, CR-1999-209480, NASA, Seattle.

[756] Peeters, P. et al. (2007a), *Air Transport Greenhouse Gas Emissions*.

[757] Penner, J. et al. (eds.) (1999), *Aviation and the Global Atmosphere*.

[758] Sausen, R. et al. (2005), *Aviation Radiative Forcing in 2000: An Update on IPCC (1999)*.

[759] Bohdanowicz, P. and Martinac I. (2007), *Determinants and Benchmarking of Resource Consumption in Hotels*.

[760] UK CEED (1998), *An Assessment of the Environmental Impacts of Tourism in St Lucia: A Report to British Airways and British Airways Holidays*, Report 5/98, UK Centre for Economic and Environmental Development, Cambridge.

[761] Gössling, S. (2000), 'Sustainable Tourism Development in Developing Countries: Some Aspects of Energy-use', *Journal of Sustainable Tourism*, 8(5), pp. 410–425.

[762] Gössling, S. (2002), *Global Environmental Consequences of Tourism*.

[763] Becken, S. (2002a), *Energy use in the New Zealand Tourism Sector*.

[764] Gössling, S. (2002), *Global Environmental Consequences of Tourism*.

[765] Watkins, K. (2006), *Human Development Report 2006 – Beyond Scarcity: Power, Poverty and the Global Water Crisis*, UNDP, New York, (Online), available: http://hdr.undp.org/en/media/hdr06-complete.pdf (14-12-2007).

[766] Ibid.

Bibliography

Abegg, B. et al. (2007), 'Climate Change Impacts and Adaptation in Winter Tourism', in S. Agrawala (ed.), *Climate Change in the European Alps: Adapting Winter Tourism and Natural Hazards Management,* OECD, Paris, pp. 25–60.

Adger, W. et al. (2007), 'Assessment of Adaptation Practices, Options, Constraints and Capacity', in IPCC (ed.), *Climate Change 2007: Climate Change Impacts, Adaptation and Vulnerability,* Cambridge University Press, Cambridge.

Adger, W. N. et al. (2005), 'Adapting to Climate Change: Perspectives Across Scales', *Global Environmental Change,* 15, pp. 75–76.

Adventure Travel Trade Association (2007), 'TripAdvisor Travelers Keen on Going Green', *ATTA Member Inkaterra Draws TripAdvisor Notice,* (Online), available: http://www.adventuretravel.biz/release041707_tripadvisor.asp (14-12-2007).

Agnew, M. and Palutikof, J. (2006), 'Impacts of Short-term Climate Variability in the UK on Demand for Domestic and International Tourism', *Climate Research,* 31, pp. 109–120.

Agnew, M. D. and Viner, D. (2001), 'Potential Impacts of Climate Change on International Tourism', *International Journal of Tourism and Hospitality Research,* 3(1), pp. 37–60.

Agrawala, S. (ed.) (2007), *Climate Change in the European Alps: Adapting Winter Tourism and Natural Hazards Management,* OECD, Paris.

Agrawala, S. et al. (2003), *Development and Climate Change in Nepal: Focus on Water Resources and Hydropower.* OECD, (Online), available: http://www.oecd.org/dataoecd/6/51/19742202.pdf (13-12-2007).

Aguilo, E. et al. (2005), 'The Persistence of the Sun and Sand Tourism Model', *Tourism Management, 26,* pp. 219–231.

Air France and KLM (2007), *Air France KLM Corporate social responsibility report 2006–07,* Air France, KLM, Paris, (Online), avalaible: http://www.klm.com/travel/corporate_en/images/CSR%20report%202006-07_tcm172-83337.pdf (14-12-2007).

AKI (2005), *Global Warming Threatens Mediterranean Tourism,* 2 July 2007, AKI, Rome.

Alberini, A. et al. (2005), *Using Expert Judgment to Assess Adaptive Capacity to Climate Change: Evidence from a Conjoint Choice Survey,* Fondazione Eni Enrico Mattei, Milano, (Online), available: http://papers.ssrn.com/sol3/papers.cfm?abstract_id=812972 (14-12-2007).

Altalo, M. and Hale, M. (2002), *Requirements of the US Recreation and Tourism Industry for Climate, Weather, and Ocean Information,* National Oceanic and Atmospheric Administrations, Washington.

Alvord, C. et al. (2007), 'Climate and Tourism on the Colorado Plateau: A Workshop Summary'. *Bulletin of the American Meteorological Society,* (Online), http://wwa.colorado.edu/products/forecasts_and_outlooks/intermountain_west_climate_summary/articles/WWA_Jun_2007_focus.pdf (14-04-2008).

Amelung, B. and Viner, D. (2006), 'Mediterranean Tourism: Exploring the Future with the Tourism Climatic Index', *Journal of Sustainable Tourism, 14* (4), pp. 349–366.

Amelung, B. et al. (2008 – in press), 'The Place of Tourism in the IPCC Fourth Assessment Report: A Review', *Tourism Review International.*

Amelung, B. et al. (2007), 'Implications of Global Climate Change for Tourism Flows and Seasonality', *Journal of Travel Research, 45* (3), pp. 285–296.

Amelung, B. et al. (2002), 'Tourism in Motion: Is The Sky The Limit?', in P. Martens and J. Rotmans (eds.), *Transitions in a Globalising World,* Swets and Zeitlinger Publishers, Linne, pp. 85–110.

Association national pour l'étude de la neige et des avalanches (ANENA) (2002), 'Prévenir le risque d'avalanche grace à la météo', *Espaces,* 190, pp. 29–31.

Asian Development Bank (2005), *Climate Proofing: A Risk-based Approach to Adaptation,* (Online), available: http://www.adb.org/Documents/Reports/Climate-Proofing/climate-proofing.pdf (14-12-2007).

Aspen Global Change Institute (2006), *Climate change and Aspen: An assessment of Impacts and Potential Responses,* Aspen Global Change Institute, Aspen, (Online), available: http://www.agci.org/pdf/Canary/ACIA_Report.pdf (17-12-2007).

Association of British Insurers (2004), *A Changing Climate for Insurance: A Summary Report for Chief Executives and Policymakers,* (Online), available: http://www.abi.org.uk/Display/File/Child/552/A_Changing_Climate_for_Insurance_2004.pdf (13-12-2007).

Australian Bureau of Statistics (2007), *Tourism Satellite Account,* National Information and Referral Service, Australian Bureau of Statistics, Canberra.

Awareness and Preparedness for Emergencies at the Local Level (APELL) (2001), *Explaining APELL,* (Online), available: http://www.uneptie.org/pc/apell/publications/pdf_files/explaining_apell.pdf (13-12-2007).

Ayuntamiento de Málaga (2007), *Ayuntamiento de Málaga Homepage,* (Online), available: www.ayto-malaga.es (10-12-2007)

Baas, P. et al. (2005), *Light Vehicle Fleet – Energy Use,* Prepared for the Energy Efficiency and Conservation Authority, *Auckland,* (Online), available: http://www.eeca.govt.nz/eeca-library/transport/report/light-vehicle-fleet-energy-use-report-05.pdf (14-12-2007).

Babikian, R. et al. (2002), 'The Historical Fuel Efficiency Characteristics of Regional Aircraft from Technological, Operational, and Cost Perspectives', *Journal of Air Transport Management, 8(6),* pp. 389–400.

Baker, J. D. et al. (2006), 'Potential Effects of Sea level Rise on the Terrestrial Habitats of Endangered and Endemic Megafauna in the Northwestern Hawaiian Islands', *Endangered Species Research, 2,* pp. 21–30.

Barnes, B. (2002), 'The Heat Wave Vacation', *The Wall Street Journal,* 2 August 2002, W1.

Barnett, J. (2001), *Security and Climate Change,* Tyndall Centre Working Paper No. 7, (Online), available: http://www.tyndall.ac.uk/publications/working_papers/wp7.pdf (17-12-2007).

Bartlett, L. (2007), 'Australia Fears Jet Flight Guilt Could Hit Tourism', Agence France-Presse, 18 April 2007 (Online), available: http://www.spacemart.com/reports/Australia_Fears_Jet_Flight_Guilt_Could_Hit_Tourism_999.html (14-12-2007).

BBC News (2006), 'Package Holiday Will be History', *BBC News,* August 26 2006, http://news.bbc.co.uk/2/hi/science/nature/5288092.stm (14-12-2007).

Beard, J. B. (1982), *Turf Management for Golf Courses,* Macmillan Publishing Company, New York.

Becken, S. and Hay, J. (2007), *Tourism and Climate Change – Risks and Opportunities,* Channel View Publications, Cleveland.

Becken, S. (2008 – accepted), 'Indicators for Managing Tourism in the Face of Peak Oil', *Tourism Management.*

Becken, S. (2007), 'Climate Change Policies for International Air Travel – A Tourist Perspective', *Journal of Sustainable Tourism,* 15 (4), pp. 351–368.

Becken, S. (2005), 'Harmonizing climate change adaptation and mitigation: The case of tourist resorts in Fiji', *Global Environmental Change – Part A,* 15 (4), pp. 381–393.

Becken, S. (2004a), *Climate Change and Tourism in Fiji: Vulnerability, Adaptation and Mitigation,* Final Report, University of the South Pacific, Suva.

Becken, S. (2004b), 'How Tourists and Tourism Experts Perceive Climate Change and Forest Carbon Sinks', *Journal of Sustainable Tourism,* 12 (4), pp. 332–345.

Becken, S. (2002a), *Energy use in the New Zealand tourism sector* (Thesis), Lincoln University, Canterbury.

Becken, S. (2002b), 'Analysing International Tourist Flows to Estimate Energy Use Associated with Air Travel', *Journal of Sustainable Tourism,* 10 (2), pp. 114–131.

Bell, G. and Chelliah, M. (2006), 'Leading Tropical Modes Associated with Interannual and Multidecadal Fluctuations in North Atlantic Hurricane Activity', *Journal of Climate,* 19, pp. 590–612.

Bell, G. D. et al. (2006a), 'The Tropics: The Atlantic Basic: State of the Climate in 2005', in K. A. Shein (ed.) (2005), *Bull. Amer. Meteor. Soc.,* 87, pp. 33–37.

Bell, G. D. et al. (2006b), 'The Record Breaking 2005 Atlantic Hurricane Season: State of the Climate in 2005', in K. A. Shein (Ed), *Bull. Amer. Meteor. Soc.,* 87, pp. 44–45.

Beniston, M. (2003), 'Climatic Change in Mountain Regions: A Review of Possible Impacts', *Climatic Change, 59* (1–2), pp. 5–31.

Bergsma, G. et al. (2007), *Biofuels and their Global Influence on Land Availability for Agriculture and Nature: A First Evaluation and a Proposal for Further Fact Finding, CE, Delft.*

Berrittella, M. et al. (2006), 'A General Equilibrium Analysis of Climate Change Impacts on Tourism', *Tourism Management,* 27, pp. 913–924.

Berz, B. (2005), 'Windstorm and Storm Surges in Europe: Loss Trends and Possible Counter-actions from the Viewpoint of an International Reinsurer', *Philosophical Transactions: Mathematical, Physical and Engineering Sciences, 363* (1831), pp. 1431–1440.

Besancenot, J-P. (1989), *Climat et Tourisme,* Masson, Paris.

Besancenot, JP. et al. (1978), 'Les Conditions Climatiques du Tourisme', Littoral, Norois, 99, pp. 357–382.

Bhatnagar, P. (2005), 'Uncertainty and Fear to Rebuild: Mississippi Officials Say Casino Companies are Hesitant to Rebuild, State could Lose Billions', *CNN,* 6 September 2005, (Online), available: http://money.cnn.com/2005/09/05/news/economy/katrina_business/ (13-12-2007)

Bicknell, S. and McManus, P. (2006), 'The Canary in the Coalmine: Australian Ski Resorts and their Response to Climate Change', *Geographical Research, 44* (4), pp. 386–400.

Bigano, A. et al. (2006), 'The Impact of Climate on Holiday Destination Choice', *Climatic Change, 76* (3–4), pp. 389–406.

Boeing (2006), *Current Market Outlook 2006,* Boeing Commercial Airplanes, Marketing, Seattle, (Online), available: http://www.boeing.com/commercial/cmo/pdf/CMO_06.pdf (14-12-2007).

Bohdanowicz P. and Martinac I. (2007), 'Determinants and Benchmarking of Resource Consumption in Hotels – Case Study of Hilton International and Scandic in Europe', *Energy and Buildings,* 39, pp. 82–95.

Bohdanowicz, P. (2002), 'Thermal Comfort and Energy Savings in the Hotel Industry', *Proceedings of the 16th Congress of the International Society of Biometeorology, 27 Oct.–1 Nov.,* Kansas City, Missouri, American Meteorological Society, Boston, pp. 396–400.

Boinet, T. (2007), 'Snowless in a Warming World, Ski Resort in French Alps bids adieu', *Associated Press,* 19 July 2007, (Online), available: http://www.iht.com/articles/2007/07/19/travel/0720francewarm.php (13-12-2007).

Bomhard, B. and Midgley, G. (2005), *Securing Protected Areas in the Face of Global Change: Lessons Learned from the South African Cape Floristic Region.* IUCN, Bangkok, and SANBI, Capetown.

Bows, A. et al. (2007), 'Technology, Scenarios and Uncertainty – *Policy Dialogue on Tourism, Transport and Climate Change: Stakeholders Meet Researchers'*, E-CLAT Technical Seminar, 15 March, 2007, E-CLAT, Paris.

Bows, A. et al. (2006), *Contraction and Convergence: UK Carbon Emissions and the Implications for UK Air Traffic,* Tyndall Centre Technical Report 40, (Online), available: http://www.tyndall.ac.uk/research/theme2/final_reports/t3_23.pdf (14-12-2007).

Boyd, A. (2007), 'Carbon Tax Threatens to Ground Asia Tourism', *Asian Times Online,* (Online), available: http://www.atimes.com/atimes/Asian_Economy/ID19Dk01.html (14-12-2007).

Braun, O. et al. (1999), 'Potential Impact of Climate Change Effects on Preference for Tourism Destinations: A Psychological Pilot Study', *Climate Research, 11,* pp. 247–254.

Breiling, M. and Charamza, P. (1999), 'The Impact of Global Warming on Winter Tourism and Skiing: A Regionalized Model for Austrian Snow Conditions', *Regional Environmental Change,* 1 (1), pp. 4–14.

Brons, M. et al. (2002), 'Price Elasticities of Demand for Passenger Air Travel: A Meta-analysis', *Journal of Air Transport Management,* 8(3), pp. 165–175.

Brooks, N. et al. (2005), 'The Determinants of Vulnerability and Adaptive Capacity at the National Level and the Implications for Adaptation', *Global Environmental Change,* 15, pp. 51–163.

Browne, D. (2007), 'Global Warming Emerges as Key Issue for Industry Leaders', *eTurboNews, Travel Industry Review,* (Online), available: http://www.travelindustryreview.com/news/5410 (14-12-2007),

Bürki, R. et al. (2003a), 'Climate Change and Winter Sports: Environmental and Economic Threats', Paper presented at the *5th World Conference on Sport and Environment,* Turin, 2–3 December 2003.

Bürki, R. et al. (2003b), 'Climate Change – Impacts on the Tourism Industry in Mountain Areas', *1st International Conference on Climate Change and Tourism,* Djerba, April 2003.

Bürki, R. (2000), *Klimaaenderung und Tourismus im Alpenraum – Anpassungsprozesse von Touristen und Tourismusverantwortlichen in der Region Ob- und Nidwalden* (Thesis), Department of Geography, University of Zurich, Zurich.

Butler, A. (2002), 'Tourism Burned: Visits to Parks Down Drastically, Even Away from Flames', *Rocky Mountain News,* July 15 2002.

Butler, R. (2001), 'Seasonality in tourism: Issues and implications', in T. Baum and S. Lundtorp (eds.), *Seasonality in Tourism* (pp. 5–22), Pergamon, London.

Byrnes, T. A. and Warnken, J. (2006), 'Greenhouse Gas Emissions from Marine Tours: A Case Study of Australian Tour Boat Operators', *Journal of Sustainable Tourism,* 14(3), pp. 255–270.

Campbell, K.M. et al. (2007), *The Age of Consequences: The Foreign Policy and National Security Implications of Global Climate Change,* (Online), available: http://www.cnas.org/attachments/contentmanagers/1278/CSIS-CNAS_AgeofConsequences_October07.pdf (17-12-2007).

Campbell-Lendrum, D. et al. (2005), *The Global Burden of Disease Due to Climate Change: Quantifying the Benefits of Stabilization for Human Health,* (Online), available: http://www.stabilisation2005.com/39_Sari_Kovats.pdf (14-12-2007).

Caribbean Hotel Association and Caribbean Tourism Organization (2007), *CHA-CTO Position Paper of Global Climate Change and the Caribbean Tourism Industry,* (Online), available: http://www.caribbeanhotels.org/ClimateChangePosition0307.pdf (14-12-2007).

Carthy, R. R. et al. (2003), 'Incubation Environment of Loggerhead Turtle Nests: Effects on Hatching Success and Hatchling Characteristics', in A.B. Bolten and B.E. Witherington (eds.), *Loggerhead Sea Turtles,* Smithsonian Institution, Washington DC, pp. 144–153.

Cavallaro, F. and Ciraolo, L. (2005), 'A Multicriteria Approach to Evaluate Wind Energy Plants on an Italian Island', *Energy Policy,* 33, pp. 235–244.

Ceron, J. P. and Dubois, G. (2006), *Demain le voyage. La mobilité de tourisme et de loisirs des français face au développement durable : scénarios à 2050:* Ministère des transports, de l'équipement, du tourisme et de la mer, Paris.

Cesar, H. (2000), *Impacts of the 1998 Coral Bleaching Event on Tourism in El Nido, Phillippines,* Prepared for Coastal Resources Center Coral Bleaching Initiative, University of Rhode Island, Narragansett.

Chan, W. W. and Lam, J. C. (2003), 'Energy-saving Supporting Tourism: A Case Study of Hotel Swimming Pool Heat Pump', *Journal of Sustainable Tourism,* 11 (1), pp. 74–83.

Chaplin III, F. S. et al. (2000), 'Consequences of Changing Biodiversity', *Nature,* 405, pp. 234–242.

Christ, C. et al. (2003), *Tourism and Biodiversity: Mapping Tourism's Global Footprint.* UNEP/Conservation International, (Online), available: http://www.unep.org/PDF/Tourism_and_biodiversity_report.pdf (13-12-2007).

Cockerell, N. (1994), 'Market Segments: The International Ski Market in Europe', *EIU Travel Tourism Analyst,* 3, pp. 34–55.

Conference Board of Canada (2007), 'Travellers Keen on Going Green', *Tourism Intelligence Bulletin,* 39, May 2007.

Crowe, R. B. et al. (1973), *The Tourist and Outdoor Recreation Climate of Ontario – Volume 1: Objectives and Definitions of Season,* Report Number REC-1-73, Atmospheric Environment Service, Environment Canada, Toronto.

Cullen R. et al. (2001), *Tourism, Water and Waste in Westland: Implications of Increasing Demand on Infrastructure,* Report No. 27/2001, Tourism Recreation Research and Education Centre, Lincoln University, Canterbury.

Dalhuijsen, J. L. and Slingerland, R. (2004), 'Preliminary Wing Optimization for very large Transport Aircraft with Wingspan Constraints', *42nd AIAA Aerospace Sciences Meeting and Exhibit,* 5–8 January 2004, AIAA, Reno.

de Freitas, C. R. et al. (2004), 'A New Generation Climate Index for Tourism and Recreation', in A. Matzarakis et al. (eds.), *Advances in Tourism Climatology,* Berichte des Meteorologischen Institutes der Universität Freiburg, Freiburg, pp.19–27.

Deravi, M. and. Smith, P. (2005), *Economic impact Alabama travel industry 2004,* Bureau of Tourism and Travel, Montgomery, AL.

Daggett, D. L. et al. (1999), *An Evaluation of Aircraft Emissions Inventory Methodology by Comparisons with Reported Airline Data,* CR-1999-209480, NASA, Seattle.

Dings, J. et al. (2000), *ESCAPE: Economic Screening of Aircraft Preventing Emissions,* (main report), Centrum voor Energiebesparing en Schone Technologie, Delft.

Dubois, G. and Ceron, J.-P. (2006), 'Tourism/Leisure Greenhouse Gas Emissions Forecasts for 2050: Factors for Change in France', *Journal of Sustainable Tourism, 14* (2), pp. 172–191.

Duval, D.T. (2006), 'Coasian Economics and the Management of International Aviation Emissions, International', *Journal of Innovation and Sustainable Development,* 1(3), pp. 201–213, and (Online), available: http://www.inderscience.com/filter.php?aid=12422 (14-12-2007).

Dyurgerov, M. (2003), 'Mountain and Subpolar Glaciers Show an Increase in Sensitivity to Climate Warming and Intensification of the Water Cycle', *Journal of Hydrology, 282,* pp. 164–176.

Eagles, P. (2001), *International Trends in Park Tourism,* Task Force on Tourism and Protected Areas, World Commission on Protected Areas, World Conservation Union (IUCN), Gland.

Easier Travel (2006), 'Climate Change to Drive Radical Changes in Global Tourism', *easier TRAVEL,* (Online), available: www.easier.com/view/News/Travel/arctiklce-66761.html (14-12-2007).

Ecologic (2007), *Time to Adapt – Climate Change and The European Water Dimension,* Key Messages, Converence, 12–14 February 2007, Berlin Germany, (Online), available: http://www.climate-water-adaptation-berlin2007.org/documents/key_ messages.pdf (13-12-2007).

European Environment Agency (2007), *Climate Change and Water Adaptation Issues,* EEA Technical report No 2/2007, EEA, Copenhagen, (Online), available: http://reports.eea.europa.eu/technical_report_2007_2 (13-12-2007).

Efron, S. (2005), 'The Race to Protect Year-round Skiing: Plan to Preserve Horstman Glacier Could be a Model for Other Resorts', *Globe and Mail,* 9 July 2007, (Online), available: http://www.theglobeandmail.com/servlet/ArticleNews/TPStory/LAC/20050709/BCGLACIER09 (13-12-2007).

Egan, T. (2005), 'The Race to Alaska Before It Melts', 925 June 2005, (Online), available: http://www.nytimes.com/2005/06/26/travel/26alaska.html?ex=1277438400anden=e88a719ca3494a76andei=5090andpartner=rss userlandandemc=rss (14-12-2007).

Elsasser, H. and Bürki, R. (2002), 'Climate Change as a Threat to Tourism in the Alps', 920, pp. 253–257.

Elsasser, H. and Messerli, P. (2001), 'The Vulnerability of the Snow Industry in the Swiss Alps', 9, 21 (4), pp. 335–339.

Emanuel, K. (2005) 'Increasing destructiveness of tropical cyclones over the past 30 years', *Nature,* 436, pp. 686–688.

European Union Road Federation (ERF) (2007), *European Road Statistics 2007,* ERF, Brussel, (Online), available: http://www.irfnet.eu/images/stat/2007/ERF_stats2007.pdf (14-12-2007).

Erickson, J. (2005), 'Changes in the Air, Part 3: Bleak Forecast for the Ski Industry', *Rocky Mountain News,* 19 March 2005, (Online), available at: http://www.rockymountainnews.com/news/2005/mar/19/part-3-bleak-forecast-for-ski-industry/ (17-12-2007).

Erickson, N. et al. (1997), *Socio-economic Implications of Climate Change for Bangladesh,* Briefing Document 4, (Online), available: http://www.waikato.ac.nz/igci/downloads/BriefingDoc4.pdf (13-12-2007).

European Commission (2007), *GALILEO European Satellite Navigation System,* http://ec.europa.eu/dgs/energy_transport/galileo/index_en.htm (14-12-2007).

EUROSION (2004), *Coastal Erosion – Evaluation of the Need for Action,* (Online), available: http://www.eurosion.org/reports-online/part1.pdf (13-12-2007).

Eyers, C. J. et al. (2004), *AERO2K Global Aviation Emissions Inventories for 2002 and 2025,* QinetiQ Ltd., Farnborough, (Online), available: http://www.aero-net.org/pdf-docs/AERO2K_Global_Aviation_Emissions_Inventories_for_2002_and_2025.pdf (14-12-2007).

Feakin, T. (2005), *Climate Change and the Threat to Global Security,* Royal United Services Institute for Defence and Security Studies, (Online), available: http://www.rusi.org/downloads/assets/HSM_05_p12-13_Climate.pdf (17-12-2007).

Federation of Hotel and Restaurant Association (2006), *Department of Tourism Matters,* India, (Online), available: http://www.fhrai.com/Mag-News/newsletDOT.asp (14-12-2007; not working).

Ford, J. and Smit, B. (2004), 'Human Implications of Climate Change in the Canadian Arctic: A case study of Arctic Bay, Nunavut', *Proceedings of the Third Northern Research Forum: The Resilient North – Human Responses to Global Change,* 15–18 September 2006, Yellowknife, Canada, (Online), available: http://www.nrf.is/Publications/The%20Resilient%20North/Plenary%204/3rd%20NRF_Plenary%204_Ford%20and%20Smit_YR_paper.pdf (13-12-2007)

Forster, P. M. et al. (2006), 'It is Premature to Include Non-CO2 Effects of Aviation in Emission Trading Schemes', *Atmospheric Environment,* 40 (6), pp. 1117–1121.

Frangialli, F. (2007), Tourism Development and Climate Change: Understanding, Anticipating, *Adapting, Participating in the Common Effort,* (Background Paper) UNWTO, Madrid.

Frangialli, F. and Passaquin, F. (2003), 'Sustainable Tourism and Climate Change: An Example in the French Alps – The Case of Morzine-Avoriaz, France', *Proceedings of the First International Conference on Climate Change and Tourism,* Djerba, Tunisia, 9–11 April. Madrid, Spain: UNWTO, (Online), available: http://www.unwto.org/sustainable/climate/pres/Passaquin.pdf (13-12-2007).

Freesun News (2005), 'The Mediterranean: Too Hot to Holiday?', *Freesun News* (Belgium), 18 November 2005.

French Environment and Energy Agency (ADEME) (2006), *Bilan carbone. Calcul des facteurs d'émissions et sources bibliographiques utilisées,* (version 4.0), ADEME, MIES, Paris.

Fukushima, T. et al. (2003), 'Influences of Air Temperature Change on Leisure Industries: Case Study on Ski Activities', *Mitigation and Adaptation Strategies for Climate Change, 7,* pp. 173–189.

German Advisory Council on Global Change (WBGU) (2007), *World in Transition: Climate Change as a Security Risk,* WBGU, Berlin.

German Advisory Council on Global Change (WBGU) (2002), *Charging the Use of Global Commons,* WBGU, Berlin, (Online), available: http://www.wbgu.de/wbgu_sn2002_engl.pdf (14-12-2007).

Giles, A. and Perry, A. (1998), 'The Use of a Temporal Analogue to Investigate the Possible Impact of Projected Global Warming on the UK Tourist Industry', *Tourism Management, 19,* 1, pp. 75–80.

Gill, J. and Watkinson A. (2004), *Linking Sea Level Rise, Coastal Biodiversity and Economic Activity in Caribbean Island States: Towards the Development of a Coastal Island Simulator,* Tyndall Centre for Climate Change Research, Technical Report 9, (Online), available: http://www.tyndall.ac.uk/research/theme4/final_reports/it1_38.pdf (13-12-2007).

Gillen, A. (2004), *Air Travel Demand Elasticities: Concepts, Issues and Measurements,* Department of Finance Canada, Ottawa, (Online), available: http://www.fin.gc.ca/consultresp/Airtravel/airtravStdy_e.html (14-12-2007).

Glantz, M. (2000), *Reducing the Impact of Environmental Emergencies through Early Warning and Preparedness: The Case of the 1997–98 El Niño.* UNEP, NCAR, UNU, and WMO.

Global Warming Art (2007), *Muir and Riggs Glaciers,* (Online), available: http://www.globalwarmingart.com/wiki/Image: Muir_Glacier_jpg (17-12-2007).

Godard, O. (2007), *Climat et générations futures – Un examen crititque du débat académicque suscité par le Rapport Stern,* Report number DDX-07-12, École Polytechnique, Paris.

Golf Environment Europe (2007), *Golf and Environment,* (Online), available: http://www.golfenvironmenteurope.org/golfandenvironment02.html (14-12-2007).

Gómez Martín, B. (2004), 'An Evaluation of the Tourist Potential of the Climate in Catalonia (Spain): A Regional Study', *Geografiska Annaler,* 86, pp. 249–264.

Gössling, S. and Hall, C. M. (2006a), 'An Introduction to Tourism and Global Environmental change', in S. Gössling and C.M. Hall (eds.), *Tourism and Global Environmental Change,* Routledge, London, pp. 1–34.

Gössling, S. and Hall, C. M. (2006b), 'Uncertainties in Predicting Tourist Travel Flows Based on Models: Editorial Essay', *Climatic Change,* 79 (3–4), pp. 163–173.

Gössling, S. and Hickler, T. (2006), 'Tourism and Forest Ecosystems', in S. Gössling and C.M. Hall (eds.), *Tourism and Global Environmental Change,* Routledge, London, pp. 95–106.

Gössling, S. and Scott, D. (2008 – in press), 'Editorial – Special Issue on Climate Change and Tourism: Exploring Destination Vulnerability', *Tourism Review International.*

Gössling, S. (2006), 'Tourism Certification in Scandinavia', in S. Gössling and J. Hultman (eds.), *Ecotourism in Scandinavia. Lessons in Theory and Practice,* CABI Publishing, Wallingford, pp. 63–75.

Gössling, S. (2002), 'Global Environmental Consequences of Tourism', *Global Environmental Change,* Part A, 12 (4), pp. 283–302.

Gössling, S. (2000), 'Sustainable Tourism Development in Developing Countries: Some Aspects of Energy-use', *Journal of Sustainable Tourism,* 8(5), pp. 410–425.

Gössling, S. et al. (2008 – submitted), 'Swedish Air Travellers and Voluntary Carbon Offsets: Towards the Co-Creation of Environmental value?', *Current Issues in Tourism.*

Gössling, S. et al. (2007), 'Diving and Global Environmental Change: A Mauritius Case Study', in B. Garrod and S. Gössling (eds.), *New Frontiers in Marine Tourism: Diving Experiences, Management and Sustainability,* Elsevier, Amsterdam.

Gössling, S. et al. (2006), 'Tourist Perceptions of Climate Change: A Study of International Tourists in Zanzibar', *Current Issues in Tourism, 9* (4–5), pp. 419–435.

Gössling, S. et al. (2005), 'The Eco-efficiency of Tourism', *Ecological Economics,* 54(4), pp. 417–434.

Great Barrier Reef Marine Park Authority (GBRMPA) (2007a), *Coral Bleaching on the Great Barrier Reef,* GBRMPA, Australian Government, (Online), available: http://www.gbrmpa.gov.au/corp_site/key_issues/climate_change/climate_change_and_the_great_barrier_reef/coral_bleaching_on_the_great_barrier_reef (14-12-2007).

Great Barrier Reef Marine Park Authority (GBRMPA) (2007b), *Great Barrier Reef Coral Bleaching Response Plan: Summer 2006–2007,* GBRMPA, Australian Government, (Online), available: http://www.gbrmpa.gov.au/__data/assets/pdf_file/0020/13169/Coral_Bleaching_Response_Plan_2006-07_Final.pdf (14-12-2007).

Green, J. E. (2003), 'Civil Aviation and the Environmental Challenge', *The Aeronautical Journal, 107,* pp. 281–299.

Green, R. E. (2003), *Global Climate Change and Biodiversity,* University of East Anglia, Norwich, Online), available: http://www.jncc.gov.uk/pdf/MJHGlobalclimatechange_14.08.03.pdf (13-12-2007).

Greenwood, G. (2005), 'What are the Important Global Change Themes and Issues in Mountain Biosphere Reserves?', in *Global Change Impacts in Mountain Biosphere Reserves,* UNESCO, Paris, pp. 179–194.

Guardian (2006), 'Climate Change could Bring Tourists to UK – Report', *The Guardian,* 28 July 2006, (Online), available: http://www.guardian.co.uk/travel/2006/jul/28/travelnews.uknews.climatechange (14-12-2007).

Haeberli, W. and Beniston, M. (1998), 'Climate Change and its Impacts on Glaciers and Permafrost in the Alps', *Ambio, 27,* pp. 258–265.

Halifax Travel Insurance (2006), *Holiday 2030,* (Online), available: http://www.hbosplc.com/media/pressreleases/articles/halifax/2007-02-14-WINTERHOLI.asp?section=halifax (14-12-2007).

Hall, C. M. (2008 – submitted), 'Tourism and Climate Change: Knowledge Gaps and Issues', *Tourism Recreation Research.*

Hall, C. M. (2006), 'Tourism, Biodiversity and Global Environmental Change', in S. Gössling and C.M. Hall (eds.), *Tourism and Global Environmental Change,* Routledge, London, pp. 211–226.

Hall, C. M. et al. (2004), 'Security and Tourism: Towards a New Understanding?', *Journal of Travel and Tourism Marketing, 15,* (2/3), pp. 1–18.

Hall, M. and Farge, D. (2003), 'Modeled Climate-induced Glacier Change in Glacier National Park: 1850–2100', *BioScience, 53* (2), pp. 131–140.

Hallegatte, S. et al. (2007), 'Using Climate Analogues for Assessing Climate Change Economic Impacts'. *Climatic Change, 82* (1–2), pp. 47–60.

Hallegatte, S. et al. (2005), *Using Climate Analogues for Assessing Climate Change Economic Impacts in Urban Areas,* Centre International de Recherche sur l'Environnement et le Développement, Nogent sur Marne (Online), available: http://www.centre-cired.fr/forum/IMG/pdf/PSICC_Partner19_qua.pdf (01-02-2008).

Halverson, J. B. (2006), 'A Climate Conundrum', *Weatherwise,* 59 (2), pp. 108–23.

Hamilton, J. M. and Lau, M. (2005), 'The Role of Climate Information in Tourist Destination Choice Decision-making', in S. Gössling and C.M. Hall (eds.), *Tourism and global environmental change,* Routledge, London, pp. 229–250.

Hamilton, J. M. et al. (2005a), 'Effects of Climate Change on International Tourism', *Climate Research, 29,* pp. 245–254.

Hamilton, J. M. et al. (2005b), 'Climate Change and International Tourism: A Simulation Study', *Global Environmental Change, 15,* pp. 253–266.

Hanlon, P. (2007), *Global Airlines: Competition in a Transnational Industry,* (third edition), Butterworth-Heinemann, Oxford.

Harlfinger, O. (1991), 'Holiday Biometeorology: A Study of Palma de Majorca, Spain', *Geojournal, 25,* pp. 377–381.

Harrison S et al. (1999), 'The Potential Effects of Climate Change on the Scottish Tourist Industry, *Tourism Management, 20,* pp. 203–211.

Hasek, Glenn (2006), 'Accor NA's Energy Star: Dan Gilligan', *Green Lodging News,* (Online), available: http://www.greenlodgingnews.com/Content.aspx?id=715 (14-12-2007).

Hawker, M. (2007), 'Climate Change and the Global Insurance Industry', *The Geneva Papers, 32,* pp. 22–28.

Hay, J. et al. (2003), *Climate Variability and Change and Sea level Rise in the Pacific Islands Region: A Resource Book for Policy and Decision Makers, Educators and other Stakeholders.* South Pacific Regional Environment Programme, Japan Ministry of the Environment, Tokyo.

Hayhoe, K. et al. (2004), 'Emission Pathways, Climate Change, and Impacts on California', *Proceedings of the National Academy of Sciences, 101* (34), pp. 12422-12427.

Hennessy, K. et al. (2003), *The Impact of Climate change on Snow Conditions in Mainland Australia,* CSIRO Atmospheric Research, Aspendale.

Higham, J. and Hinch, T. (2002), 'Tourism, Sport and Seasons: The Challenges and Potential of Overcoming Seasonality in the Sport and Tourism Sectors', *Tourism Management, 23* (2), pp. 175–185.

Hoegh-Guldberg, H. and Hoegh-Guldberg, O. (2004), *The Implications of Climate Change for Australia's Great Barrier Reef,* WWF Australia, Sydney.

Holland, G. and Webster, P. J. (2007), 'Heightened Tropical Cyclone Activity in the North Atlantic: Natural Variability or Climate Trend?', *Philansophical Transactions of the Royal Society,* (Online), available: http://publishing.royalsociety.org/media/philtrans_a/Holland%20and%20Webster%201.pdf (13-12-2007)

Hu, Y, and Ritchie, J. (1993), 'Measuring Destination Attractiveness: A Contextual Approach', *Journal of Travel Research,* 32 (20), pp. 25–34.

Hulme, M. (ed.) (1996), *Climate Change in Southern Africa: An Exploration of Some Potential Impacts and Implications in the SADC Region,* Climatic Research Unit, University of East Anglia, Norwich.

International Business Leader Forum (2007), *Going Green: Minimum Standards Towards a Sustainable Hotel,* (Online), available: http://www.iblf.org/media_room/general.jsp?id=123932 (10-12-2007).

International Snowmobile Manufacturers Association (2006), *International Snowmobile Industry Facts and Figures,* (Online), available: http://www.snowmobile.org/pr_snowfacts.asp (17-12-2007).

International Union of Railways (2007), *Energy Efficiency Technologies for Railways – Database, International Union of Railways,* Paris, (Online), available: http://www.railway-energy.org/tfee/index.php?ID=200 (14-12-2007).

Intergovernmental Panel on Climate Change (2007a), Summary for Policymakers and Technical Summary, in S. Solomon et al. (eds.), *Climate Change 2007: The Physical Science Basis. Contribution of Working Group I to the Fourth Assessment Report of the IPCC,* Cambridge University Press, Cambridge and New York.

Intergovernmental Panel on Climate Change (2007b), Summary for Policymakers, in M. L. Parry et al. (eds.), *Climate Change 2007: Impacts, Adaptation and Vulnerability. Contribution of Working Group II to the Fourth Assessment Report of the IPCC,* Cambridge University Press, Cambridge and New York.

Intergovernmental Panel on Climate Change (2007c), *Climate Change 2007: Mitigation. Contribution of Working Group III to the Fourth Assessment Report of the IPCC* [Metz, B. et al. (eds.)], Cambridge University Press, Cambridge and New York.

Intergovernmental Panel on Climate Change (2007d), *Guidance Notes for Lead Authors of the IPCC Fourth Assessment Report on Addressing Uncertainties,* (Online), available: http://www.ipcc.ch/pdf/supporting-material/uncertainty-guidance-note.pdf (17-12-2007).

Intergovernmental Panel on Climate Change (2002), *Climate Change and Biodiversity* (Technical Paper V), IPCC, Geneva.

Intergovernmental Panel on Climate Change (2001), *Climate Change 2001: Impacts, Adaptation and Vulnerability – Contribution of Working Group II to the Third Assessment Report of the IPCC,* [J. J McCarthy et al. (eds.)], Cambridge University Press, Cambridge and New York.

Intergovernmental Panel on Climate Change (2000), *Special Report on Emissions Scenarios, IPCC,* Geneva, (Online), available, http://www.grida.no/climate/ipcc/emission/index.htm (01-02-2008)

IUCN (2006a), *Coral Reef Resilience and Resistance to Bleaching, IUCN Global Marine Programme,* (Online), available: http://www.iucn.org/dbtw-wpd/edocs/2006-042.pdf (13-12-2007)

IUCN (2006b), *Managing Mangroves for Resilience to Climate Change,* IUCN Global Marine Programme, (Online), available: http://www.iucn.org/dbtw-wpd/edocs/2006-041.pdf (13-12-2007)

IUCN (2004), *Securing Protected Areas in the Face of Global Change: Issues and Strategies,* (Online), available: http://www.iucn.org/themes/wcpa/pubs/pdfs/securingpas.pdf (13-12-2007).

IUCN (2003), *Evaluation of the Cape Floral Region for the World Heritage Committee,* World Heritage Nomitation – IUCN Technical Evaluation, (Online), available: http://whc.unesco.org/archive/advisory_body_evaluation/1007rev.pdf (14-12-2007).

Iyer, P. (2007), '20 Places to see before they die', *Condé Nast Traveler,* May 2007, (Online), available, http://www.concierge.com/cntraveler/articles/detail?articleId=10772 (14-12-2007).

Local Governments for Sustainability (ICLEI) (2007), *About ICLEI – Local Governments for Sustainability,* (Online), available: http://www.iclei.org/index.php?id=global-about-iclei (10-12-2007)

Jahn, G. (2005), 'Glacial Cover-Up Won't Stop Global Warming, But It Keeps Skiers Happy', *Environmental News Network,* (Online), available: http://www.enn.com/top_stories/article/2060 (13-12-2007).

JAL (2007), *CSR Report 2006,* Japan Airlines, Tokyo, (Online), available: http://www.jal.com/en/corporate/csr2006/index2.html (14-12-2007).

Jang, S. C. (2004), 'Mitigating Tourism Seasonality: A Quantitative Approach', *Annals of Tourism Research, 31* (4), pp. 819–836.

Janzen, F. J. (1994), 'Climate Change and Temperature-Dependent Sex Determination in Reptiles', *Proceedings of the National Academy of Sciences, 91,* pp. 7487–7490.

Johnson, A. (2005), 'Early Start to Hhurricane Season Forces Travelers, Resorts to Adjust', *The Wall Street Journal,* 21 July 2005, D5.

Johnston, M. (2006), 'Impact of Global Environmental Change on Tourism in the Polar Regions, in S. Gössling and C.M. Hall (eds.), *Tourism and Global Environmental Change,* Routledge, London, pp. 37–53.

Jones, B. and Scott, D. (2006), 'Climate Change, Seasonality and Visitation to Canada's National Parks', *Journal of Parks and Recreation Administration,* 24 (2), pp. 42–62.

Jones, C. D. et al. (2006), 'Impact of Climate-carbon Cycle Feedbacks on Emissions Scenarios to Achieve Stabilisation', in J. Schellnhuber et al. (eds.), *Avoiding Dangerous Climate Change,* Cambridge University Press, Cambridge, pp. 323–331.

Jones, G. et al. (2005), 'Climate Change and Global Wine Quality', *Climatic Change, 73* (3), pp. 319–343.

Jorgensen, F. and Solvoll, G. (1996), 'Demand Models for Inclusive Tour Charter: The Norwegian Case', *Tourism Management, 17,* pp. 17–24.

Jorgensen, M. W. and Sorenson, S. C. (1997), 'Estimating Emissions from Railway Traffic', *Report for the Project MEET: Methodologies for Estimating Air Pollutant Emissions from Transport,* Department of Energy Engineering, Technical University of Denmark, Lyngby, (Online), available: http://www.inrets.fr/infos/cost319/MEETDeliverable17.PDF (14-12-2007).

Kim, B. Y. et al. (2007), 'System for Assessing Aviation's Global Emissions (SAGE), Part 1: Model Description and Inventory Results', *Transportation Research,* D 12, pp. 325–346.

Kim, B. Y. et al. (2006 and 2005), System for Assessing Aviation's Global Emissions (SAGE), Version 1.5, *Global Aviation Emissions Inventories for 2000 through 2004,* Federal Aviation Administration, Washington DC, (Online), available: http://www.faa.gov/about/office_org/headquarters_offices/aep/models/sage/media/FAA-EE-2005-02__SAGE-Inventory_Report-Text.pdf (14-12-2007).

Kjellström, E. et al. (2006), *Modelling Daily Temperature Extremes: Recent Climate and Future Changes over Europe,* (Online), available: http://prudence.dmi.dk/public/publications/PSICC/Kjellstrom-et-al.pdf (14-12-2007).

Klein, R. J. T. et al. (2005), 'Integrating Mitigation and Adaptation into Climate and Development Policy: Three Research Questions', *Environmental Science and Policy, 8,* pp. 579–588. and (Online), available: http://www.tyndall.ac.uk/publications/working_papers/wp40.pdf (13-12-2007).

Knauer, S. (2007), 'Endangered Ski Slopes in the Bavarian Alps: Snow Cannons Against the Apocalypse', *Spiegel Online,* 3 January 2007, (Online), available: http://www.spiegel.de/international/spiegel/0,1518,457498,00.html (13-12-2007).

König, U. (1998), *Tourism in a Warmer World: Implications of Climate Change due to Enhanced Greenhouse Effect for the Ski Industry in the Australian Alps,* Wirtschaftsgeographie und Raumplanung, Volume 28, University of Zurich, Zurich.

König, U. and Abegg, B. (1997), 'Impacts of Climate Change on Tourism in the Swiss Alps', *Journal of Sustainable Tourism, 5* (1), pp. 46–58.

Koohafkan, P. (2006), 'Conservation and Adaptive Management of Globally Important Agricultural Heritage Systems (GIAHS)', *International Conference on Endogenous Development and Bio-Cultural Diversity,* 3–5 October, 2006, Geneva, Switzerland, (Online), available: http://www.bioculturaldiversity.net/Downloads/Papers%20 participants/Koohafkan.pdf (13-12-2007)

Kovats, R. S. and Ebi , K. (2006), 'Heatwaves and Public Health in Europe', *The European Journal of Public Health, 16* (6), pp. 592–599.

Kozak, M. (2002), 'Comparative Analysis of Tourist Motivations by Nationality and Destinations', *Tourism Management, 23,* pp. 221–232

Lagadec, P. (2004), 'Understanding the French 2003 Heat Wave Experience: Beyond the Heat, a Multi-Layered Challenge', *Journal of Contingencies and Crisis Management, 12* (4), 160-169.

Lamers, M. and Amelung, B. (2007), 'The Environmental Impacts of Tourism to Antarctica: A Global Perspective', in P. Peeters (ed.), *Tourism and Climate Change Mitigation: Methods, Greenhouse Gas Reductions and Policies,* Breda: NHTV, Breda, pp. 51–62.

Lea, A. S. and Saunders, M. A. (2006), 'How Well Forecast Were the 2004 and 2005 Atlantic and US Hurricane Seasons?', *Weather,* 61, no. 9, pp. 245–249.

Leckebusch, G. C. and Ulbrich, U. (2004), 'On the Relationship between Cyclones and Extreme Windstorm Events over Europe under Climate Change', *Global and Planetry Science,* 44, pp. 181–193.

Lemoine, N. and Bohning-Gaese, K. (2003), 'Potential Impact of Global Climate Change on Species Richness of Long-distance Migrants', *Conservation Biology, 17,* 2, pp. 577–586.

Lesser, M. (2007), Coral Reef Bleaching and Global Climate Change: Can Corals Survive the Next Century?', *Proceedings of the National Academy of Sciences,* 104 (13), pp. 5259–5260.

Létard, V. et al. (2004), *Rapport d'Information Fait au Nom de la Mission: La France et les Français Face à la Canicule: les Leçons d'une Crise,* Report No. 195 (2003-2004) to the Parlament, Government of France.

Liotta, P., H. and Shearer, A.W. (2005), *The Use of Scenarios in Assessing Climate Change, Human Security, and Potential Outcomes, Pell Center for International Relations and Public Policy,* (Online), available: http://www.gechs.org/downloads/holmen/Liotta_Shearer.pdf (17-12-2007).

Lohmann, M. and Kaim, E. (1999), 'Weather and Holiday Preference – Image, Attitude and Experience', *Revue de Tourisme,* 2, pp. 54–64.

Lollino, G. and Audisio, C. (2006), 'UNESCO World Heritage Sites in Italy Affected by Geological Problems, Specifically Landslide and Flood Hazard', *Landslides, 3* (4), pp. 311–321.

London Climate Change Partnership (2002), *Climate Change Impacts in a London Evaluation Study, Final Report,* (Online), available: http://www.london.gov.uk/gla/publications/environment/londons_warming_tech_rpt_all. pdf (13-12-2007).

Lowe, J. (2003), *The Effects of Climate Change on Storm Surges Around the UK, in The Big Flood: An International Scientific Meeting on North Sea Storm Surges.*

Lowe, J. A. and Gregory, J. M. (2005), 'The Effects of Climate Change on Storm Surges Around the UK', *Philosophical Transacation Royal Society,* (A) 363 (1831), pp. 1313–1328.

Luckman, B. and Kavanagh, T. (2000), 'Impact of Climate Fluctuations on Mountain Environments in the Canadian Rockies', *Ambio, 29,* pp. 371–380.

Lumsdon, L. et al. (2006), 'Transport for Tourism: Can Public Transport Encourage a Modal Shift in the Day Visitor Market?', *Journal of Sustainable Tourism,* 14 (2), pp. 139–156.

Luterbacher, J. et al. (2007), 'Exceptional European Warmth of Autumn 2006 and Winter 2007: Historical Context, the Underlying Dynamics and its Phonological Impacts', *Geophysical Research Letters,* 34, pp. 1–6.

Maddison, D. (2001), 'In Search of Warmer Climates? The Impact of Climate Change on Flows of British Tourists', *Climatic Change, 49* (1/2), pp. 193–208.

Martens, P. et al. (1999), 'Climate Change and Future Populations at Risk of Malaria', *Global Environmental Change,* 9(1), pp. 89–107.

Martin, C. and Chehebarf, C. (2001), 'The National Parks of Argentinian Patagonia – Management Policies for Conservation, Public Use, Rural Settlements and Indigenous Communities', *Journal of The Royal Society of New Zealand, 5* (4), pp. 845–864.

Masson, P. J. et al (2007), 'HTS Machines as Enabling Technology for All-electric Airborne Vehicles', Superconductor Science and Technology, 20 (8), pp. 748-756.

McBoyle, G. et al. (2007), 'Climate Change and the Future of Snowmobiling in Non-Mountainous Regions of Canada'. *Managing Leisure,* Volume 12, Number 4, pp 237-250.

McBoyle, G. and Wall, G. (1992), 'Great Lakes Skiing and Climate Change', in A. Gill and R. Hartmann (eds.), *Mountain Resort Development,* Policy and Research, Simon Fraser University Burnaby, BC, pp. 70–81.

Mieczkowski, Z. (1985), 'The Tourism Climatic Index: A Method of Evaluating World Climates for Tourism', *Le géographe canadien,* XXIX (3), pp. 220–233.

Mills, E. et al. (2005), *Availability and Affordability of Insurance under Climate Change: A Growing Challenge for the US, Ceres,* (Online), available: http://www.ceres.org/pub/docs/Ceres_insure_climatechange_120105.pdf (13-12-2007).

Ministère de l'Économie, de l'Industrie et de l'Emploi (France) (2007), Memento du Tourisme 2007, (Online), available: http://www.tourisme.gouv.fr/fr/z2/stat/memento/memento_2007.jsp (07-04-2008).

Ministry of Culture and Tourism of Indonesia (2005), *Tourism in Indonesia,* (Online), available: http://www.world-tourism.org/tsunami/reports/Serial7.pdf (14-12-2007).

Ministry of Tourism of India (2004), *India Tourism Statistics 2003,* Market Research Division, Ministry of Tourism, Government of India, New Delhi.

Mintel International Group (1991), 'Special Report – Holidays', *Leisure Intelligence,* Mintel International Group, London.

Mitchell, T. and Tanner, T. (2006), *Adapting to Climate Change: Challenges and Opportunities for the Development Community,* Tearfund Report, Institute of Development Studies, Brighton, (Online), available: http://www.tearfund.org/webdocs/website/Campaigning/policy%20and%20research/Adapting%20to%20climate%20change%20discussion%20paper.pdf (17-12-2007).

MSNBC (2007), 'Toyota Worldwide Hybrid Sales Top 1 Million', *MSNBC,* 7 June 2007, (Online), available: http://www.msnbc.msn.com/id/19088667/ (14-12-2007).

Muller, B. (2002), *Equity in Climate Change: The Great Divide,* Oxford Institute for Energy Studies, Oxford University, Oxford.

Munasinghe, M. and Swart, R. (2000), 'Climate Change and Its Linkages with Development, Equity, and Sustainability', *Proceedings of the IPCC Expert Meeting, Columbo, Sri Lanka, 27–29 April 1999,* LIFE, Columbo, RIVM, Bilthoven, and World Bank, Washington, DC.

Myers, N. et al. (2000), 'Biodiversity Hotspots for Conservation Priorities', *Nature, 403,* pp. 853–858.

National Bureau of Statistics of China (2007), *China Statistical Yearbook – 2006,* (Online), available: http://www.stats.gov.cn/tjsj/ndsj/2006/indexee.htm (17-12-2007).

National Drought Mitigation Center (1998), *Reported Effects of the 1997–98 El Niño,* National Drought Mitigation Center, Lincoln, Nebraska, 11p.

National Ski Areas Association (2007), *Green Power Program Fact Sheet,* (Online), available: http://www.nsaa.org/nsaa/press/0607/green-power-fact-sheet.asp (14-12-2007).

Network for Soft Mobility in European Tourism (2007), *NETS Hompage,* (Online), available: http://www.soft-mobility.com/english/index.htm (10-12-2007)

Ngugi, V. W. et al. (2003), *Application of Climate Information and Predictions in Mitigating the Impacts of Drought on Tourism in the Gha (Great Horn of Africa) Region,* UNWTO, Madrid.

Njegovan, N. (2006), 'Elasticities of Demand for Leisure Air Travel: A System Modelling Approach', *Journal of Air Transport Management,* 12, pp. 33–39.

Nogués-Bravo, D. and Araújo, M.B. (2006), 'Species Richness, Area and Climate Correlates', *Global Ecology and Biogeography,* 15, pp. 452–460.

Nukubati Islands (2007), *Environment and Ecology,* (Online), available: http://www.nukubati.com/environment.asp (14-12-2007).

O'Brien, R. (2007), 'Guardian Insurance', *2nd UK-Caribbean Business Forum on Climate Change,* Trinidad and Tobago, 8 June 2007.

OECD (2006), *Climate Change and Winter Tourism. Report on Adaptation,* (Online), available: http://www.oecd.org/dataoecd/58/4/37776193.pdf (14-12-2007).

Olefs, M. et al. (2007), 'The Role of Artificial Increase of Accumulation within Glacier Skiing Resorts: A Feasibility Study', *Geophysical Research Abstracts,* 9, 06576, (Online), available: http://www.cosis.net/abstracts/EGU2007/06576/EGU2007-J-06576.pdf (13-12-2007).

Ontario Ministry of Tourism and Recreation (2002), *If the Future Were Now: Impacts of Aging in the Canadian Market on Tourism in Ontario,* Ontario Ministry of Tourism and Recreation, Toronto.

Paavola, J. and Adger, W.N. (2002), *Justice and Adaptation to Climate Change,* Tyndall Centre for Climate Change Research Working Paper 23, (Online), available: http://www.tyndall.ac.uk/publications/working_papers/wp23.pdf (17-12-2007).

Pachauri, R. K, Jallow, B. (2007), *Presentation of the WG I Report at the GMEF and UNEP GC-24 Nairobi, 6 February 2007,* (Online), available: http://www.ipcc.ch/pdf/presentations/wg1-report-2007-02.pdf (13-12-2007).

Pack, T. (2004), 'Florida Tourism Problem: Survey Shows 1 in 4 Less Likely to Visit Florida Next Year', *Tribute Business News,* (Online), available: http://www.hotel-online.com/News/PR2004_4th/Oct04_FloridaNextYear.html (14-12-2007).

Parry, R. (2005), 'Cherry Trees Programmed to Blossom for Tourists', *The Times Online,* 9 June 2005, (Online), available: http://www.timesonline.co.uk/tol/news/world/article1080206.ece (13-12-2007).

Pateman, E. (2001), 'Rising Energy Costs Cause Concern in the Lodging Industry', *Hotel Online Special Report,* March 2001, (Online), available: http://www.hotel-online.com/News/PR2001_1st/Mar01_Pateman_Energy.html (17-12-2007).

Patz, J. A. et al. (2005), 'Impact of Regional Climate Change on Human Health', *Nature, 438* (17), pp. 310–317.

Paul, A. (1972), 'Weather and the Daily Use of Outdoor Recreation Areas in Canada', in J. Taylor (ed.) *Weather Forecasting for Agriculture and Industry,* David and Charles Newton Abbott, pp. 132–146.

Peeters, P. (2007), *Tourism and Climate Change Mitigation – Methods, Greenhouse Gas Reductions and Policies,* NHTV Academics Studies No. 6, NHTV, Breda University, Breda.

Peeters, P. et al. (2007a), 'Air Transport Greenhouse Gas Emissions', in P. Peeters (ed.), *Tourism and Climate Change Mitigation – Methods, Greenhouse Gas Reductions and Policies* (pp. 29–50), NHTV Academics Studies, No. 6, NHTV, Breda University, Breda.

Peeters, P. et al. (2007b), 'Major Environmental Impacts of European Tourist Transport', *Journal of Transport Geography, 15,* pp. 83–93.

Peeters, P. et al. (2005), *Fuel Efficiency of Commercial Aircraft: An Overview of Historical and Future Trends,* Peeters Advies/National Aerospace Laboratory, Amsterdam, (Online), available: http://www.transportenvironment.org/Downloads-index-req-getit-lid-398.html (14-12-2007).

Peeters, P. et al. (2004), *European Tourism, Transport and Environment,* (Final Version), NHTV CSTT, Breda.

Peeters, P. and Middel, J. (2006), 'Historical and Future Development of Air Transport Fuel Efficiency, *Transport and Climate Change (TAC) Conference,* 25–29 June 2006, Oxford.

Pelling, M. and Uitto, J. (2001), 'Small Island Developing States: Natural Disaster Vulnerability and Global Change', *Global Environmental Change Part B: Environmental hazards, 3* (2), pp. 49–62.

Penner, J. et al. (1999), *Aviation and the Global Atmosphere: A Special Report of IPCC Working Groups I and III,* Published for the IPCC, Cambridge University Press, Cambridge.

Perry, C. P. (2003), 'Reef Development at Inhaca Island, Mozambique: Coral Communities and Impacts of the 1999/2000 Southern African Floods', *Ambio, 32* (2), pp. 134–139.

Pittock, A. B. (2006), 'Are Scientists Underestimating Climate Change?', *Eos, 87* (34), pp. 340–341.

Pounds, J. A. et al. (2006), 'Widespread Amphibian Extinctions from Epidemic Disease Driven by Global Warming' *Nature, 439,* pp. 161–166.

Prather, M. and Sausen, R. (1999), 'Potential Climate Change from Aviation', in J. E. Penner et al. (eds.), *Aviation and the Global Atmosphere: A Special Report of IPCC Working Groups I and III,* Cambridge University Press, Cambridge, pp. 185–215.

Price, J. and Glick, P. (2002), *The Birdwatcher's Guide to Global Warming,* National Wildlife Federation and The Plains, Virgina, and American Bird Conservancy, Virginia.

Price, M. (1999), *Global Change in the Mountains,* Parthenon, New York.

Prideaux, B. (2006), 'The Use of Scenarios to Project the Imapct of Global Warming on Future Visitation to the Great Barrier Reef', *Tourism After Oil: ATLAS Asia Pacific 2006 Conference,* 2–5 December 2006, Dunedin.

Professional Golfers Association of America (2007), *PGA CEOs Detail Golf's Economic Impact at Global Economic Summit,* (Online), available: http://www.pga.com/news/show/2007/news/summittranscript012507.html (14-12-2007).

Prom Perú (2004), *Perú: Perfil de turista extranjero 2003,* Prom Perú, Lima.

Pulles, J. W. et al. (2002), *AERO Main Report: Aviation Emissions and Evaluation of Reduction Options,* Dutch Ministry of Transport, Public Works and Water Management, Den Haag.

Raksakulthai, V. (2003), *Climate Change Impacts and Adaptation for Tourism in Phuket, Thailand,* Asian Disaster Preparedness Centre, Pathumthani.

Randerson, J. (2006), 'Med to Lose Pull as Earth Heats Up', *The Guardian,* 9 August 2006, (Online), available: http://www.guardian.co.uk/science/2006/aug/09/travelnews.environment (14-12-2007).

Raupach, M. R. et al. (2007), 'Global and Regional Drivers of Accelerating CO2 Emissions', *Proceedings of the National Academy of Sciences, (early edition),* (Online), available: http://www.pnas.org/cgi/reprint/0700609104v1.pdf (14-12-2007).

Reiser, A. and Simmons, D. G. (2005), 'A Quasi-Experimental Method for Testing the Effectiveness of Ecolabel Promotion', *Journal of Sustainable Tourism,* 13 (6), pp. 590–616.

Research and Markets (2004), *Opportunities in the Global Golf Club Market 2004–2010,* (Online), available: http://www.researchandmarkets.com/reportinfo.asp?report_id=227053 (14-12-2007).

Reuer, M. (2006), 'Regional Challenges of Future Climate Change: Endless Summer or Business-As-Usual?', *The 2006 Colorado College State of the Rockies Report Card* (pp. 85–103). Colorado Springs: Colorado College.

Reuters (2005), *Global Warming to Wreck Med Paradise,* 2 July 2007 Reuter, London.

Richardson, D. M. et al. (2000), 'Invasive Alien Species and Global Change: A South African Perspective', in H.A. Mooney and R.J. Hobbs (eds.), *Invasive Species in a Changing World,* Island Press, Washington DC, pp. 303–350.

Richardson, R. and Loomis, J. (2004), 'Adaptive Recreation Planning and Climate Change: A Contingent Visitation Approach', *Ecological Economics, 50,* pp. 83–99, and (Online), available: http://www.nrel.colostate.edu/projects/star/papers/Richardson&Loomis-2004.pdf (14-12-2007).

Rixen, C. et al. (2003), 'Does Artificial Snow Production Affect Soli and Vegetation of Ski Pistes? – A review', *Perspectives in Plant Ecology, Evolution and Systematics,* 5 (4), pp. 219–230.

Royal and Ancient Golf Club of St. Andrews (2000), *On Course for Change – Tackling the Challenges Facing Golf in the First Decades of the New Millennium,* Fife, The Royal and Ancient Golf Club of St. Andrews, St. Andrews.

Ruosteenoja, K. et al. (2003), *Future Climate in World Regions: An Intercomparison of Model-based Projections for the New IPCC Emissions Scenarios,* The Finnish Environment 644, Finnish Environment Institute, Helsinki, (Online), available: http://www.environment.fi/download.asp?contentid=25835&lan=en (20-12-2007).

Rutherford, M. C. et al. (1999), 'Climate Change in Conservation Areas of South Africa and its Potential Impact on Floristic Composition: A First Assessment', *Diversity and Distributions,* 5 (6), pp. 253–262.

Sandals Resorts (2006), 'Blue Chip Hurricane Guarantee', *Beaches,* (Online), available: http://www.beaches.com/general/hurricane.cfm 13-12-2007.

Santer, B. D. et al. (2006), 'Forced and Unforced Ocean Temperature Changes in Atlantic and Pacific Tropical Cyclone Genesis Regions', *Proceedings of the National Academy of Sciences,* USA 103, 13, pp. 905–910, and (Online), at: http://www.pnas.org/cgi/reprint/0602861103v1 (13-12-2007).

SAS Group (2002), *The SAS Group Environmental Report 2001,* SAS Group, Stockholm, (Online), available: http://www.corporateregister.com/search/report.cgi?num=7097-ERzVbHgl4X2 (14-12-2007).

Saunders, M. A. and Lea, A. S. (2006), 'Hurricanes and Global Warming'. Presentation at *Oxford University Centre for the Environment,* May 2006.

Saunders, S. and Easley, T. (2006), *Losing Ground: Western National Parks Endangered by Climate Disruption,* The Rocky Mountain Climate Organization, Louisville, CO and Natural Resources Defense Council, New York.

Sausen, R. et al. (2005), 'Aviation Radiative Forcing in 2000: An Update on IPCC (1999)', *Meteorologische Zeitschrift,* 14 (4), pp. 555–561.

SBB (2007), *SBB Environmental Topics – Energy,* (Online), available: http://mct.sbb.ch/mct/konzern_engagement/konzern_umwelt/konzern_energie.htm (14-12-2007).

Schafer, A. and Victor, D. G. (2000), 'The Future Mobility of the World Population', *Transportation Research - A, 34,* pp. 171-205.

Scott, D. (2006a), 'Climate Change and Sustainable Tourism in the 21st Century', in J. Cukier (ed.), *Tourism Research: Policy, Planning, and Prospects,* Department of Geography Publication Series, University of Waterloo, Waterloo, Ontario, pp. 175–248.

Scott, D. (2006b), 'Global Environmental Change and Mountain Tourism', in S. Gössling and C. M. Hall (eds.), *Tourism and Global Environmental Change,* Routledge, London, pp. 54–75.

Scott, D. and Jones, B. (2006a), *Climate Change and Seasonality in Canadian Outdoor Recreation and Tourism – Executive Summary,* Report prepared for the Government of Canada Climate Change Action Fund, University of Waterloo, Waterloo, Ontario.

Scott, D. and Jones, B. (2006b), *Climate Change and Nature-Based Tourism – Executive Summary,* Report prepared for the Government of Canada Climate Change Action Fund, University of Waterloo, Waterloo, Ontario.

Scott, D. and Jones, B. (2005), *Climate Change and Banff: Implications for Tourism and Recreation – Executive Summary,* Report prepared for the Government of Canada Climate Change Action Fund and Town of Banff, Alberta, University of Waterloo, Waterloo, Ontario.

Scott, D. and McBoyle, G. (2006), 'Climate Change Adaptation in the Ski Industry', *Mitigation and Adaptation Strategies to Global Change,* [Electronic], SpringerLink.

Scott, D. et al. (2008a – in press), 'Climate Change Adaptation in the Recreation and Tourism Sector', in K. Ebi and P. Hoeppe (eds.), *Biometeorology for Adaptation,* Springer, New York.

Scott, D. et al. (2008b – in press), 'Climate Preferences for Diverse Tourism Environments: Evidence from Canada, New Zealand and Sweden', *Climate Research.*

Scott, D. et al. (2007d – in press), 'Climate Change Vulnerability of the Northeast US Winter Tourism Sector', *Mitigation and Adaptation Strategies to Global Change,*

Scott, D. et al. (2008d – accepted), 'Climate Preferences for Tourism: Evidence from Canada, New Zealand and Sweden', *Climate Research.*

Scott, D. et al. (2008e – in press), 'Exploring Potential Visitor Response to Climate-induced Environmental Changes in Canada's Rocky Mountain National Parks', *Tourism Review International.*

Scott, D. et al. (2007a), 'Climate Change and Québec's Ski Industry', *Global Environmental Change, 17* (2), pp. 181–190.

Scott, D. et al. (2007b), 'Using an Analogue Approach to Examine Climate Change Vulnerability of the New England (USA) Ski Tourism Industry', *Proceedings of the 3rd International Conference on Climate, Tourism and Recreation,* International Society of Biometeorology, Commission on Climate Tourism and Recreation, Alexandropolis, 19–22 September 2007.

Scott, D. et al. (2007c), 'Implications of Climate and Environmental Change for Nature-based Tourism in the Canadian Rocky Mountains: A Case Study of Waterton Lakes National Park', *Tourism Management, 28* (2), pp. 570–579.

Scott, D. et al. (2005a), *Climate, Tourism and Recreation: A Bibliography –1936 to 2005,* University of Waterloo, Waterloo, Ontario.

Scott, D. et al. (2005b), *Climate Change: A Long-term Strategic Issue for the National Capital Commission (Tourism and Recreation Business Lines) – Executive Summary,* Report prepared for the National Capital Commission, University of Waterloo, Waterloo, Ontario.

Scott, D. et al. (2005c), 'The Evolution of the Climate Change Issue in the Tourism Sector', in M. Hall and G. Higham (eds.), *Tourism Recreation and Climate Change,* Channelview Press, London, pp. 44–60.

Scott, D. et al. (2004), 'Climate Change and the Distribution of Climatic Resources for Tourism in North America', *Climate Research, 27* (2), pp. 105–117.

Scott, D. et al. (2003), 'Climate Change and the Skiing Industry in Southern Ontario (Canada): Exploring the Importance of Snowmaking as a Technical Adaptation', *Climate Research, 23,* pp. 171–181.

Scott, D. et al (2002), *The Vulnerability of Winter Recreation to Climate Change in Ontario's Lakelands Tourism Region,* Department of Geography Publication Series Occasional Paper 18, University of Waterloo, Waterloo, Ontario.

Shea, E. L. et al. (2001), *Preparing for a Changing Climate: The Potential Consequences of Climate Variability and Change – Pacific Islands,* US Global Research Program, East-West Center, Honalulu, Hawaii.

Shine, K. P. et al. (2005), 'Scientific Issues in the Design of Metrics for Inclusion of Oxides of Nitrogen in Global Climate Agreements', *Proceedings of the National Academy of Sciences, 102* (44), pp. 15768–15773.

Sievanen, T. et al. (2005), *Nature-based Tourism, Outdoor Recreation and Adaptation to Climate Change,* FINADAPT Working Paper 11, Finnish Environment Institute, Helsinki.

Simmons, P. (2005), 'Swiss Plan to Wrap Up their Glaciers', *The Times,* 30 March 2005.

Simpson, M. C. (2008 – in press), 'Global Climate Change and the Implications for Tourism Resilience in Small Island Developing States (SIDS)', in *Building Tourism Resilience in SIDS: Maximising Economic Benefits and Sustaining Tourism Development,* SIDS Tourism Organization, Bahamas.

Simpson, M. C. (2003), 'Tourism, Livelihoods, Biodiversity, Conservation and the Climate Change Factor in Developing Countries', *NATO Advanced Research Seminar on Climate Change and Tourism: Assessment and Coping Strategies,* November 2003, Warsaw.

Simpson, M. C. and Ladle, R. (2006), 'Selecting and Evaluating Destinations for the Sustainable Tourism Zone of the Caribbean (STZC)', Keynote Presentation at the *7th Meeting of the Experts in Sustainable Tourism Indicators Association of Caribbean States (ACS) Technical Seminar,* Bayahibe.

Skinner, E. et al. (2004), 'Does Stewardship Travel Well? Benchmarking, Accreditation and Certification', *Corporate Social Responsibility and Environmental Management,* 11, pp. 121–132.

Smith, S. et al. (2006), *Air and Rail Competition and Complementarity,* (Final Report), SDG Project, Number P206600, Steer Davies Gleave, London, (Online), available: http://ec.europa.eu/transport/rail/studies/doc/2006_08_study_air_rail_competition_en.pdf (14-12-2007).

Sonmez, S. (1998), 'Tourism, Terrorism, and Political Instability', *Annals of Tourism Research,* 25, (2), pp. 416–456.

South Pacific Tourism (no date), *A Green Business Benchmark,* (Online), available: http://nztri.aut.ac.nz/pacifictoolkit/pages/viewsuccess.php?successstory=16 (14-12-2007).

Stern, N. (2006), *The Economics of Climate Change: The Stern Review,* Cambridge University Press, Cambridge.

Sustrans (2007), *Sustrans Homepage,* (Online), available: http://www.sustrans.org.uk (10-12-2007)

South West Climate Change Impacts Partnership, Devon County Council and South East Climate Change Partnership (2007), *Climate Change and Tourism in the South of England,* (Online), available: http://www.oursouthwest.com/climate/archive/tourism-leaflet-2007.pdf (17-12-2007).

Swedish Railways (2007), *SJ Environmental Calculation,* (Online), available: http://www.sj.se/sj/jsp/polopoly.jsp?d=6783andl=en (14-12-2007).

The CAN Corporation. (2007), *National Security and the Threat of Climate Change,* http://securityandclimate.cna.org/report/National%20Security%20and%20the%20Threat%20of%20Climate%20Change.pdf (17-12-2007).

The Economist (1998), 'Winter Wonderlands', *The Economist,* 31 January 1998.

The R&A (2004), *Climate Change,* (Online), available: https://www.bestcourseforgolf.org/content/environment/key_environment/climate_change/en (14-12-2007).

Thomas, C. D. et al. (2004), 'Extinction Risk from Climate Change', *Nature 427,* pp. 145–148.

Thompson, L. et al. (2002), 'Kilimanjaro Ice Core Records: Evidence of Holocene Climate Change in Tropical Africa', *Science 298,* pp. 589–593.

Thorne, P. (2006), *World Snowdomes,* Snow Hunter Ltd, Kiltarlity Inverness.

TNS-Sofres (no date), *Description du Suivi de la Demande Touristique,* (Online), available: http://www.tns-sofres.com/sofres/secteurs/sesame/souscription-suivi-demande-touristique.php (07-04-2008).

Tommasini, D. (2003), *Personal Communication,* North Atlantic Regional Studies (NORS), University of Roskilde, Roskilde.

Tompkins, E. and Adger, N. (2003), *Building Resilience to Climate Change through Adaptive Management of Natural Resources,* Tyndall Centre for Climate Change Research, Working Paper 27, (Online), available: http://www.tyndall.ac.uk/publications/working_papers/wp27.pdf (13-12-2007).

Tourism Authority (2006), *Thailand Tourism Statistics Main Page,* (Online), available: http://www2.tat.or.th/stat/web/static_index.php (14-12-2007).

Transportation Association of Canada (1999), 'Transportation and Climate Change: Options for Action', Options Paper of the *Transportation Climate Change Table,* November 1999, (Online), available: http://www.tc.gc.ca/programs/environment/climatechange/subgroups1/Options_Paper/English/Trans_Final_OR-en.pdf (14-12-2007).

Travel Insurance Web (2007), *TIW Customers Willing to Pay Green Flight Tax.* http://news.bigg.net/n37667-TIW_Customers_Willing_to_Pay_Green_Flight_Tax.html (14-12-2007)

Twinshare (2005), *Twinshare: Tourism Accommodation and the Environment.* http://twinshare.crctourism.com.au/aboutTwinshare.asp (14-12-2007).

Uemura, Y. et al. (2003), 'Potential of Renewable Energy Sources and its Applications in Yakushima Island', *Renewable Energy, 29,* pp. 581–591.

United Kingdom Centre for Economic and Environmental Development (CEED) (1998), *An Assessment of the Environmental Impacts of Tourism in St Lucia: A Report to British Airways and British Airways Holidays,* Report 5/98, CEED, Cambridge.

United Kingdom Department for Environment, Food and Rural Affairs (DEFRA) (2005), *Climate Change Impacts on Sea Level in India,* Department for Environment, Food and Rural Affairs, London, (Online), available: http://www.defra.gov.uk/environment/climatechange/internat/devcountry/pdf/india-climate-4-sealevel.pdf (13-12-2007).

United Kingdom Department for International Development (DFID) (2004), *Adaptation to Climate Change: Making Development Disaster-proof,* Department for International Development, London, (Online), available: http://www.dfid.gov.uk/pubs/files/climatechange/6disasterproof.pdf (13-12-2007).

United Kingdom Department for Transport (2007a), *Attitudes Towards Transport,* (Online), available: http://www.dft.gov.uk/pgr/statistics/datatablespublications/trsnstatsatt/ (14-12-2007).

United Kingdom Department for Transport (2007b), *Public Attitudes Towards Climate Change and the Impact of Transport,* (Online), available: http://www.dft.gov.uk/pgr/statistics/datatablespublications/trsnstatsatt/attitudestoclimatechange (14-12-2007).

United Kingdom Met Office (2007), Seasonal forecasts, UK Met Office, Exeter (Online), available: http://www.metoffice.gov.uk/weather/world/seasonal/index.html (01-02-2008).

Union of Concerned Scientists (2007), *Northeast Climate Impact Assessment,* (Online), available: http://www.northeastclimateimpacts.org (13-12-2007).

United Nations (2007a), 'Climate Change and Development Must Be Tackled Together – Ban Ki-moon', *UN News Centre,* 9 May 2007, (Online), available: http://www.un.org/apps/news/story.asp?NewsID=22498&Cr=commission&Cr1=sustainable (13-12-2007).

United Nations (2007b), *UN Millennium Development Goals,* (Online), available: http://www.un.org/millenniumgoals/ (13-12-2007).

United Nations Educational, Scientific and Cultural Organization (2006), 'Water and Tourism', *UNESCO Water Portal Weekly Update,* No. 155, (Online), available: http://www.unesco.org/water/news/newsletter/155.shtml (17-12-2007).

United Nations Educational, Scientific and Cultural Organization (2005), *Global Change Impacts in Mountain Biosphere Reserves,* UNESCO, Paris.

United Nations Educational, Scientific and Cultural Organization (2002), *Mountain Summit Opens In Kyrgyzstan,* Press Release No.2002-84, (Online), available: http://www.unesco.org/bpi/eng/unescopress/2002/02-88e.shtml (17-12-2007).

United Nations Educational, Scientific and Cultural Organization – World Heritage Centre (2007), *Case Studies on Climate Change and World Heritage,* UNESCO-WHC, Paris, (Online), available: http://whc.unesco.org/documents/publi_climatechange.pdf (07-01-2008).

United Nations Environment Programme (2007a), 'Insuring for Sustainability: Why and How the Leaders are Doing it', UNEP Financial Initiative, UNEP, Geneva

United Nations Environment Programme (2007b), *Europe Set for Warmer Northern Winters, Hotter Southern Summers and Worsening Droughts and Floods,* Press release, 10 April 2007, (Online), available: http://www.unep.org/Documents.Multilingual/Default.asp?DocumentID=504&ArticleID=5560&l=en (17-12-2007).

United Nations Environment Programme (2003), *Switched on: Renewable Energy Opportunities for the Tourism Industry,* UNEP, Paris, (Online), available: http://www.iclei-europe.org/fileadmin/user_upload/tourism/Switched_on_2003_1-5.pdf (14-12-2007).

United Nations Environment Programme (2002a), *How Tourism Can Contribute to Environmental Conservation,* (Online), available: http://www.uneptie.org/pc/tourism/sust-tourism%5Cenv-conservation.htm (13-12-2007).

United Nations Environment Programme (2002b), *Inventory of Glaciers, Glacier Lakes, Glacier Lake Outburst Floods Monitoring and Early Warning Systems in the Hindu Kush-Himalayan Region, Nepal and Bhutan,* International Centre for Integrated Mountain Development, UNEP, (Online), available: http://www.rrcap.unep.org/glofnepal/start.htm (14-12-2007).

United Nations Environment Programme (2000), *'Natural Selection: Evolving Choices for Renewable Energy Technology and Policy',* DTIE, Paris, (Online), available: http://www.unep.fr/energy/publications/files/naturalselection.htm (14-12-2007).

United Nations General Assembly (1994), *Report of the Global Conference on the Sustainable Development of Small Island Developing States:* UN General Assembly, New York, (Online), available: http://www.un.org/documents/ga/conf167/aconf167-9.htm (13-12-2007).

United Nations Global Compact, (Online), available: http://www.unglobalcompact.org (13-12-2007).

United States Environmental Protection Agency (1999), 'Global Climate Change: What Does it Mean for South Florida and the Florida Keys', *Report on the Environmental Protection Agency Public Consultations in coastal cities,* May 24–28. Washington, DC: Environmental Protection Agency.

Uyarra, M. et al. (2005), 'Island-Specific Preferences of Tourists for Environmental Features: Implications of Climate Change for Tourism-Dependent States', *Environmental Conservation, 32* (1), pp. 11–19.

van den Brink, R. M. and van Wee, B. (2001), 'Why has Car-fleet Specific Fuel Consumption not Shown any Decrease since 1990?, Quantitative Analysis of Dutch Passenger Car-fleet Specific Fuel Consumption', *Transportation Research Part D, 6,* pp. 75–93.

Visit Scotland (2004), *Greening Scottish Tourism: Ten Best Practice Case Studies,* (Online), available: http://www.greentourism.org.uk/greening-scotland-booklet.pdf (14-12-2007).

Wall, G. (1992), 'Tourism Alternatives in an Era of Global Climate Change', in V. Smith and W. Eadington (eds.), *Tourism Alternatives,* University of Pennsylvania, Philadelphia, pp. 194–236.

Walther, G. R. et al. (2005), 'Climate Change and High Mountain Vegetation Shifts', in G. Broll and B. Keplin (eds.), *Mountain Ecosystems,* Springer Publishing, New York, pp. 77–96.

Watkins, K. (2006), *Human Development Report 2006 – Beyond Scarcity: Power, Poverty and the Global Water Crisis,* UNDP, New York, (Online), available: http://hdr.undp.org/en/media/hdr06-complete.pdf (14-12-2007).

Webb, L. et al. (2006), *Wine Industry 'Winners and Losers' from Climate Change (in Australia),* Commonwealth Scientific and Industrial Research Organisation, Dickson.

Webster, P. J. et al. (2005), 'Changes in Tropical Cyclone Number, Duration, and Intensity in a Warming Environment', *Science,* 16 (309), No. 5742, pp. 1844–1846, (Online), available: http://www.sciencemag.org/cgi/content/full/309/5742/1844 (13-12-2007).

Wheeler, D. (1995), 'Majorca's Water Shortages Arouse Spanish Passions', *Geography, 80,* pp. 283–286.

Wheeler, S. (1998), *Planning Sustainable and Livable Cities,* Routledge, New York.

Wickers, D. (1994), 'Snow Alternative', *Sunday Times* 27 November 1994.

Wilbanks, T. J. et al. (2007), Industry, Settlement and Society, in M. L. Parry et al. (eds.), *Climate Change 2007: Impacts, Adaptation and Vulnerability. Contribution of Working Group II to the Fourth Assessment Report of the IPCC,* Cambridge University Press, Cambridge and New York, pp. 357–390.

Wilby, R. et al. (2004), *Guidelines for Use of Climate Scenarios Developed from Statistical Downscaling Methods,* IPCC, Task Group on Data and Scenarios Support for Impacts and Climate Analysis, Geneva.

Williams, P. et al. (1997), 'The Influence of Weather Context on Winter Resort Evaluations by Visitors', *Journal of Travel Research,* Fall, pp. 29–36.

Wilton, D. and Wirjanto, T. (1998), *An Analysis of the Seasonal Variation in the National Tourism Indicators,* Canadian Tourism Commission, Ottawa.

Wipe, S. et al. (2005), 'Effects of Ski Piste Preparation on Alpine Vegetation', *Journal of Applied Ecology,* 42, pp. 306–316.

Wit, R. C. N. et al. (2002), *Economic Incentives to Mitigate Greenhouse Gas Emissions from Air Transport in Europe,* 02.4733.10, CE, Delft, (Online), available: http://www.rapportsysteem.nl/artikel/index.php?id=121&action=read (14-12-2007).

Wolfsegger, C. et al. (2008 – in press), 'Climate Change Risk Appraisal in the Austrian Ski Industry', *Tourism Review International.*

Wonderful Copenhagen (2007), Free City Bikes, (Online), available: http://www.visitcopenhagen.com/composite-378.htm (10-12-2007)

Wood, J. et al. (2004), *Long-Term World Oil Supply Scenarios,* United States Energy Information Administration, (Online), available: http://www.eia.doe.gov/pub/oil_gas/petroleum/feature_articles/2004/worldoilsupply/oilsupply04.html (14-12-2007).

World Bank (2007), World Bank Country Classification by Income Group (Online), available: http://go.worldbank.org/K2CKM78CC0 (07-04-2008)

World Meteorological Organization (2007), *Expert Team on Climate and Tourism,* (Online), available: http://www.wmo.ch/pages/prog/wcp/ccl/opags/opag4/et4.3/et4.3_members_tors.htm (17-12-2007).

World Meteorological Organization (2005a), *The Abridged Final Report with Resolutions and Recommendations of the Fourteenth Session of the Commission for Climatology,* Beijing, China, 3–10 November 2005, WMO-No, 996.

World Meteorological Organization (2005b), 'Special Issue on Climate and Tourism', *World Climate News, 27th edition,* (Online), available: http://www.wmo.int/pages/publications/world_climate_news/documents/wcn27.pdf (17-12-2007).

World Meteorological Organization (1988), *Technical Regulations,* Vol. I, WMO Publication No. 49, WMO, Geneva.

World Tourism Organization (2007a), *UNWTO World Tourism Barometer,* Vol. 5, 1, UNWTO, Madrid.

World Tourism Organization (2007b), *Tourism Factbook,* UNWTO, (Online), available: http://www.wtoelibrary.org/content/v486k6/?v=search (14-12-2007).

World Tourism Organization (2007c), *UNWTO Approximations of Consistent Worldwide Tourism Volumes,* (unpublished).

World Tourism Organization (2007d), *Basic References on Tourism Statistics,* (Online), available: http://www.world-tourism.org/statistics/basic_references/index-en.htm (01.04.2008).

World Tourism Organization (2006), *Tourism Market Trends: World Overview and Tourism Topics,* (2005 Edition), UNWTO, Madrid.

World Tourism Organization (2003), *Climate Change and Tourism: Proceedings of the First International Conference on Climate Change and Tourism,* Djerba, Tunisia, 9-11 April 2003, UNWTO, Madrid.

World Tourism Organization (2000), *Tourism Vision 2020, Volume 7: Global Forecasts and Profiles of Market Segments,* UNWTO, Madrid.

World Tourism Organization and World Meteorological Organization (1998), *Handbook on Natural Disaster Reduction in Tourism Areas,* UNWTO, Madrid.

World Wide Fund for Nature (2003), *Development in the Drought: The Incompatibility of the Ebro Water Transfer with Sustainable Development in the Southeast Region of Spain,* WWF, (Online), available: http://assets.panda.org/downloads/developmentinthedrought_5104.pdf (17-12-2007).

Xiong, W. et al. (2007), 'Climate Change and Critical Thresholds in China's Food Security', *Climactic Change, 81* (2), pp. 205–221.

Yapp, G., McDonald, N. (1978), 'A Recreation Climate Model', *Journal of Environmental Management, 7,* pp. 235–252.

Yohe, G. W. et al. (2007), 'Perspectives on Climate Change and Sustainability', in M. L. Parry et al. (eds.), *Climate Change 2007: Impacts, Adaptation and Vulnerability. Contribution of Working Group II to the Fourth Assessment Report of the IPCC* Cambridge University Press, Cambridge and New York, pp. 811–841.

Zhou, Y. and Tol, R. S. J. (2005), 'Evaluating the Costs of Desalination and Water Transport', *Water Resources Research, 41,* (3), W03003.

DATE DUE